EACH TO THE OTHER

Books by Christopher La Farge

HOXSIE SELLS HIS ACRES
EACH TO THE OTHER

CHRISTOPHER LA FARGE

Each to the Other

A NOVEL IN VERSE

NEW YORK COWARD-McCANN, INC. MCMXXXIX

Typography by Robert Josephy

TO

MY FATHER, MY MOTHER

AND MY WIFE:

NOT TO PAY THEM A DEBT

BUT TO ACKNOWLEDGE IT

PROLOGUE

ERE is no tragedy. These are my days
Life-weighted, turned and measured in the scale
Of my own inches: only that, no atom more,
No plus nor minus subscript to its sum.
They tell me, those who know the incredible mass
Of man's recorded cries, that in each one
Born to the burden of unasked existence
There lives one story. Very well, here's mine
Laid out in words, each verb a piece of me,
Each noun an echo, every adjective
Reflecting the hot circumstance of living
Within my bounds, my flesh, my blood, my eyes,
My fingers crooked to catch the fantasy
Of explanation. Here's a crackling light
Flung from my poles will make my flesh transparent,
My skeleton appear before its due time,
Untendoned, bare, supported by a light
Beyond our understanding. But my life,
The reason I am I, the flesh I bear,
The colour of my eyes, the thoughts that throw
Expression in the conduct of my bones,
Are all past comprehension. In your eyes
I shall find reason by your reasoning,
Exist unshadowed if your light be such
That it surround me, compass me, contain me:
Read then with eyes, but let your thoughts be waves
That tune to the reception of your heart.

I cannot see the end of circumstance,
It is so infinite. One's days are bought
With the bright coin that chance minted and flung
Within grasp or beyond reach. Thus I owe
Double a debt for unpaid days of blazing
Life, but the grey, accounted, paid-up hours
Must somehow balance. What's a will, a passion,
A hope, ambition, hate, what's love, what's love

(Passionate echo flung: What's love?)
But the conclusion of those columned days
That bred a total? If I write them neatly,
Figure on curious figure, orthodox,
Illogical, unexplained, inevitable,
Perhaps the end of that long sum may read:
On such a day could Thomas Cottrell die
In the full measure of his circumstance.

Here's birth, then: here's the first great flagrant fact,
The cry that neither night nor day contains,
The metaphysical hour shattered and split,
The question asked once more, in vain, the flood
Of flesh and spirit joined in one deep river
Of chancéd being. So my mother bore
A twin to change, a fellow to the child
That the large earth had laboured to produce
Great with its time; so Change and I became
Step-brothers of one moment, grafted shoots
To an old tree, and all around us sprouted
Numberless brothers in the same regard.
I know now how birth was: the simple, hard fact
Caused but the usual ripple:
                              She who lies
Content with pain and the essential joy
Of fierce relief attainable: all agony
Banded and wrought to fit the subtlest curve
Of incommunicable trial—so labour runs
Its proved course, sears, divides the spirit clean
To warring elements: the Would-be-done,
The Pride-of-doing, the supernatural sense
Of life's evolving flood beyond whose pain
Is anaesthesia;
                  He who walks in strange
Disjointed terror, hopeful-hopeless, daring
The cruellest vision not unbelievable;
Drunk with strong drink, so that the dumb and dread
Murder of passion might be lifted past
The crass reality, and seek a sphere
In far heroics something less than God;
Intolerable weight of tiny thoughts
Piled, pyramided on the uneasy brain,
Founded in gravity upon the spirit

4

Dark struggling in its ignominious midnight,
Before-dawn blackness of its own device,
Sombre unpiercable dusk from which shall spring light
More bright than day; the unadmitted hope
Of glory beyond reason, clouded, fogged
By a dim sense of this continuous scene
Ten billion times become conglomerate man.

So I became and was. The great way stretched
Hard, long, and wonderful before their eyes
Who did not make the road but set my feet
To tramp, to travel, to what terminus
In what direction set, they did not know.
(Passionate echo flung: They did not know!)
They knew their fetters—after they were forged,
Fleshed to their flesh. Some strike the fetters free
To flash upon the ground, to trample them,
Till they have tangled in their feet, self-bound;
Some wear them as a charm and draw protection
From the unseen by linked spells wrought in chains;
Some never feel the close-fit miracle-manacle,
But in strange ignorance of bonds, move slow
With doubled step up the long steep of doubt
Twice doubting, twice dismayed, yet still alone;
Some polish up their links as ornaments
And send their jingle gaily as they move,
Bracelets of pretty living; some can pull
Endless apart till tension stills the chime
Of living movement, and the stronger draws
The weaker, all unwilling, down the road
Hedged with the shadows of their star-bred thoughts.

But this lies all before. You see the circle
Now in its first phase, the fresh lighted moon
Held in circumference of the old. The whole curve
Shall round and fill, repeat—variety
Can lie but in its loop. As for those two,
My parents' circle widened with the pain,
The exaltation, the forgone liberty
Loin-wrought in passion for an end obscure,
Brave, mad, mysterious—and most usual.
This is my story, this the seed of me
Borne dubious on the wind of my own breath,

5

Not theirs. A hundred generations flowed
And could not pause for mine, for me, for them,
And must roll onward to great hundreds more.
This puzzle of lapped circles is so hard:
Which is my own? What's I? What's Tom to whom?
Is Tom my ego, or my ego, Tom?
Was Tom before or shall be after me?
Am I the negative through which a sharp light
Evokes clean outline, or but the tarnished image
Some other light has modelled from the grey?

No matter! I'll write truth, words, joy, decision,
The passion of my own circle, all enclosed,
Here spread, here told—the Me that came from life,
Gave life, was given love, gave love, gave Me,
Gave joy, received it, battled circumstance,
Dwelt on the earth excited, could excite,
Touched glory (whether dream or real, no matter),
Built, patched and mended, saw his current flow
To light a love, to light his harm, his grief,
His children and his spirit. Here's Tom, here's I:
Father, son, husband—and the aching child
Filled with the grieving joy of life's design
Half understood then, still but faintly seen.
O grand good spectacle of planted life!
What tragedy can touch it, what despair
Can harm its essence, when about its roots
Flowed once the nourishment of consummate love?

PART ONE

*Y*OU MUST attend the satisfactory dusk,
The rise of evening, the decline of day,
Dew on the leaf's reanimated musk
When bats are pendulums on the western grey,
The space of resting before night's begun,
The hours of day all gathered to their sheaves,
The stones still warm from the remembered sun,
Cicadas' opening rustle in the leaves:
That is the manifest and pregnant hour
When all the softness of first morning light,
The noon's high torrent from its southern tower,
Long, priestly shadows of day's aconite,
Are to their essence in dark hours refined
To strike starred flint-flame to the steel of mind.

HERE'S the first image: my grandfather's house
Lay near the village of Cottrellton; our own
Was distant half a mile from his and stood
On the tide's inlet known as Oyster Cove.
The way between us: a contenting road,
The summer dust so easy to disturb
From its warm nest, whence it flew out to spin
In wreathing motes: an endless, dusty joy
Scaled to my inches, so that many worlds
Announced their boundaries in its travelled yards.
My nine years swelled with freedom as they passed
Beyond the cedar park that hid the yellow
Of our ramshackle house.

                         The summer sun
Made minutes endless and the months so long
One could not stretch their reach, as stars remain
The teasing edge of all things limitless.
There swept on me the prickling sense of life
Too fine to waste, too great for measured haste,

9

Too strong for the immediate response:
And I seized handfuls of the sandy dust,
Flung out its mist about me, left the road,
Tore wildly up the slope to a stone ledge,
And breathless on its peak, stood still to feel
The battering blood turn stillness into speed
And speed to life's bewilderment while, stretched
Before my eyes, all summer and the sea
Clothed my enriched and inarticulate mind.

I do not know how long before the need
Of action closed thought's chasm; some interruption:
Perhaps the white swords of a seagull's wings
Clove sea-borne idleness, perhaps the wind
Crept for a whispered, aromatic pause
Through dark green islands of the sculptured bay
That grew about me, or but the recurrent ache
Of pleasure's hours became immediate
And their postponement hateful; but I moved
On toward the grey house to the south of me.

This mood was shattered by the strident voice
That called my name: "Hello there, Tom, you're late,
Hurry up, boy, the horses are all saddled
And you have kept me waiting." There he sat
On the stone terrace, bent and motionless
In crippled attitude.
                         "You, John!" he shouted,
"Bring out those animals, the boy is here.
By God, the mornings would be afternoons
If you'd your way. Hell, dammit, by the Lord,
The man's asleep!"
                       He slowly turned his head
And looked at me with sharp and fretful eyes.
"You tell your father that his fancy friend,
That Doctor Morrison, came here yesterday,
And wished to put me permanently in bed.
Put me in bed! By God, would he conserve
My years by bedding me? Where's your riding kit?
You don't expect to ride in cotton shorts
And shame the family by your skinny knees
And silly sneakers, do you?"
                               I heard the clatter
Of the led horses. "They told me you were worse

And wouldn't like to ride today," I said,
Confused and angry.
                          "Ha! They told you so?
Hell's bells and bracelets, Tom, you'll have to watch
The world you live in if it's girt about
With nincompoops like Doctor Thingummy
And your God's-idiot father. One small pain
And he goes howling Mercy to his bed
While that soft, charitable fool, his wife,
Injects the morphia for his hiccup. Hell!
Here are the horses. Will you ride, or not?"
I was too young to carry one demand
Against another and more peremptory one:
So I said, "Yes, I'd love to," and my words
Were truthful.
                     Now there followed a sharp scene:
John Ward led up the horses; he was tall,
Immensely strong, with a lean, pallid face
Deep-lined in humour and in reticence.
My horse was near a pony, fifteen hands,
A pretty chestnut mare, a gentle creature
Whose spirit ran to willingness and swift flight;
Grey Hen, the mare that my grandfather rode
Was a great creature of near eighteen hands,
Gigantic to my eyes, most beautiful;
Her fine long barrel in its dark grey coat
Swayed to the graceful length of easy strides.
With John there came another man, Jake Caswell,
As big as John but lean and young and blonde,
With empty features; an ex-army man.
He was the fascination and delight
Of both my elder brother and myself:
Not for himself; but he possessed a bow
Made in Japan, and this he let us shoot
Under his skilful guidance who could hit
Small marks at full a hundred yards away
With home-made arrows; a queer, silent man
Nursing a grudge we did not understand
In these young summers.
                                First they mounted me
(My stomach tense against the trembling fear
That then attended each initial movement
Of eager riding); then they stooped to him

11

Who still sat bent upon the terrace edge,
And lifted him between them till they set
His crouched and crippled body in the saddle,
Where he became, as if by some enchantment,
Part of the horse he rode so firmly on.
They put his feet in stirrups, placed the reins
In his stiff-seeming and expectant hands,
While he said "Thank you," gathered up his reins,
Cried out, "We're off, by God, we're off at last!"
Lifted his horse in three steps to a canter,
And rode, a misty, bent-backed, Centaur-thing
Along the roadway bright with burnished dust.

I caught him up beyond the sounding drums
Of battered boards that hooves made resonant
Over the short-bridged inlet. Thence we rode
In silence eastward as our custom taught,
Avoiding roads, but seeking ragged fields
Where the crushed pungence of sweet-fern could rise
In wilding air; over the ancient walls
Half tumbled in grey beauty; under trees
More wide than tall, green spreading of grey boughs
In twisted summer opulence of fat leaf;
Through still, thin brooks whose water seemed to flow
In hesitant small movements, rippled-brown,
Cress-full, green-banked. We did not talk, we rode,
Our pace determined by the path we found:
Now walking with the echo of deep stone
In subterranean music to our tread;
Now trotting muffled over soft grey moss,
The only sound the creak of friendly leather,
The light swish-rustle of a fetlock drawn
Swift through the low-bush huckleberry grown
In olive patterns—then a cantered breeze
Across a rock-rimmed pasture to the wall
Whose lift would give us the familiar flight
Through air and heart, the triumph of descent
To tumbled hoof-beats and the steady sense
Of joy accomplished.
                              So we rode. His voice
Slashed at the summer with each hearty *Damn*
That jolts provoked. He used to cry, "By God!
That briar nicked me," or "Damn, hell and blast!

May the Almighty strike all woodchucks dead!
They've filled this field as full of cursed holes
As is a blasted pepper-pot." We'd go
Awhile in silence, then his voice would rise
Incredible in strength and carrying power,
And I'd hear curses (splendid to my ears
Accustomed only to the soft restraint
Of Mother's voice and Father's cool, detached
And cultivated phrases) swing and crack
Across the pastures, or through exciting trees.
We followed on the course of Seldom Brook,
Up its mild valley, through the Gardner Woods,
And then drew rein most suddenly. We stopped
Close to the brink of Pender Spring: it lay
Deep in a close, green hollow, ringed about
With thriving maple, choked with clethra growth,
With spice-bush and witch-hazel's fine-drawn lines
Of sparse and spreading green.
                              Grandfather made
A motion to keep quiet. So we stood,
Our horses' silence broken by the swift
And rippled sound of ruffled velvet breath
Through shaken nostrils, the impatient clump
Of nervous foot on dry and dissonant ground.
The old man edged Grey Hen most gingerly
Till it was side by side with my small mare.
He whispered, "Listen!"—paused, then said again
In a low voice I had to strain to hear,
"A hermit thrush—full late—a second nesting,"
And sat quite silent then, his head cocked forward,
His eyes upon the trees whose mossy roots
Wove a piled prison for the stilly spring.
I heard the thrush as it began to raise
Its yet imperfect song,
Notes sweet and long,
A tentative of praise
All ended suddenly, as though unsure,
Testing the silence, and began
Once more and ran
Its gamut now so pure
That delicacy was robust and strong,
Its tiny flame a blaze
To heal, to cure.

13

Grandfather spoke. "There now! You heard it, boy.
There's truth, eternal truth. Don't monkey with it!
Remember it. You're young. Recall the facts.
You heard a hermit thrush when you were nine
While riding out in June with an old man
Whose curses take the place of energy
More reasonably expressed. You hear?"
                                        I said,
"I heard the song. I wish he'd sing again."
"There's no use wishing. It's all over, Tom.
The bird is gone."
                    "Where has he gone?"
                                        "He's flown
Into your mind to hide." I laughed. He cried:
"You keep him there, young fool, you keep him there.
You just remember that he sang for you
Without his willing—sang for his brown mate,
And all the listening trees. He sang for worms,
He sang for eggs—for life and death and love,
And normal appetites—and if you found
His song was beautiful, you've yourself to thank.
If you can keep it so, its beauty stays,
But once you start to fuss about it, son,
And add your meanings to its simplicity,
It will be gone and never will come back.
You understand?"
                    I could not answer him,
For he was past my comprehending then,
Though then, as now, I tried to search for words
I could not find to utter.
                            "God Almighty!
What torture is like wisdom's final sight
Of its obliquity? Look here, look here!
You heard a thrush sing and you liked its song."
I nodded. "But the song was just a part
Of nature's program—like your breath—your hunger—
The beating of your heart. The fact is simple,
The act is clean and beautiful and fine
As long as it remains a fact of nature
And is not tortured by your mind to art,
Its clear notes pricked upon a human scale."
He searched my face with his enquiring eyes.
"You cannot understand. You are too young.

14

But you'll remember. And as the time returns
When this experience has grown old to you,
You'll add my words to meanings. Look, your father
Would dress the evening star in a white tie
And give it cocktails, to fit it to the scheme
Of his world-fitted life. Your blessed Ma
Would add a surplice to cover up the spots
That poor Jack-in-the-Pulpit likes to wear,
And from his nodding would see God grow great
While Jack was host to fertilizing flies.
Oh, if I could still draw as once I drew,
I'd fit your fingers for an artist's life,
And drill your spirit to an eager search
For truth, that simple, devastating line
That needs no meaning greater than itself."
He flinched and cried, "God's pestilence descend
On all mosquitoes! Let's get on!"
                                    He turned
And trotted off; I followed in his wake
Till, as the suffocating dust he raised
Made breathing horrible, I caught him up,
And as I did so he called out to me:
"I wish we could be Moslems, Tom, see here:
Cry 'Allah!' to the fields, they'll answer you,
Fling back the simple echo, unconstrued—
Cry 'God!' and back the whipping echo comes
Across the loud presumption of your mouth.
We'll gallop." So he gave his horse her head
And on we galloped over empty fields,
His strident voice loud-shouting as he rode,
Allah il Allah to Rhode Island skies.
All rides with him I loved. This ride became
Part of the treasure of my silent youth.

BE QUICK to see your unity dissevered,
For by your quickness you may save your heart
The pain it suffers when it has endeavoured
To hold together matters that must part.
Split up to regiments your soul's great corps,

15

That they may meet the multiple, wide foe
Whose flanking armies wage a single war
While on all fronts their hostile numbers show.
And when the peaceful unity you exhume
From its thick teguments of warful death,
Make many-candled day in flames resume
Whose fluttering souls extinguish at a breath;
So mourn for unity but one briefest night:
The stars are but one universe in sight.

WHEN I was ten, my brother Joss was twelve,
And we played much together; so my years
Were far advanced by striving to his age
And in all matters aiming at his mark.
I followed silently upon his lead,
And he forever followed Father's word,
So that our playing was a constant practice
To be as perfect in all games as he.
We shot, played tennis, golf. Joss always won,
Having more quickness and that singular
Incredible eye that can relate all movement
To instantaneous action; and to this
He added Father's swift facility,
That dangerous gift that gives an aptitude
For all new matters, and so breeds contempt
Of plodding progress, and tunes the mind to feel
After the easy conquest of first steps,
All further effort's an indignity.

We played one day at shooting at a mark:
A small, boy-manufactured man-of-war
Made solid of one wooden block and plated
With a wild miscellany of old metals,
Furnished with masts of twisted iron wire,
Turrets of spikes that pierced tomato cans,
Guns of great nails, small flags flown lavishly
In fierce, bright colours on a cotton thread.
She floated thirty yards or so off shore
In her still anchorage of Oyster Cove.
We'd fire alternately with our twenty-two,
Ten shots a turn, and then row out to score

16

The hits we'd made and mark the damages
With dabs of red paint on ourselves and them.
Joss shot the forward turret clean away
With two successive shots, the bullets singing
Their tuneless, angry song of ricochet.
I cried, "Yay! Wonderful!" Joss grinned and said,
"Go up and get another turret, Tom,
They're in the shed next to the studio,
And bring the hammer and some nails. I'll row
Out to the boat and fetch her in to mend."
I turned and scrambled up the rocky shore,
Dove through the tunnel we had jointly made
Under the wild grape's shaggy raftering
(Whose crotches held the secret, treasured pipes
In which we smoked corn-silk or dried sweet fern,
Foul leaves, or tea, depending on the season),
Passed through the sassafras that fringed the lawn,
And left the green day for the cool, brown night
Whose damp perpetual air the shed enclosed.
There's a sweet, ever-freshness in the sight
Of sunlit trees framed in a shadowed door:
I turned to notice them, as I have stood
Vanished, untarnished many moments since.

Perhaps the image of what followed then
Remains so clear because the hard, dark line
Of jamb and lintel (sharpened by the stripe
Of pale reflected light on inner rabbet)
Added a fourth dimension to the scene,
Removing me in space and time to stand
Unused spectator at my elder's play.

I heard my mother's voice before she came
Into my picture. She called out: "Christopher!
Oh, Christopher!" The lovely sound grew loud,
Fulfilled its instant beauty and so fled
To faintness in the passion of the sun.
She moved into my vision and she stood
Attentive, white-clad, firm upon the ground.
I heard the loud scrape of a wooden chair
In the adjacent studio, and it made
An angry noise. Then followed Father's voice:
"Curse it! This makes me sympathize with Dad

And his profanity." Then somewhat louder:
"For heaven's sake, Maria, must you yell
Directly by my window?"
                              She replied:
"Sorry, Josiah. But I've looked high and low
And can't find Christopher. Did I disturb you?"
"Disturb?" he answered, "with that clarion voice?
I sent Chris off to get the pictures back
From Mrs. Herendene. I'll be bound he heard
Your call down at North Ferry. What are miles
To such a bugle call?"
                              She laughed. He said,
"The boys go on to Father's for the night?
They ride with him?" She nodded. "Good enough.
I'd rather that they rode than played with Jake.
He's not responsible."
                              She said, "A bow?
A bow and arrows? Could they hurt themselves?"
"No, not the shooting—Jake. He's a queer lot,
He has been since you sacked the girl. I know
He still bears me a grudge through all the years,
Army and everything. He won't believe
She really stole things, thinks it's something else."
He paused and added, "Or so I suppose."
I saw my mother lift her head and look
Most sharply at the window, her lips apart,
As though she were about to speak; but then,
She dropped her eyes and closed her lips again,
And joined her fingers tightly overlapped.
He said, "Well?"
                              Then she raised her eyes to him
And spoke: "And when will Christopher be back?"
"He left at ten—he should be back by lunch,
He drove your bay mare in the run-about."
She said, "Oh, but you might have asked, Josiah."
After a moment's pause I heard his steps,
The slam of his screen door, and soon he stood
Within my picture. He made her beauty seem
Heavy and ponderous by contrasting grace.
She did not look at him. He stood and stared,
With eyes half-closed against the beating sun,
And stroked his cheek with fingers fine and strong.
He said at length: "I could not use the pair,

18

I need them for this afternoon."
                              She stirred,
And echoed him: "The pair—this afternoon?"
He looked at her a moment silently,
And so repeated it, "This afternoon."
"You have forgotten, this is August fifth."
He frowned and said, "The fifth?"
                              "I promised Aunt Emily
I'd meet her at East Greenwich and drive over.
I wanted Christopher to make the garland
For Father's grave."
                    "Oh yes. I did forget.
Your—shall I say—memorial tendencies
Are punctual, always, but beyond my scope."
He paused a second, and a flashing smile
Lighted his face. "If I should predecease you,
And die in February, do take care
Not to get influenza at my grave
And follow me through force of piety."
She said, "I hate that sort of joke, Josiah."
"I know you do. Perhaps that's why my imp
Suggests them to me. Take the pair, of course."
He leaned toward Mother then, and took her hand,
Saying, "Dear Maia, don't be vexed with me,
You shall have Chris this afternoon, you know,
But let me have them for tomorrow morning.
My need is urgent."
                    She withdrew her hand.
"Where must you go?"
                    "To Providence—Bottomley
Has offered me a thousand dollars flat
For the complete set, and I'm going to sell it.
I don't think it's worth waiting for the sale
Of individual drawings."
                        Mother said,
"A thousand dollars? But, it's not enough!"
"I know it's not. But then—I need the money."
She sighed and answered, "Yes. I know you do.
Perhaps it's better so. Bills are so hateful."
He said, "See here, the bills are not so bad,"
And pulled some letters from his pocket. "Look,
I've just had this. It's frightfully exciting."
He opened one and stuffed the others back

19

Into his pocket—but one letter bent
And tumbled to the ground without his seeing,
And he continued: "It's from Walter Moore,
Just came this morning. He's starting in a week
To take his yacht to Norway, and he asks
If I can join him. Naturally, I'll go."

What shocked me then was that my mother dared
To look so at my father, that great figure,
Symbol of power and of perfect doing.
I'd never seen her wear a look like this,
So stern and disapproving, so contained
That even I could feel her pulses throb
With their locked energy. But she said nothing.
So Father spoke; the passion in his voice
Was hot and evident: "Perhaps you think
Painting is nothing—you're entitled to—
Your own opinion is your own. You know,
Or should have known, the day you married me
That art was not a product of the home
Like needlework or knitting. Shall I sit
Forever at your side, and throw away
The grand good moments of an artist's life?
The moments that excite, that feed the mind,
Let loose the power? Must I rusticate
Forever here, or dull the edge of thought
With but domestic gabble for my mind?
Here's a great chance, new worlds to see, to paint,
Thrown in my lap—and you look daggers at me,
Because I take the money I have earned
To reinvest it in producing more.
Must I continue hacking illustrations
For puerile books when there is offered me
Free passage, now, at last, to proper work?"
He paused. There was a silence. Then he kicked
The ground a little, and I recognized
Most shockingly, the weakness of that gesture
Which I so often used.
                              Then Mother said:
"You don't mean half of what you say, Josiah.
By all means go if you believe it best."
"Best, best, believe, believe, words, words, and words!
This is the essence of my life. Be sure

20

I shall not fail to go. I have to go.
You might have made it possible for me
To leave in happiness, not in discontent."
She said, "How long shall you be gone away?"
"Oh, I don't know—a month, or two or three,
Not more, I daresay. But you've changed your mind?
You do approve?"
                              "You know I can't approve."
Then suddenly he turned cool, and so his voice
Took on its grace and charm, but so detached
He might have been addressing civilly
A slight acquaintance. "That's very interesting.
Your reasons, I'll suppose, are adequate.
The home is greater than its single parts,
The family is the nation's ancient strength,
And that great bulwark of our ancestry,
Our pure, New England ancestry (from which
My lamentable father so departed
In marrying an Italian) rests on these
Great bourgeois principles: that a tradesman's debt
Must be more honoured than a public bond,
And all our living, to whatever end,
Is wanton if it's pleasant. Dear Maria,
How widely do we differ!"
                              So he turned
And walked away. I heard the screen door slam;
Once more I heard his steps on the board floor
Beyond my shed wall, and it made my stillness
Seem doubly guilty.
                              Mother stood and stared
At his departing, then turned away—but paused,
Her eyes upon the letter on the ground.
She picked it up and held it in her hand
In indecision. Then she reached inside,
Pulled out the letter from its envelope,
Cast one quick glance at it, and thrust it back
To its white sanctuary. Then a trembling
Shook her all over, violent but brief.
She dropped the letter to the ground again
And walked away; her passing from the frame
Of this my picture left an emptiness
More solid than the sunlight on the trees
That wove their green against the violent sky.

I had forgotten boats and turrets now,
And wished for one thing only: to escape
This dark, surrounding dampness of cool air
That so preserved discomfort. So I left it,
And stood a moment, blinking on the lawn,
Looking about for witnesses: there was none.
But suddenly my mother reappeared
Around the barn that joined the studio
And called my name, but softly, and I ran
With curious eagerness to her.
                                    "Look," she said,
"Your father dropped a letter. Take it to him."
She pointed to the letter on the lawn,
White stain on dusty green. "I must suppose
That it concerns his plans. I do not know."
She smiled at me, that rapt and lovely smile
That so embraced and comforted, but yet
Seemed indecisive in its goodness. "Run!
He may be missing it." She turned again
And walked slow step on step, beyond my sight
And past my comprehension.
                                    In my turn
I picked the letter up and looked at it,
But as it merely had my father's name
And our address on its concealing face,
It did not help me. So I carried it
Up to his studio door, and knocked and heard
His voice say "Come!" I opened and went in.
"What is it, boy?"
                                    "A letter for you, Father.
Mother just saw it lying on the grass
And told me it was yours." I did not mean
To say as much, for all my words then seemed
A terrible deceit, a fearful trap
To trip me into punishment.
                                    He sat
Before his desk and looked at me a while,
His pen in one hand, and the other feeling
His chin in his habitual gesture.
                                    "Well,
Just give it here."
                                    I did so, and he took it,
Turned it twice round, and dropped it on his desk.

22

"Good! Thought I'd lost that one. Where was it, Tom?"
"Outside the shed," I answered.
                              "How do you know?"
"I picked it up when Mother showed it to me."
His voice turned hard and bitter and he said,
"How clever of your mother to have guessed
That it was mine! All right, Tom, thank you, boy,
You run along now. I'm a busy man."
I said, "You're welcome," and went out again
Into the hot day.
                    There I stood and scratched
My leg in indecision and dismay,
Till Joss came running and cried out, "You, Tom!
For goodness' sake!"
                        I said, "Oh golly, Joss,
They . . . well, they . . ." but I could not finish it:
What had They done? But Joss was not amused,
He pushed me roughly and went past me then,
And I just followed him.

                          2

                    All morning long
His energy drove thinking clean away.
My father did not come to lunch. And after
We ran off to our room to change. We found
Agatha there, short, pink, her apron hung
Forever on the bias. We shouted at her:
"Good morning, Agatha. A balmy day!"
"Good afternoon, by grace of God," she said,
"But balmy none the less."
                            "Be off, get out,
We've got to change our clothes."
                                  "Don't bother me,
I've got to pack your nighties."
                                "Agatha!"
I cried again, "Go 'way, we've got to strip."
And Joss said, "Agatha, the Good Book says:
'Thou shalt not look upon my nakedness.'"
She laughed deliciously and said, "Since when?
You sprats, I've pulled the blessed underdrawers
From off your bottoms since you had the things."
"Which, underdrawers or bottoms?"
                                  "Get along.

                          23

I'll tend my business, get you to your own."
We were defeated, so we dressed while she
Packed our excitement in a leather case.
We trod once more that most delicious road
Past Wych Pond to Grandfather's distant house,
Our hands upon the double-handled bag
For half its honour.
                    All that afternoon
We rode, we three, till the slant light proclaimed
Our giant-shadowed growths might touch the stars
And light them for our resting. Joss and I
Raced through our changing in the big blue room
Whose matting smelt as Indian baskets do.
Then down the winding stair, always in haste
(Our faces damp with that symbolic film
Of customary washing which our years
Dared not omit), and out on the wide porch
To sit in rocking chairs and hear them creak,
Look for the first and hesitating flash
Of Chepaug Lighthouse as the tangled sun
Escaped the trees and hid behind the grey
And many-angled roofs of Cottrellton.
From time to time we'd hear the vivid oaths
Rip out above our heads as steadfast Charles,
Tall, black and gentle, changed Grandfather's clothes.

I had no time to think then. Life was filled
Too full of the unusual in this house.
We dined in lavish style. He gave us wine,
And bade us note its flavour and its name;
And talked of many grand, romantic things:
Of battles and their men, stupidities
He said he had committed when his youth
Was deep in wrathful doing. All his talk
Was salted by the spice of his enjoyment.
He seemed so small and weak, so hunched and crippled,
Once you removed him from his giant horse—
Unable to move from one room to the next
Without a strong man's aid; and yet a boy
So soon forgot his weakness, for his strength
Rallied his spirit to his body's spite;
And so his tongue became a flashing sword
To cut his bonds, and in our youthful eyes

24

(Which shun and dread the crippled, awkward thing)
He was heroic.
                    Afterwards he'd read
Most violently from his curious books,
Olla Podrida, Moby Dick, perhaps
A passage from Suetonius, Hamlet, Lear—
Oh, most unsuitable! But I loved them then
As they took rich, incalculable life
Through my obscuring mists of unlived years,
Beneath the warmth of his impassioned voice
Hot with the fusing of so many days,
Still radiant for the days yet unfulfilled.

When he had finished reading on this night,
He sat awhile, the book upon his lap,
And silence lay on us. My mind returned
Inconsequent to the morning and I said:
"Grandfather, tell me, for I'd never heard it,
Was Grandmother an Italian?"
                              "God Almighty!
Is this what Shakespeare makes you think about?
Of course she was. Just look at Joss, his eyes
Are purely hers, Italian eyes." Joss blushed,
And giggling, shifted in his seat.
                                  "Be off!
It's past your time for bed. Be off, you two.
And tell your father to teach you of your roots.
By God, next thing you know you'll sign your name
Cottrell of Cottrellton—though he knows full well
Its founder's not our kin. Coincidence,
Most handy if you wish to be a snob.
Your good grandmother died when Joss was two,
She never saw you, Tom. The worse for you!
Her warmth was like no other's on this earth,
It glowed in song—as a flame burns, she sang—
And all the pity is, Josiah's got
Her grace alone of all her shining gifts—
Perhaps he'll get cantankerous when he's old
And so take after one of us at least."
Joss laughed. Grandfather shouted out, "Be off!
Smile you my speeches, as I were a fool?
Goose, if I had you upon Sarum plain
I'd drive you cackling home to Camelot."

25

We said goodnight reluctantly, and made
Boy's crablike progress through the pleasant hall,
Up the dark stair to our sweet-smelling room.
Our beds were cool and large. We did not talk,
For Joss was tired and soon dropped asleep,
Leaving me desperately alone, to feel
The day rush back in unaccustomed tides
Across my mind. The strange and passive room
Re-echoed with the ticking of its clock
Loud in my ears; the night resumed its sounds
Of soft waves woven in incessant song
Of toads and crickets, and the pulsing beat,
So strangely out of harmony, that my heart
Tapped on my eardrums pillowed desperately
Against this waking. So the scene returned,
Hard, clear, incomprehensible; these two,
My father set against my mother—words
Flung like sharp knives, to cut, to cut again;
Unity shattered to two warring parts,
Dissevered whole—that told me I must turn
To one by one, and must forever face
Two ways to loving.
                        Then the letter grew
To a great white and terrible extent,
White against green, a glaring, endless thing
That covered me. And so I woke again
From my uneasy sleep and heard the clock,
And turned my mind with effort to retrace
My just position in this twisted room,
Heard waves and soft wind and the clock-beat merge
With the soft pulses of my younger heart,
And into the great deeps of sleep so slipped
Past the unlighted passages of night.

NO MEASURE timed for youth in all this hard world!
So hemmed about with the unending star-years,
Star chained to far star, dissipant comets furled

26

In a dark mantled ordering that never veers;
Light become slave to mensurable time-flow,
Time lamed and halting, so do seconds, sharp split,
Cloven and broken to their fractions, climb slow
Million on million down the minute's deep pit.
How place child's heart-beat in the thunder's crashed light?
Slow beat, pulse beat, zero to all far space,
Mountain unmovable to the atom's flashed flight—
Zero's infinity, in the atom's star race.
Pillow your head, child, night may be short, long—
No matter, heart-beats measure your dream song.

IT'S CURIOUS the way slight boyhood matters stick tight
In my lame memory. I can forget the whole lot
Of what must have seemed, once, important incidents,
And so leave a year naked save for its number:
Just think how terrible to lose a whole year
Out of the few minutes we're granted to scratch our marks on
    earth!
And then some idiotic small word, dim smell, or slight taste,
Or fluttered sound like paper trembled at a cool spring
    window,
And back rush images as clear, as clean, as lighted
As they are root-clipped—or so detached
That they no longer fit equations of a whole scheme,
Or join the spine of growth. They're like the group pictures
Of small boys at school: unless I have written the names
I cannot ever remember more than a bare half
Of the vaguely familiar faces, such clear young faces,
Each face foretelling something, like a weather-vane—
A whole line of little barometers reading, from left to right:
FAIR BUT CHANGE.
So as I go about this daily work of scratching the dust
Of my own youth, I turn up the old arrow-heads
Of my own ancestry, the primitive weapons I once used
To pierce the tigers, the lions, the stampeding buffaloes,
Or the other, hostile Indians on the warpath, softly
On the warpath, of my mind. These were the figments of
    triumph
That a silent boy wove to his need from his silence.
The hard part is that I can't always recall

When the arrow was made, or why I made it, or bought it,
Or begged it—and worse: if it missed its aim
And let the enemy by. But I suppose not: if they had come
Past the arrow that flew to the string of my mind,
I should have perished, utterly, immediately,
For one can't then lose in an imagined contest,
Losing in so many of the hard fights of the stiff day,
The real battles, the endless competitions with all those faces
Over the neat collars, under the brushed hair, the faces named
And having now no name except the great group names
Which were: *Triumph* and *Conform* and, like the barometers,
CHANGE—*before we have to change you!*
                                        The things I did well
They did not do. They'd say 'Just run and catch.'
I'd run, but like as not I'd trip, before I caught,
Having feet that were clumsy and hands that were awkward,
And loving a horse too well for a football's comfort
To my fingers.
                        So these images come up now unbidden,
Unwelcome, nearly useless, but the mass picture is Me:
Film on film, confusing all the surroundings,
But not me—I'm clear—blazing clear, young Tom,
Clumsy, silent Tom changing and changing:
Clear sky to cirrus cloud, cirrus cloud to cumulus,
Cumulus to thunder-head, black cloud, wind-reaved,
Lightning-roasted, pushed here, there and back again,
But still a cloud, still a sky-dweller, still remote,
Commonly silent—even the thunder is not of me,
Nor is the lightning of me, but of the wild faces that hedged
    me
Compelling this outburst, that collision—this static fierce
Blast of blazed heat to hurt—not in heaven, just high—
Too well removed, over-silent, only resenting the one thing,
The everlasting command, the eternal necessity: CHANGE!
So, after a while, you learn, if you're Tom; you do change,
You learn to look down, you learn to pick your feet up
So that you're not the one boy who stumbles on the smooth
    stone,
And you learn to use your head, hands, eyes, to save,
To save, to protect, to cover the inside up, to hide it,
To keep intact the passionate life of you, of YOU!
And never let anyone know that you're doing it, hiding it,
Keeping it—oh, not because you don't want to tell it,

But because you have not learned to speak of the inside
As if it were the outside and like your clothes, outgrown,
Outmoded, torn, burned, frayed: your spirit can ravel
Before you are old enough to bind its edges with the thin
    thread
Spun from your own growing.

THIS pleasing silver is but water falling,
Those high and magic mountains are but mist
In cloudy shadow, and the music calling
Is but the wet wind that the wet trees twist;
This leisure's but the season's idleness
Enforced by trailing rain; this printed page
Is stabled Pegasus, haltered bridleless
To chew the cud of his imprisoned rage;
This luminous moonstone's but an oval drop
Creeping upon the sky-infuséd glass;
That flash of pallid gold is but the sop
That storms throw out to Cerberus as they pass:
Yet these false treasures in the memory blaze
Brighter than sunlight on the cloudless days.

I'LL SING you now a broken song about one grey day
When the mild rain fell steadily and the city's long streets
    Shone like pale rivers and the horses' heavy
    Down-stroke repeated rhythm of four great feet
Starred the dark mirror held to the wet fleeting clouds,
Scattered in covey the disturbed drops idly gathered
    In slant-seen silver puddles, and awoke
    Echoes from empty-seeming, withdrawn faces
        Of the endless ranks of buildings.
It may be that because of this day now I remember
My mother always as of rain, or days of rain,
    As grey surrounded, yet never grey herself:
    But bright in colour, like colour when the raining

Skies so enwrap the world too close-held in its tissues
Of soft sad monochromes, the subtle background raising
  Passion for colours flung against its veiling,
  Burning of reds against the greens grown violent
    Under the wet sky, under the rain.
So she remains in image, not too clearly discovered,
  Forever mixed with thought of rain in my mind
That of its youth, was free from impress of manifold images,
  Freedom obscured by the veil of immature years,
    Strong colours veiled as rain veils distance.

I think it must have been in March because the rain
Was warm, yet ice in the gutters persisted, porous and rotten.
  So did the hybrid day breed a confusion,
  Season on season city intermingled:
All spring in air and rain, the subtle spring-rain feeling,
Winter in all the chill, mean, penetrating dampness,
  Spring in the gutters, glutted with grey water,
  Swirling and joining at the corner culverts,
    Winter in icy dams that turned it.
It's all a part now of the thousand wintry spring
Rain-and-ice-coated days that I have seen go past
  The misted window of my unwearied years
  That eager watched them at a welcoming sill.
Yet I recall still feeling the warmth that grew about me,
Warmth from Mother's presence as we sat near together
  Huddled within our hansom cab and seeing
  Long black trees on Madison Avenue, dripping,
    Streets reflecting dark brown buildings.
The sound of horses' feet fills all my childhood memory:
  This sharper city sound seems to return now
Always with that wet hiss and whisper before the clump
  Of the weary down-step, peaceful in rhythm,
    Battering sadness into memory.

But I was not sad then. This was a holiday, extra,
Wonderful swift release from the rub of school's day-by-day
  Suddenly granted because some small boy blossomed
  Into the heaven-sent pink small spots called measles.
Mother was gay too, in her tempered manner of gaiety,
Humming a small tune over and over again, smiling,
  Nodding her head to questions if nods would answer,
  Or breaking her tune off short, to fill the hansom

30

With the warm music of her deep voice.
It was great fun to see the black umbrellas scurry,
Legs that finished off at the top in spreading, headless
    Japanese fantasy hats at rakish angles,
    Headless people dashing about, their shadows
Lying vertical, stumpy under the pattering feet,
Rippled, reflected shadows, bright in the puddles of rain,
    Mushroom shadows, dodging about, inedible
    Toadstool shadows, with scalloped black umbrellas
        Growing in motion on the wet streets.
Somehow it made the airless hansom, window down-drawn,
    Warm and comforting, full of the smell of horses,
Full of Mother and me on a holiday expedition,
    Mother humming and rain on everyone else
        But not on us: we were safe—a short space.

Then I thought of a picture I'd seen Father make once:
Great fat pines, swift brush-drawn in luminous black ink,
    And I said, "Shame that Father's not here, too,
    He'd have drawn those umbrellas hiding people."
Mother said, "Yes . . . yes," but no more, and I looked at her
Seeing her face go solemn and still and endlessly distant.
    If I'd been older, I'd have asked her right out
    What was the matter—but youth's flood of questions
        Dams at the locked gate of older sorrow.
We drove awhile in silence, until I, grown afraid
Of this long, trying wordlessness, which could not be other
    Than disapproval (silence being but that
    Wherein one's small sins by contemplation grew
To punishable size) spoke up, but heard my voice beat
Round the enclosure of the cab's confining walls
    Louder than my intention, and so whispered:
    "Where are we going, is it far from here—
        Whose house is it where we're going?"
Perhaps because my sudden shout aroused her mind
    And then my whisper came so suddenly,
My mother burst out laughing, and the soft, deep notes
    Filled the cab with such music and relief
        That I too laughed aloud with her.

She must have put aside whatever thoughts had risen
Hard and unwelcome in her mind, for when she spoke
    Her voice was placid and contented—not gay

31

(Who did not know the rootless life-in-air state
That gaiety demands, its bubble floating wind-borne
Past puncturing thorns of the close-bushed realities),
    But a pleased, forward-looking tone of voice
    Whose quality proclaimed good things yet coming:
        All trouble well endured, would lighten.
"We're going (she said) to my Aunt Emily's house. She died
Some months ago in England. She was buried there, far off,
    You did not know her—she was very old then,
    Content to let life's burden slip off her shoulders.
She's left the contents of the house to me, for my use,
Either to keep or sell, or give away as suits
    My own convenience—for when old people die
    They will these long accumulated mere things
        To those they love, or pity, most."
She looked at me but I was silent in my interest.
    "We meet Mr. Leighton there—cousin Evelyn Leighton";
She paused but added quickly, "A very distant cousin,
    He knew Aunt Emily well, and truly loved her,
    And so he's coming too—to help me."

I saw the colour flood her cheeks so slowly, hotly,
And she said, "It is hot and close here—here in a hansom.
    We're nearly there. I'm glad. A breath of fresh air
    Is what we both need. Closed cabs are so stuffy."
The horse clip-clopped along the street a short while more
And we two stared out through the steamy, rain-streaked
        window.
    I wished that the cool rain could be here within
    The thick air, but be dry, refresh our breathing,
        And without wetting us, cool our faces.
Then the cab stopped at last. Up popped the funny small
        hatch,
Down came the driver's voice: "Hope youse got an umbrella."
    Short sharp clap as back he snapped the hatch top,
    Rattle and click-click-click as the window slid up,
Creak and whine as he swung the black doors open widely,
Sway and heave as he pulled the restless horse to stillness,
    Rustle and swish and sway as Mother arose
    Pulling her cloak about her and cried, "Now, Tom,
        Run for it, child, for it's raining hard!"
Mother's idea of running didn't come up to mine,
    But even so, I had to stand on the pavement

Until she showed me the house by climbing the broad brown
    steps;
  I tumbled up after her, and we two stood panting,
    Hid from the rain, under the stone porch.

Mother unlocked the big white door and we entered the
    house:
Here it was colder than the March day, here lingered reluctant
  January and February together
    Keeping each other cold and hiding from spring.
Mother called: "Evelyn!" but her voice resounded, unanswered,
From the dull gold of the unlit hall, the uncarpeted stairs.
  "He's not here yet. Perhaps he hasn't a key.
    We'll go upstairs now. Tom, I'll show you the room
      Where I was happy, when I was your age."
So we climbed in darkness up to a third floor bedroom,
Smelling the dust aroused, the acrid smell of disuse,
  And Mother pulled up the blinds of a rear window
    Letting the grey light into the patient room.
"Dear, dear room! Sweet room! How sad that I could leave
    you!
How gaily I left you! How sad to return like a ghost walking,
  Phantom of all my youth here gathered, here walled.
    What can I do with the stuff of a vanished day?
      Years, piled up! Years, all gone!"
Then her voice changed. She said, "I must run to the front
    room,
  Open a window there. Possibly Evelyn's come."
So she rushed from the room. I heard steps deepening silence,
  It lay heavily on me. I stood, listening,
    Watching locked doors: doors to strange rooms.

Thirteen still waits the unknown from cupboards' closed doors,
  So I was glad when I heard her steps returning,
    Even more glad when she entered the room, dispelling
      Need to watch tensely for the uncertain.
She said, "He hasn't come yet. I hope that he doesn't fail me.
  Look, Tom! These are my books, these my beginnings,
    I lived here long after Mamma had died
      When I was seven—until I married."
She began then to pull off the yellow newspaper covers
  Over the book shelves; but she'd stop to listen
    Every so often, saying, "Maybe that's Evelyn,

Did you hear anything?" I'd say, "No, nothing."
"Sense and Sensibility here next to Little Women,
   Norse Mythology, Lang's Red Fairy Book—
   Did I read you The Death of Koshchei the Deathless?
   Did you hear anything?" I'd say, "No, Mother."
"It was given me after I grew to a woman—I loved it."
   There she broke off to listen; went on: "I remember
   How this room once looked: it was buried in flowers,
   Wonderful roses—still I smell them."
Knock at the front door, then. Her hand went up to her
      throat—
   She stood so, still—then called beautifully, loudly:
   "Evelyn! Evelyn! I shall come down!"

She ran out of the room and down the stairs. I followed,
   Slowly and cautiously, through unfamiliar darkness,
   Hearing her steps clatter ahead on the steep stairs,
   Hearing the front door open, and a man's deep voice
      Saying, "Maia, Maia, belovéd!"
Then the front door slammed shut; pale light vanished again,
   The darkness echoed my steps with a chill caution,
   And I went on, down toward the darker silence
   Lying below me, past doors on doors shut
      On the unnamable, maybe not locked;
Turned the head of the next flight. She said, "That's Tom
      now."
   So I continued down toward the two dark figures
   Silhouetted against the blue-grey fanlight,
   Man and woman, against the lucent grey glass
      Two dark figures, close together.
Soon I was at the bottom and Mother said, "Come here, Tom,
   This is your cousin Evelyn, Evelyn Leighton."
He said, "How do you do?" but he sounded angry:
   I was unwilling to say more to him.
Then he spoke again and he said, "Maria, for God's sake,
   Give your boy an errand or he'll be bored here;
   I didn't come for this—you know it!"

Mother stood, fingers twined, looked from one to the other,
   Painfully twisting her fingers. But Evelyn smiled,
   Smiled, with his eyes hard, smiled with his mouth alone,
      Wide smile that quite overbalanced his eyes.
"This is no day to tackle long listing of these many things.

34

It's too cold here, isn't it? You feel it, Tom?
Too cold and grey and dismal. Did you two open
   Any of those big windows above?"
I spoke: "It was black." He said, "Black? I should hope so!
Blacker, by George, than the inside of a cow."
   I thought: he means to be funny. Mother said, "Yes,
   Windows are open both front and back."
It seemed less dark now; eyes (perhaps mind) grew accus-
   tomed:
   I saw his face more clearly, the huge smile spreading
As though to embrace both Mother and me within it,
   But the eyes still cool, still unsmiling.
"What do you say? Shall we knock off now?" She said, "Yes."
"Run upstairs then, Tom, that's a good fellow,
   Shut those windows," said Evelyn, "then we'll be off—
   You're not afraid of this big dark house?"
I said, "No, not afraid," and turned to leave them, feeling
   Torn between thoughts of those strange rooms above,
   These two people waiting below me.

So I climbed steadily up the stairs, not daring to stop,
Simply because I'd said that I was not afraid, yet fearful,
   Greatly disliking this blond man with the wide smile
   Covering anger and calling to Mother: 'Belovéd!'
I looked back from the top step of the first flight. They stood
Just exactly as I'd left them standing, too still,
   Tense and still, looking up, waiting, waiting—
   Pose of expectant stillness for him—for Mother?
   I couldn't tell, she was a dark shape.
So I went up, past all the closed doors, listening hard,
Hearing no sound at all, no voice, no movement below,
   Climbed to the top floor, followed the strange hall forward,
   Entered the front room. There was the window open:
This was the window out of which she had watched to wel-
   come . . .
Evelyn, Evelyn, I shall come down . . . but she hadn't seen
   him.
   I closed the big paned window with a fine bang,
   The good noise cheered me up and I pulled the shade down,
   Let it snap up to hear it rattle.
I pulled it down again and ran from the dark to the back
   room,
   Death of Koshchei the Deathless, smell of roses,

35

Slam bang down went the open window, shade down, dusk
      followed,
   Fled down stairs in the dusk, clatter on the bare boards,
      Last flight: they stood silent below me.

Stood everlastingly silent, it seemed. But she said he had come
Here but to see her, to help her. Why were they silent, like
      this?
   It was so queer, uncomfortable. I felt more awkward
   Even than usual, clumping downstairs to join them;
But as I reached them they began talking, almost as though
I were a key to unlock speech, open a closed door leading
   Into the room of their present, critical living,
   Into the room of decision—not shrouded with papers
      Placed to protect the past, cover memory.
Mother then asked me, had I closed down the windows? I
      nodded.
"Then we'll go now, Tom." Evelyn said, "And tomorrow?"
   Mother replied, "Tomorrow? There is no tomorrow.
   Come, Tom, we'll go now." Evelyn seized her arm,
Said in his deep voice, "You can't keep me dangling, Maria,
If there is no tomorrow, there's no hereafter, but only—
   Only Josiah—so we are saying Good-bye.
   Murder your heart and happiness—if you must murder."
      Mother said, "Evelyn! Evelyn! Tom's here!"
Then he burst out, "Is it my doing? Did I bring him? Ask
      him?
   Did I compose a trio to test life, love?
Patience must be prepared for more postponement, always?
   Passion await on schoolboys? I wait no longer!"
      So he ceased and departed. The door shut.

So ends the broken song, in the blue light of evening
While mild rain fell invisibly, and the city's smooth streets
   Shone like metal rivers, and horses' heavy
   Down-stroke repeated rhythm of four shod feet
Starred the gold mirror held to the brightness of yellow lights,
Spattered in sparklets all disturbed drops idly gathered
   In slant-seen golden puddles, and awoke
   Echoes from the warm and light-pierced faces
      Of the endless black of buildings.
Past all the years I can still feel the sobs that shook
Mother pressed near me in the hansom's cloister, her voice

36

Saying over and over: "I loved him, I loved him!
Never tell anyone, Tom, my darling, I loved him."
So there re-echoed in my mind the words she'd said:
'She was content to let life's burden slip off her shoulders,'
    And I saw Christian freed from his vast bundle
    In a great flood of heavenly light, while I
        Shouldered the bundle in the darkness.
The sound of horses' feet recalls now the child's memory:
    This sharper city sound seems to be singing
Christian, Christian, in soft whispers before the dull clump
    Of the homeward down-step, rhythm of woman's sobs
        Battering sadness into memory.

DEPRIVE me not, O past, departed days,
Of all the flavour of your sharper taste,
Nor dressed alone in sombre memory's greys,
Discard spring colours in your mourning haste;
Bury not warmth that once had lit the fire
To kindle joy because my earth seemed young,
That nourished all beginnings of desire,
Or mulled the wine of youth upon my tongue;
Deprive me not of all the little words
That sang the sweet unprompted song of boy,
Cloud not the daytime of the speaking birds,
Nor wash the fabric clean from stains of joy—
And from these flavours, fire, colour and stain,
I'll build your image, till it live again.

I SLEPT alone, in this my thirteenth year;
Joss was away at school. I tumbled out
On this particular and happy day,
Dressed with the dilatory sense that time
Was endless where a quarter of an hour
Lay between future fact and present me;
Then down to breakfast, still an eager meal,

Vast quantities always ravenously consumed.
When Agatha came in, I cried aloud
In haste to be the first, "A balmy day!"
"Balmy, indeed. Well you may say the same.
Your mother wishes you to speak to her."
She looked at me and added: "Seems a shame
You haven't any appetite these days."
"I have!" I cried. She said, "Who's balmy now?"
Burst into laughter and so left the room.
"That Agatha!" I said. Then I went up
And knocked at Mother's door. She called, "Come in,"
And in I ran and kissed her. She said, "Careful,
Or you'll upset the tray." She looked so gay
That I felt even gayer than I had,
And said, "That dreadful Agatha just caught me.
I'll catch her next time, though." My mother laughed.
"You'll have to get up early to catch her.
Tom, will you skate to school?"
                                    I answered, "Yes."
"Then take the trolley home. Your game's today?"
"It is," I said.
                    "Play well. Have a good time.
I wish I could be there to see you play.
You've got a heavenly day—oh, blessed April,
It makes me long for Cottrellton."
                                    I kissed her,
And left the room, put on my skates and cap,
Picked up my school case, and so left the house,
And felt the warm sun, the caressing air,
Smelt April all about, and whizzed along
In grand excess of springtime energy.

That morning I had luck. I caught a hitch
On an express truck, hanging comfortably
To leather covered chains behind its door,
And truck and I went up Fourth Avenue
Drawn at vast speed by a fine pair of greys.
Policemen, mellowed by the mist of spring,
Turned Irish eyes away and did not see;
Another small boy joined me, on one skate,
Clutching his school books by a leather strap,
A yellow cap on his dark, curly hair.
He stayed a moment only and then said,

38

"Jees, it's too fast for me. My brother pinched
The other skate. I'll flop and hoit myself."
I said, "It's slick." He looked at me and cried,
"Ah, you got two skates, what the hell. My Ma
Will skin me if I rip this pair of pants."
The truck slowed down and he dropped off, to yell,
"Remember me to Mrs. Vanderbilt!"
I thumbed my nose at him, and he called out:
"Oh, Clarence, naughty, naughty! Poppa spank!"
But we (my truck and I) resumed our speed
In grand progression, and he soon grew small
Until his swift limp disappeared from sight.

All morning at St. David's School I swam
On a strange wave: unusual success.
I who was near the bottom of my class,
So slow to learn, so plodding in advance,
That day knew all the answers. I, alone,
Remembered, after everyone had failed,
To cry out *fregi* as the aorist tense
Of simple-seeming *frango*. My reward
Was but the smiles that covered the chagrin
Of all the brighter members of my class.
My sums were all correct—perfection grasped
In this bewildering field where Numbers swept
Like uncontrollable and wingéd wasps
About my frightened head. My master said,
"Well, Cottrell, that's a give-away. I'll expect
Your sums to be like this from now straight on.
I fancy it's been laziness."
                              Even that
Could but uplift me.
                      After school was out,
My friends and enemies alike called out,
"I fancy it's been laziness, oh, boy!
Yea, Fregi Cottrell, fancy laziness!"
But all attention is a form of praise
To any singular and awkward boy,
And is his armour, ready-made for him
By just the thrusts that thought him vulnerable.
So it became to me—for I remember
My feeling of elation, strong and sure,
More sure than usual, stronger than my day

Could commonly account me.
                              Still the horn
Had not yet emptied pleasure's measure out.
That afternoon we played a baseball game
Against a team of somewhat smaller boys
From Bannerman's Academy. We won,
And finding no great triumph in the event
Were yet contented that our score was large,
Our season well begun. I played that day
In center-field—with no security
That I should grace the post again: my hands
Were awkward to a catch, my feet were slow,
But being near the oldest boy in school
They judged I should have had experience
To compensate.
                    I caught a towering fly,
And though I fell in catching it, hung on,
And rising, threw the ball the whole way home
(Further than I had ever thrown before)
To land directly in one long straight bounce
Clean to the catcher. So they caught the small
And struggling runner who was dashing home,
And thus my action blotted out the one
And final hope of Bannerman's to score.
But now on my return, they did not jeer,
Nor tease me further, but they said, "Good work,"
"Good stuff, old Cottrell," "Cottrell, that was slick,"
And I just grinned and scuffed the earth and said,
"Aw, cut it out!" but knew my cup was full.

But now, day over, I was homeward bound.
Dusk crept upon the city as the sun
Fled the tall towers to meet the marrying sky,
And all the corners of this rectangular
And builded earth were webbed with the blue shade
Of day's new absence.
                            To my present pride
Was added one more dignity: as the dark
Deepened, the motorman of the trolley car
(By whom I stood) said, "Son, turn on the lights."
Simple and precious privilege! I climbed
On the small strapontin and switched them on,
And standing by the motorman, I shared

With him the official darkness of his place,
And in my mind performed the miracle
Of whirling brake and lever as my heel
Beat out the grand good clangour of a bell
Which his, more actual, could but echo to.

But triumphs end, and soon I walked alone
In early darkness on the friendly street,
And tasted these good moments in my mind,
Knowing obscurely of the need to tell them,
The hard, vain search for words in which I might dress
Pictures so clear, so bright that in my boy's mind
They shone with passionate fierce intensity.
I became conscious of my brother's absence, so far,
So far away my father, to whose ears this tale
Needed no dressing. Could Mother comprehend it?
Where was the word, the phrase to make such things clear?
How could you tell a woman? but she'd listen,
Warmly attentive, perhaps not understanding,
Yet in an eager, groping, loving manner,
Just as though she were trying, with her two eyes
Steadily on me, to see down inside me,
Follow the spirit, though the story's matter
Knocked at her ears in vain.
                        So in the twilight
Young Tom mounted the stoop and rang the doorbell,
Peeked through the sidelights in his fine impatience,
Saw the sweet face of Agatha draw near him,
Heard the door click and open, leaped inside,
Cried out, "We beat them, Agatha, we beat them!"—
Heard her say, "Fine! That's fine! A visitor's here,
Give me your things, Tom, Mother's in the front room",
Slipped off his coat and cap, and once more awkward,
Opened the door of the front room and entered.

There in the green-covered chair with pink flower-patterns
Sat cousin Evelyn Leighton, face awry with his great smile;
    Mother sat on the sofa in the lamplight,
    Face flushed and glowing. She was also smiling.
They both started to speak at once, their voices clashing,
Then as suddenly stopping, cried out, "Sorry—excuse me."
    Silence a small sweet second, a pause, a pulse-beat,
    And my mother said, "Come, Tom, did you beat them?"

41

My tongue said "Yes," but my heart was silent.
Evelyn said, "Well done, boy. Well, Maria, I'm off now."
"No, not yet," she answered. "Tom must go up and get ready,
  Supper is waiting for him, and we'll talk then,
  He shall tell everything. My, I long to hear it!"
Evelyn looked at me and he said, "I think that he'd rather
Tell the tale while it's hot, isn't that so for a fact, Tom?"
  It was so, or had been—but I felt flow
  Anger like darkness, over the mind and body
    Like the shadows on tall towers.
Who was he to interpret between me and my mother?
  Mother was trembling, and I trembled too.
Who was he to turn the taste of triumph to anger?
  Mother was trembling, but for what she trembled
    I knew not, nor whence came anger.

He took the bull by the horns, and said, "Tom, we're fated
Always to get in each other's hair. I'm awfully sorry.
  We'll start fresh for the next time, so our meeting
  Will be arranged for the joy of all three of us.
Maybe some day we'll go off on an expedition, we three,
Hire a hack and go off for the whole good spring day
  Up in the country. Right?" But I was thinking,
  Hearing my mother weep in the close, dark hansom,
    Sobs and torn words and the horse's clatter.
What I said was but an excuse, unconscious refusal:
  "Father is coming home in a day or so."
Evelyn reddened and turned to my mother, saying, "Maria,
  Don't say I haven't tried. Can you do nothing?
Now I shall say good-night." He left us. Again we listened,
  Heard the door close, the beat of his feet on the stoop,
    Battering anger into memory.

SUN, moon, stars, earth and heaven, cloud and sea
Bind aerial filaments to the ear of youth
And in gigantic code vibrate the key
In messages of untranslated truth,

Mystic arrangements of his life received
Beyond the power of human comprehension,
Not understood but heard, and heard, believed,
Incredible logic in a strict declension:
Logic of moon-rise, of the heavy tides,
Torpor and energy of noonday sun,
Trinity's unity that thrice divides,
Life that is lost and instantly is won:
When the man blooms, the boy is left behind
Deaf to such messages, to their mystery blind.

✦   ✦

ONE SUMMER passed, long winter nearly gone,
Spring threatening softness to the rigid hills: spring,
Troubler of action, saying *yes* and *no,* softly
In the same breath, disturbing breath, singing
Wildness and ease and power, but all these
Songs for the future, never now. I heard it
Strange and familiar in new hills, among the few
Familiar trees, the like unlikeness of birds
Among strange branches. But I bore this fever,
This discontent exalted, the lax sinew,
The moodiness, the passion in a fresh blade
Green in the winter brown, the mystic blue
Turning to trembling the young heart bewildered
Beneath an easier sky, trembling and rueful:
As though all spring lay in the gate of one trap
Sprung for an action or an indecision,
Offering happiness in captivity, no hurt,
Only the season's madness for your prison.

This was a hard time: a new school, little help,
Life to adjust to new ways just as life grew
Slender on a new vine, budded stem feeling
Sap flow, spring flood; life and the season truly
Now at first coincident; hard, sweet juncture
Tearing like flood water through the soft banks
Of this my new meadow, making a new bed,
Flooding the secret thickets that grew rankly,
Confident and rootless—brown flood, singing flood,
Builder, destroyer, thirst for him who drank it.

Joss was no help to me, he loved no one then,
His love was but affection, like the glancing
Riffled reflection of a flowing river.
Easter was near at hand and Joss, entranced,
Plotted his holiday of ten days' fishing
Off with my father. Mother was in Europe
Travelling with her feminist friend, Miss Darnley,
Sending me postal cards, covered with the sloping
Delicate writing of her love, thin, strong
Wire to link all distance to illusion.
I was to go that Easter to the country,
Stay with my grandfather—I had no refusal.
Spring in Rhode Island, I did not know its measure:
Summer and Cottrellton in my mind confusing.

Mild April day when John Ward drove me from Chog's Cove
Home by the wet roads. I talked of my new school easily,
I could let go to him, he was so removed.
But soon I became aware of the country, beastly,
Bare and brown and wet, withholding, hiding,
Under transparent thickets, under its open fields,
Hard, unwelcoming. Where was the green, the softness,
Where was the blue sea? Here the water was grey steel
Measured against the thin and the miserly blue
Of the April evening sky.
                                        We ceased from talking,
Jogged along in silence. I looked about me
Trying to love it, trying to find love, sulky,
Hurt by the need to change, the eternal changing,
Love that could run, could gallop, but never walk.

Then this mood changed over, for there were houses,
Roofs and familiar trees and familiar faces,
Curve of the shore, old friends of boulders spouting
Spray in a hiss and a gurgle from gravel-sprent water;
Known good music of horses' hooves on bridge-boards
Rattled and drummed over the mud-banked inlet;
Yellow sides gleaming, seen as never before,
Of *our* long house shining through leafless branches;
Turn in the road, no change, perhaps no wetter
Than after a good north-easter—smell of the salt sea
Fiercer and sharper, cutting—it did not matter,
It was the sea-scent, breath of the live sea spreading

44

Over my spirit, down in my heart to settle;
Now the mauve of the roof, the grey of the building,
Pale clear shadow on the great mass of barn;
Chepaug Lighthouse, white on a pallid ocean,
Holding the last light of day like fire drawn
Hard on an east sky, moth-wing flick of yellow
Vanishing light as it greeted the leaning dusk,
Bent to the mirror of evening caught in the sea;
Grandfather's house! Negro voice of Charles, soft, husky,
Welcoming child-man, late small boy, new-sprung youth—
Lights in the warm hall, and a great warm voice
Shouting aloud, "By God! but the boy's on time!"
Charles took my bag. I welcomed the pleasant noise
Grandfather made as he called me. I ran to him,
Flung myself into his arms that gripped like a vise,
Grateful and loving and happy and sorry together,
Needing a thousand things I could not name.

Then I went up into the sweet-smelling blue room:
There was my bag, and here a heavenly sameness,
And above all, I was at last alone,
Free from the endless watch of the other boys' eyes,
Free from the crowded, the unassimilated
Torturing novelty of the too-new school life.
Supper and brief talk followed, but I grew drowsy,
Eyelids weighted and clumsy, the vision blurred;
Soon I went up to bed, savouring freshly
That great luxury, solitude, not being herded,
Sense of the shut door: sense of the open window,
Stir of the waves for my ears alone occurring.

2

Then the good morning came, shrouded in gentle light,
The sun too lazy to quit his heavenly harem
Of softly feminine clouds.
                                    I rose to the tinkle
Of breakfast silver, borne on the languid air
Through my peaceful window. I heard the vibrance,
Cut by curious curses, that grandfather's voice had,
Piercing the wooden walls; sometimes I'd hear
Soft music of Charles's words, not gay, not sad,
Just pleasant and steady:

45

Ununderstandable chorus,
Sung to the fall of the waves on the shore, addressing
Pagan music to honour the moon's pale image,
Western moon in the water; the calling, restless,
Distance-strained of dissonance, fat gulls feeding
At the innumerous, ceaseless, Ephesian breasts
Of the breathing water.
                    Charles came into my room,
Tall and black and solid, straight as an arrow,
Goodness walking, smile with a large reserve,
Face that echoed peace and a touch of sorrow,
Voice of the deep wind in the home-bound rigging.
"Well, good morning! Slept well, Mr. Tom, didn't you?"
"Morning, Charles," I said. "I slept well, thank you.
What will the weather be like?" He went to the window,
Peered a moment out at the day. "Good weather,
Sun is coming, he's going to rise up soon,
We'll be warm after lunch. Mr. Cottrell tells me
He's not feeling too spry, getting up noontime.
Breakfast is ready. Will I close the window down?"
"No, don't bother. Oh, Charles, I must have been loony
Not to have wanted to come here." Strange how easy
Talk could run with a man like Charles, when speech
Dried in my throat with my equals! He tipped back
His dark head a bit and he laughed. "We'll teach you
All you got to know about springtime hereabouts."
Then he turned and made for the door. My suitcase
Lay by the foot of the bed, and he didn't see it.
He tripped over it, stumbled forward, his face
Brushing the foot of the bed as he fell resounding
Onto the matted floor.
                    I cried, "Oh! Charles!
Golly, you must be hurt!" But he said nothing,
Picked himself up and brushed his clothes, a scar
Of blood on his dark face. Then he looked at me,
Saying quietly, "Well now, that was a jar."
I said, "Yes, I'll bet, but Charles, you didn't swear?"
I was thinking of Grandfather.
                              "No sir, no.
No good use to swearing." I said, "No use?"
"Some there is that does, but some don't do so—
No sir, I don't swear." He stood a moment
Looking away beyond me, but his deep eyes

46

Fled to far space not caught with walls or doors.
Then he smiled a little.
                              "I was surprised
Right in the centre of cuss-words once. Long ago
When I was young and hearty and full of the devil,
I near to broke my shin on a stone—the plough
That I was follering down a loamy level,
Jammed up on a rock and I tripped. Then I cut loose,
And Mr. Tom, the words I used then was evil,
But flowed in a smooth fine flow. I was accustomed.
So I was cussing, till presently the Lord Jesus
Stood in the furrow and He said, 'See here, Charles,
You got no business to talk so—it plumb freezes
My bones to the marrer to hear you abuse My name.'
And I said, 'Sorry, Lord Jesus,' and He said, 'Son,
Don't go to cussing again.' Then He went away.
I haven't swore since that time. I couldn't have done it.
I told your grandmother and she comprehended, and—
I told Mr. Cottrell."
                              "Oh—what did he say?"
"I really don't know," said Charles. "Mr. Cottrell stood
And stared at me for a spell without no saying
And then said something, it must have been foreign language,
I didn't just catch what it meant."
                                        Then he turned away,
And left the room and the door shut, most slowly,
Softly as always, leaving his presence behind.

3

Later that afternoon I went down to the stable
Looking for something to occupy body and mind
Left to themselves on a spring day. John Ward sat
On a wooden chair in the first pale, meagre sunlight,
Cleaning the curb chains, that he'd pick up dripping
Out of a bucket of brine. I remembered one bright
Joke I had heard before and I said, "Well, John,
I see you're fond of pickles." He looked at me
With solemn eyes and held up a clanking curb-chain,
Shook it and answered slowly, seriously,
"Some is and some is not. Now you take Jake,
He don't speak often, but gracious, seemingly,
He's crazy when it comes to pickles. I've seen him

47

Swallow 'em for an hour. Pickled green gages."
"I meant this brine, this pickle."
                              John shook his head,
Answered, "You've got to do something to earn your wages.
Horses are turned to grass when there's none to ride 'em."
"Are they all turned out?" I asked.
                              "You aiming to ride?
Thought you could ride in April?"
                              "But John, why not?"
He rubbed at his chain and he looked at it smiling widely.
"Bits in pickle and horses out in the meadow.
Bridles and saddles to clean and wash, work for fair, boy.
Who's going to curry the horses? Their coats is longer
Than a boy's hair is who hasn't had a hair-cut."
I put my hand to my hair and he laughed aloud.
"Where is Jake?" I asked.
                              "He's down to the Bear Bog,
Fixing the fencing. You better go down and help him.
He's digging holes."
                              I turned away, feeling gloomy,
But as I moved he said, "It just might happen
A horse could be handy to ride by tomorrow noon,"
But he added quickly: "If your grandpop should say so."
"That'll be grand," I said. "I knew you were joking."
"Did you?" he answered. "You better go look for Jake,
I've got no time for chatter," and then he poked
His hand in the brine pail, swishing the chains around.
I turned and left him, feeling a bit uncertain
If he were joking or not.
                              Then I went down
To the bay's edge to hear the treble waves hurtling
Grey-green music against the bass of the shore.
I followed the mark of the tideline, leaping and hurdling
Brown and grey rocks, feeling the sun grow warm,
Watching the pale sky luminous to the northward,
Watching the pink flush grow on the huckleberry
Under increasing light as the sun came forth
Clothed in his silken shade and his satin shadow.
The tide was low and a rock we called the Heron,
Swayed in the water as the drifting gradual
Mass of its glittering seaweed, waving, stirring,
Followed the water's motion.
                              I left the shore there,

48

Pushed through the briar and berry and under the thorn,
Climbed to the rise where the naked maples fairly
Bridged the hollow of blue in the western sky.
You had to dodge the blackberry there, its tearing
Tentacles clung and ripped, overarching the bay,
Mingled with wild rose; the underbrush grew thickly
Along the edge of the maples, dead meadow-sweet,
Steeple-bush whips for the legs and the sharper pricking
Of catbriar strands from a fallen birch to a maple.
Up in the grove it was clear, once you got past this:
I'd just raised the hard, sharp line of the stone ledge
Pointing the north star now and for everlasting,
Great curved circle of stone on the edge of the Bear Bog,
When I heard voices.
                    I said, I'm alone, I'm an Indian,
Weekaho Hotanka, I'm the Black Raven,
I'll be a Sioux, there's no one to see me, no grinning
Boys to make fun of me. This is the way to scout people,
Indian manner, alone. Now keep your chin down,
The top of your head won't show the way your face will.
So I crept through the brush, slow inch on inch,
Got through the undergrowth to the clearer maples,
Paused by a rock to breathe, thinking, This is a cinch,
When I get good and close I can hear what they're saying,
See them without their seeing me, Indian-sneaking.
Then I thought: I wonder who's talking to Jake?
So I listened. I couldn't be sure who was speaking
Just at first, for I heard between my heart-thumps
Only Jake's flat voice ring.
                    Then I crawled up nearer,
Heading for one great boulder right on the steep edge
Overlooking the hollow: there I'd see clearly
Into the open bottom, the great bare rock,
See who was talking to Jake without much fear
That they could see me once I was close behind it.
So I crawled in a wide curve, carefully circling,
Getting the boulder between me and the mingled
Voices dimly heard now through the jerky
Breath of the hostile scout who crept on the warpath.
Then I was there at last and I lay still, panting hard,
Waiting for breath to cease from the noisy drumming
That deafened the ears. Heart beats slowly retarded,
The voices began to come clearer, clearer, close to me.

49

Suddenly I became aware of the wonderful music,
Tuned by Yankee rocks to the clear perfection
Of Charles's utterance.
                    Why was Charles there using
Singing words to the emptiness of Jake?
I couldn't imagine the picture, my mind refused it.
I crept up closer and peered through a cleft in the rock:
The Indian play was forgotten, just Tom astonished
Froze to the spectacle there below him.

Jake was kneeling and on his face the passionate,
Hungry look of a man wrapt in his inner
Self spread out to the sun. I hardly knew him:
Where was the empty expression, the dull, detached,
Walking strength of his silence? The usual, rueful
Pucker of brow bewildered but uncomprehending?
Charles stood up behind him, arms outflung,
Close to the curve of precipitous sunlit rock,
Fingers bent in the fissures to which they clung,
Head thrown back, the whites of uplifted eyes
Bright in his good face.
                    His words were lunging
Waves of sound that beat on the closeted air,
Caught in the cup of the land that so enclosed them,
Rock for a locked door, circled earth for a wall.
Charles was praying loudly, the words arose then
Carrying clearly: "Hail Mary, full of Grace,
The Lord is with thee: blessed art thou among women,
And blessed is the fruit of thy womb, Jesus,
Holy Mary, Mother of God, pray for us sinners,
Now and at the hour of our death. Amen!"
Jake's thin whine of a voice echoed *Amen,*
His body weaving slightly from side to side.
Charles left his rock and stood by Jake then,
Joined his palms together as Jake did,
Lifted his eyes to the sky again,
Cried with a loud voice, "Lord have mercy!"
"Lord have mercy," echoed Jake's voice,
Growing higher, shriller, more thin,
Organ notes of Charles, rejoicing,
Alternating now, faster and faster,
"Christ have mercy"—the answer, "Christ have mercy."

"Christ hear us"—thin ringing echo, "Christ graciously hear
     us."
Repeated, "Christ graciously hear us," hard and piercing.
Jake bowed his head then, swaying,
Fingers twitching together, palms moving,
Rubbing each other, slowly, ecstatically.
Silence a moment, the warm sun glowing,
Caught in the hollow. Sweet goodness again,
Charles's voice a deep earth groove
Sluicing the water of fine passion:
"Mirror of justice, Seat of Wisdom,
Cause of our joy, spiritual vessel,
Singular vessel of devotion,
Mystical Rose, Tower of David,
Tower of Ivory, House of Gold,
Ark of the Covenant, Gate of Heaven . . ."
Jake looked up at Charles and my blood ran cold,
It frightened me, there was froth on the edge of his lips.
Charles was moving his feet to the beat of the words:
"Morning Star, Health of the sick,
Refuge of sinners . . ."
                              The froth grew worse,
Jake unclasped his hands, they were shaking and trembling,
Twisted his body around like the neck of a bird,
Till he faced towards Charles. He lifted up his hands,
Laid them on Charles's thigh, and a quavering *Aaah!*
Came from the back of his throat. Charles hesitated,
Cried again in a loud voice, "Morning Star!"
The great hands fluttered upon his leg and thigh—
Then Charles shouted loudly, "Lamb of God!"
Turned and threw Jake down with a swinging blow
Till his body lay sprawled, his face in the soft brown sod,
And Charles stood over him, fists clenched, crying,
"Lamb of God who takest away the sins of the world—
O Lamb of God, who takest away the *sins of the world!*"
Then silence a heart beat, and Jake stirred;
His voice, thin and nasal and flat and creepy,
Answered obedient: "Spare us, O Lord."

I felt bewildered and slightly sick at my stomach;
Dropped my head and crept away from the boulder,
Crawled through the maple grove, through clammy mosses,

51

Feeling the shade grow chill, my body grow colder,
Out to the warm sun, crash through the brush to the good
    shore,
Sick and troubled and stirred in a terrible manner.

This still clings to my mind in the sensitive hours,
Flutters my heart with a hot and terrible fanning
As I creep down the knife edge of my thin pride
Between the light and the darkness.

4

In those days it was always so hard for me
To tell a story, save by writing it down
For no eye but my own. The searching toil
Of finding words, the sentences rankly grown
In thickets line on line, impassable, dense,
Calling for infinite labour to cut in short lengths
And bind to usable faggots.
                              So that evening
I sat in misery, wishing I had the strength
To tell my story. Grandfather asked of my new school;
I answered him; but then at last he spoke
Of this close here and now, saying, "Well, Tom,
What did you do this afternoon?" The smoke
Of his cigar wreathed up under the warm lamp,
Fled like a mist from the top of the shade, thin and ghostly,
Hypnotizing my mind. I answered, uncomfortable,
"Nothing so very much. I went to the stables."
"See John Ward?"
                  "He said I could ride tomorrow,
If you'd say yes. He said that he might be able
To get the horses ready by noon tomorrow.
He always calls you my grandpop."
                                   Grandfather laughed.
"Yes, he would. We might go riding together.
After you'd seen John—what did you do after?"
"I walked up the shore a bit. As far as the Heron.
The tide was low. The country looks kind of funny
Without any green leaves."
                          "They'll come soon enough.
I like it this way, soft colours under the pale sun."
I said nothing, I watched the smoke. The fine smell

Permeated the room. "I used to go gunning
Up by the Bear Bog." Then he smoked in silence,
Looking at me, and I avoided his eyes,
Twiddling my fingers.

"Tom, have you been into mischief?"
I said, "No," but I knew my colour was rising
As though I were guilty of something. He said, "You're sure?"
I didn't know how to answer.

"You're troubled by something.
Something you've done or seen. Better let me help you."
How does he know? I thought, and I felt a lumpy
Substance caught in my throat and I couldn't speak,
But I wanted to cry, feeling desperately ashamed
Of the mere wanting. But how could you ever begin?
Bits of fierce-coloured images blew to a flame
Inside my mind—but the words, where were the words?
Where was the speech that wouldn't stumble lamely?
Wasn't it telling tales? I'd been in hiding,
Listeners never hear good—but the end of that said:
Of themselves. This wasn't of me, but of Jake and Charles,
Of something good and of something sickening, mad,
Out of the reach of day or the day's shining.
Where were the words?

"I think you're beginning to grow,
That's a hard process. Nobody really can lift you
On to the final answers, for all our knowing
Stems from experience. Incomprehensible things
Beyond experience yield to the explanations
Thoughtfully given by age. You won't believe now,
But when it happens to you, your new sensation
Casts a familiar shadow." His voice was gentle,
Strong and kind, but free from that curious passion:
Usual weave of its strength.

"It was Charles and Jake."
That was the best I could do. Grandfather spoke slowly:
"What did they do, Tom?"

"Well, I saw Charles praying,
Down by the Bear Bog. I was behind a boulder."
"Was he alone?"

"No."

"Jake was there?"

"Yes, kneeling
In front of the great rock," and I added quickly,

53

"I hid there, they didn't see me." His embracing
Voice like the feel of strong arms in night's sickness,
Sounded toward comfort: "Did the praying upset you?"
I said, "No, it was wonderful, Charles's praying."
"Jake?"
      "His face was funny."
                    "What sort of funny?"
"He looked all queer and white, and he kept on swaying,
He looked at Charles." I shuddered a little. "He grabbed
    him."
"Jake did?" I nodded, I heard the scene replayed
In the hollow of echoing brain.
                    "What did Charles do, boy?"
"He pushed him down and Jake fell. Charles went on.
He went right on with his praying and Jake answered,
Lying there on the ground, his head sort of bent down,
He sounded different."
            "And then?"
                        "I ran away then,
They didn't see me. I didn't want to be seen."
"You were troubled by this?"
                    "I felt kind of sick. I ran."
"I see," said Grandfather. He'd been watching me keenly,
Now he lifted his eyes and smoked in silence,
But sweeter, more comforting silence I never knew:
His presence wrapped me, I felt no longer like crying,
The words had eased me, confession's comfort grew
With the elapsing pulse-throbs; there was no anger
Battering at me for a fault told truly.
Finally, though, he spoke, his voice still gentle,
Somewhat removed now.
                "The flaw of untransmuted
Iron runs through the stuff of all our steel—
But Jake's not steel, really—more like the roots
Of some big tree gnawed by the blind creeping
Slugs of an old soil.
                Dammit, if you were older,
I'd give you instances of fine men corrupted—
Even the fine ones go. Jake was a soldier.
Joined the army a good while back—poor chap,
He was in love with a girl who worked for your mother,
But she as an odd one, a kleptomaniac, really,
Stole a bit of money, silver and other

Oddments about the house. And she was pretty,
Neat and good at her job, and made no bother
With extra work. But finally she was caught out,
Too much money had disappeared. They sacked her.
They could have prosecuted—I should have done so,
But then, your mother is soft. Jake was distracted.
The girl just disappeared and he couldn't find her,
He drifted off in search and he joined the army,
Angry and never believing the girl was guilty.
He saw his service and I think it's harmed him,
He has faced death, and by God, yes, mutilation,
Out in the Philippines—saw his friends go in an agony
Of hard, animal cries—he had to go forward, then.
Discipline. Now that's over. His spirit flags, he
Utters his animal cries in peace and in weakness,
A false flame lighting his spirit. Poor spirit lagging!
There are some fine new engines get on the wrong track,
Rush like the devil backward—perhaps someone
Opened a switch through error. All that power
Speeds to collision, a vast wreckage dumbly
Pointing the failure of a system. Desperate,
Fearful reminder of man's ever-fallible
Self-direction. Most of us need some power
Edged with a clear promise, a threat so terrible
We shall pay heed to it.
                              We fear the power of Hell,
Beg for a final reward and pay to get it,
Sin and repent, and repeat—obscurely believing
Only that in the end it is always better,
Safer and better, to conform to the general
Rule than deny it. So we try to fettle
Destiny with a fear. Yet even in misery,
Weak with our desperate weakness, or strong in strength,
Torn with terror, or blinded with our self-hood,
We cry, 'Iō moi moi, pōs an oloiman!' "
He looked at me. "You don't know what that means,
It says, 'Woe! Woe! if only I could die!'
You see? Not even fear's valid, when our life
Tinkles to shards from moulded form and so lies
Shattered about us.
                              It's a short road from fear,
To say—perhaps you can translate," he paused;
" 'Certum est quia impossibile.' Well, Tom?"

55

I said, "I think so. 'It is'—well—'sure because
It is impossible.'"
                                "That's it."
                                                "What does it mean?"
"What does it mean? It's the hair line of the law,
The point where light emerges from all darkness
While yet the source of light and dark's unquestioned;
It's music from the spheres, or a dog's barking
Under the high moon that's no moon to him;
It is the shut door of the thinking mind,
Back of whose opaque panels lies a great world
Moving, ununderstandable, through the vast, blind
Reaches of mystery . . .
                                But this is not mine, Tom—
I'm an old plodder, scratching his too-real head,
Feeling his own aches, watching the slow night fall
On his long day. Just an old horse-car, ready
To have a fine machine replace him, yet still
Following down the silver-worn tracks steadily.

When your grandmother lived, she trod so lightly
On the mysterious path. She said the night-time
Brought the spirit of God down, close and happy,
Back of the stars—that even the thunder and lightning
Spoke the voice of God's mercy. I used to tell her
All the credible reasons for the bright flashing
Sword of the storm and she would say, always laughing,
'Dear Enrico, how blind you are—or how bashful:
Naked before the Lord who made your nakedness.
Must your Mr. Franklin's pure scientific rovings
Lead my God down a string to be put in a bottle?
God is electric, so? E pur si muove!'
Ah, but I'm rambling, now—and by God Almighty,
My blasted cigar's gone out."
                                He turned slowly,
Felt for a match and struck it. The soft glow lighted
Warmth for the lines of his face.
                                        "Negroes are curious,
There's a quality in them beyond our knowing.
Most that we see in them is surface, spurious,
Worn for our seeing. Now, my wife Francesca
Moved with the grace of a child in mind and body,
Never grew old for the small things. So Charles adored her.

56

First he adored her, then he adored her God,
Left his way for hers. He was strong and gentle,
Quiet about the house. All the dogs and cats
Followed him round, adoring. But your grandmother
Said he was too damn quiet, she missed the rattle
Of her Italian servants. But soon his laughter,
Deep and rich and easily roused, could matter
More to her pleasure, so she then declared,
Than the style she first had missed.
                                        All life I've tried
To cultivate one philosophy—never succeeded—
Tried to make ambition grow side by side
With a full content in living. Too hard for me.
I needed discontent to reach the high places,
Whipped myself with the whips of my own wishing,
Saw my life go downward toward mean failure,
Or saw it rise to incredible heights. The price
Was but an unequal spirit.
                            She knew the answer:
Followed a clear path, lightly, not over-wishful,
Saw the whole pattern of life in an hour's chance
Occupation. She saw that the sum of living
Made but the sum of years spent on this planet,
Neither more nor less—that the good was good,
The evil, evil, the purpose of life was living,
That the end of life was death and a clear hereafter
Grown from the tree of life as sure as leaves
Follow the pattern that the maple's good sap
Orders upon them.
                    This she drew from religion,
Drew from a near God, from a Virgin Mary
Fruitful in help and comfort, a loving Son
Close to her goings. These things she proclaimed.
Charles couldn't follow her realistic credo—
He took the substance and fitted it to his spirit,
Followed her, joined her church—but not as she'd do,
Bearing the burden of life because you were living,
But in the passion of burdens borne, the great need
To feel the load was part of the vast, loving
Substance of God's will, mystical yet explicit."

Grandfather paused a moment, then said, "I'm talking
Over your head. Is this way beyond you? Is it?"

I said, "No, sir."
            "Anyway, it'll be good for you,
Chuck you into the water and let you swim,
Damn deep water."
                    I said, "Oh, but Jake?"
"Jake—yes—I hadn't forgotten—we're coming back to him.
It's not easy.
                There are some things we ought not
Ever attempt. Mucking about with the other
Fellow's poor, single life is one. You'll see that—
Sure as God made little apples, some day you'll bother
Trying to fit your cap to somebody else's
Head or trying to alter his cap or his clothes, or
Change the shape of his clothes to the ones you wear.
It is a bad idea. It's always dangerous.
Nearly always it fails. Hardest thing in the world
Is to get under your own skin. It's no damn use
Thinking you'll ever be able to creep in under
Somebody else's: most skins fit too tightly.
Leave them alone. Offer them help if they need it,
Offer them help for *their* need—but walk lightly
Over the other chap's lawn. Don't leave your great heel marks
Scarring his surface. His grass grows his own way.
Don't you try to weed it for him, not ever—
Maybe he likes to see grass starred with the blazing
Stars of the dandelions. It's none of your business.
You can happily occupy all your own days
Keeping your own lawn pure and perfect and green.
You never feel the wind that bends the spirit
Unless that spirit is yours. Maybe it's better
His spirit should be bending, that he may hear it:
Music of wind in his branches that sing to the blowing
Your ears are deaf to.
                        There's the whole thing. Your Grandmother
Swept on her own course, never once interfering,
She and I so different, respecting each other,
Leaving each other alone, with our own foibles,
With our own singularities, helping, not haltering
Seeing no purpose served by trying to change
Fundamentals of life. One tree can alter
The whole last shape of another one growing beside it,
Just by its shade, but the growth of neither need falter;
They go on—though in the final growing

58

Their roots, interlocking, weaving together,
Suck the same moisture. Ring the bell, I want whisky."
I rose and rang the bell.

                          "It's no matter whether
Your intentions are good or bad or average,
Proselytizing's the trouble. Now there's the thing
Grandmother never did. She went her own gait,
Straight and happy and good, not ever bothering
To interfere, but setting her fine example—
And Charles just followed her of his own volition.
There's the difference."

                          Charles came into the room.
"Did you ring, Mr. Cottrell?"

                                "Hell and perdition!
Where's my whisky, Charles?"

                                "Just getting it ready,
It's but a quarter past nine. There's milk in addition
For Mr. Tom."

              "Oh." Grandfather looked at his watch.
"Quarter past nine. I thought that it must be later.
Fetch it along, Charles." Charles said, "Yessir," and vanished.
"Damn!" said Grandfather, "he never keeps me waiting,
Ought to have known. I curse and I find he's right."
He sighed and shook his head. "There are some times, though,
When I wish he'd get angry, too, for nothing at all,
And let me feel superior. Fritter and fry me!
Well, where were we? Oh yes, now take your father,
Not inconsiderable really, a genuine talent,
Clever enough, but vain and conceited as hell.
He's all mind and body. Your mother's all heart,
He tries to make her fit to his life of ethics,
She tries to make him into a moral party,
Be a good influence. Gosh! it makes me weep.
Here I sit with seventy well behind me,
The end of my days in sight, a battered old tramp
Fetching an unknown port, with a chart designed
For inland waters—hoping to see great sights,
And seeing mostly a spiral of greedy gulls
Diving for scraps of offal.

                          I, too, was an artist,
Just beginning to learn that the longest pull
Was when you'd begun to learn that you'd just begun
The job of learning.

And then I jumped in a river,
Jumped in hot and sweaty to icy water,
Pulled out a poor damned soul who had tried to deliver
His body from slow dissolution: so he returned
To the long business of watching corruption dissever
Life from his members—in a lawful manner.
Also the Hero painted no more thereafter:
Damned if he'd watch his pure strong line grow shaky,
Pallid, impure, a subject for tears and laughter,
Frans Hals painting after his death had seized him.
Fine job, interference."
     I heard the tinkle
The glasses made on the tray that Charles was carrying.
Grandfather laughed, and all the deep, clear wrinkles
Marking his face, grew curved in the yellow light.
His great voice had gone back to its usual strength
In these last moments, and I felt comforted,
Loving the grand sound and the splendid lengthy
Words that poured out from him, half-understood,
Beating like breakers from whose green and drenching
Down-curve one issued sputtering and breathless,
Fearful and yet refreshed.
     So I no longer
Hated the thought of meeting with Charles alone
Out in the corridor.
      Charles entered; his strong
Hands placed the tray down softly by the chair
Grandfather sat in. He said, "Anything more now?
Biscuits and milk here." Grandfather said, "Thank you.
Charles, the boy here, playing down by the shore,
Got up close to the Bear Bog. He heard you praying."
"Did he now?" said Charles.
       "Yes, and he watched you,
Saw Jake, too."
    "Good gracious."
        "He didn't like it.
Something wrong there, Charles."
       "Yes, Mr. Cottrell,
Something mighty wrong. I'm sorry he seen it."
He shook his head.
      "It seems to me you've botched it—
Mind you, I put no blame. He's a poor sort, man,
Leave him alone. Let the priest do priest's business,

Wanting to help is not enough."
                        "You're right, sir."
"He's no-account, Charles. Evil has often arisen
Out of the fine things. There! we'll say no more, now,
I'll be going up in about ten minutes."
Charles just nodded and left us. We sat in silence,
Having our drinks, and when my milk was finished,
Grandfather said, "Go up to bed now, boy,
You should be tired. Good night."
                        I left him quickly,
Going up to the blue room, now not so happy
In its solitude. Soon the day had thickly
Peopled my mind in the darkness with its figures,
Terrible figures, and I felt the sickness
Born of the afternoon return upon me.
How many times since have I hid my eyes
Praying the light of day would return to blind me,
Banish the night-wrought memories that arise
Out of the darkness!
                        My new world was changing—
Safe and firm no longer: but all the splendid
Words that Grandfather spoke were comfort's echo,
Doubled in meaning now, day's fury ended.
Yet all the swift-made, rapidly imposed,
Close-fitting garments that civil anno domini
Nineteen hundred and ten had patiently wrought
(Year upon failing year had patterned the solemn trial
For this late model), ripped, ravelled, and were cut then
Clean by the sharp shears of one common night.

WHEN winterberry lifts its scarlet flame
Against the ashes of December sky,
Winter itself must bear another blame:
Mother-of-spring whose warmth is but a lie.
But of these flames of static providence,
Shall growth and motion once again be born,
Opening in moist and pearly innocence

61

Where the fierce redness of their shell is torn.
And shall I then remember the still hour
Of patient buds upon a blacker stem,
Or when the leaf has flung aside the flower,
Shall I remember innocence of them?
When winterberry lifts again its flame
I shall be old, and innocence a name.

⸱   ⸱

THESE adult affirmations are so hard!
I conjure night
Back to the youthful sorrow,
Back to the flooding joy whose sharper light
Pierced through the flesh unquestioning; I borrow
Sleep from a past of darkness brightly starred.
Now of my need
I'll recreate the images of youth
Before it ended, while its affirmation
Pointed unmeasured truth:
No puzzle of the day sleep could not solve:
So the bright glare of day blinds older eyes
That once had knowledge of the night's creation,
Seeing the whole great universe revolve
In shallow and tumultuous constellation
Of the field's fireflies.
So you shall see
The ghost of Sally, with her eyes of blue,
The auburn glinting of her hair, the three
Dimples of mouth and chin.
There is no true
Sally but this who moves upon the way
Of youthful rule,
Of memory's distant, thin
Trail of the summer's past, recaptured day,
In dress of green as cool
As water's wavering reverse that weaves
Its image leaves.
I give you Sally for your own to keep
Forever as an image in the pale
Flame of the summer evening, under deep
Spreading of maples by the tiny strand
Of sharply scented sand

On Nyas River with its wavering veil
Of sun-bred mist;
I give you Sally, pretty and unkissed,
But you must place my shadow by her side,
And hear our laughter ring upon the clear
Silence of evening, hear the small and dear
Words of our inexperience that abide,
The echoes of our pleasure that persist.
I give you all our innocence to hold:
It walked the lengthened hill
Past the dim cedars that were dark and bold
Against the still
Enchantment in the levels of the sky
Graded to promises of night's advance,
Toned to the promise of the night's romance,
And all the high
And quivering words that lay upon our hearts:
Unspoken love's delicious counterparts.
She leaves in darkness and I touch her hand,
Stealing the handkerchief that can retain
The essence of her being in its sweet,
Its delicate and bland
Memory-disturbing scent that fills my brain
In absence with defeat
That still I had not touched her with my lips.
We speak, with joy made actual by sorrow,
Thinking but this: tomorrow and tomorrow—
And so we part. She slips
Into the darkness.
So my path must lead
Along the road to home: to home, alone,
Yet not a tragic loneliness
Wrought of an absence in a love's distress,
But a companioned loneliness, a zone
Walled by the images my mind could breed
Of Sally in a thousand dimly known
Phases of living;
So at home to see
The others of my world but as the ghosts,
Sally the one reality,
Her hidden handkerchief forever giving
Floods of sweet sadness, welcome as the hosts
Of inward images not ever clear

Nor wanted clearly.
                    Then at last to bed,
To press the scented souvenir and feel
        The hour grow near
(As sleep descends upon the pillowed head)
When courage like a shining sword of steel
Shall arm me to the capture of all bliss,
When on indefinite morrows I shall press
My lips to Sally's cheek in love's caress
        And feel her kiss
Brush on my own, and know that all the deep
World of our love is ours to hold and keep.
Sally is fled. So fled the bright pretence
Of love; so fled my youth, my innocence.

PART TWO

WHO SHALL be judge? Or by what witnessed act
Shall we sum up the measure of a worth?
By the response denied? Who has not lacked
The power to respond in the heart's dearth?
By this fine qualified philosophy?
That pure production of a workman's skill?
This will to do? Or doing's scarcity?
This crumbling weakness, or the strength that still
Flexes its muscles when the need is fled?
Who shall be judge? for in the rarely seen
Close-covered precinct of the quick and dead
Acts of the soul, you find the one just mean.
I leave these judgments to the God whose birth
Turned hopeless burial to the quickening earth.

AT Christmas time, in my first year at Harvard
(While I was home to have my holidays
And, Christmas over, we sat of an evening
Having our tea, my parents and myself),
My father said, "I'm going south to shoot,
Near Tallahassee, Walter Moore's preserve.
He said that I might bring you, Tom, or Joss,
Whichever one was free. Since Joss has gone
Up to Quebec to have his winter sports,
Would you like going?"
                    "Would I not!" I cried,
"There's nothing that I'd rather do. I'd love it."
"Good!" said my father.
                    Mother echoed him,
Adding, "How lovely for you, Tom—at last—
To get such shooting."
                    "You'll be alone," I said.
"You're sweet to think of it—it makes no difference."
"She won't be long alone," my father said,

67

"I'll wager Ethel Darnley'll soon be here."
She flushed and said, "I've asked her here, of course,
Tom doesn't mind her."
                          Father simply laughed.
I felt the usual discomfort grow
Out of their voices.
                          "After all, why not?
And Evelyn," said Father, "for a beau,
Steady old Evelyn. Who'll be beau for Ethel?"
I held my breath in terror. Surprisingly,
Mother looked up and smiled and said, "Of course,
I'll get Fred Hammond."
                          "Godfrey!" Father said,
"I don't see how you do it."
                          "Not I—for Ethel."
"Or Ethel either."
                          But she laughed again.
"When shall you two great shooters leave me now?"
"We'll leave on Saturday," Father said. "That gives
Tom one full week at Overton and three days
To get back up to Harvard."
                          "How nice!" she said,
"A solid week. I am so happy, Tom,
That this has happened for you."
                          Then we turned
To fascinating talk about our clothes,
Our guns and cartridges.
                          There's an enchantment
Stored richly in the memory of such things:
The shape of boots seen in the dusk of closets,
The green and yellow of the cartridge tubes
Jumbled in canvas bags, the acrid, sharp,
And unforgettable smell of oil on steel
As leather cases open to let loose
Scents of anticipation. So we lived
A hundred past experiences again,
Unspoken save in the clear images
That light the mind. And still I have not learned
How to escape the excitement of a list
Whose pencilled column speaks of remedy
Against the possibles of stormy skies,
Against the briars thick around the knee,
Against the water waded to retrieve

68

The crippled bird, the glove against the thorn,
The maculate hat against the glaring sun,
The knife, the match-safe—oh, all the treasured toys
That deck our liberation with their bright
Promise of joy released upon the fields,
Promise of happiness floated on the cool
Shadows of tangled trees.
                                        This joy was mine
For two interminable, happy days
While Father shopped with me and we laid out
Our things on beds (to Agatha's disgust).

We took the midnight train on Saturday,
And dined at home beforehand, just we three.
Our talk was desultory during dinner:
I asked some questions about this and that
Concerning quail and how one shot the doves
That Father had described.
                                        He said, "They're swift,
They're very high and clever on the wing,
It'll be something new to you to shoot
High birds. But it's a really pretty sport.
The places where one shoots, the time of day,
Are singularly lovely."
                                        Mother said,
"It's always sounded so."
                                        "You've never seen it,
Have you, Maria?"
                                        "No, I never have.
I don't know that I'd like it if I did—
I never yet have overcome the sense
Of pity for the bird."
                                        "You humanize
His animal sensations."
                                        "So I do.
But I can't help it—it's beyond my power—
It spoils the sport for me. It always has."
"It always has," he said. She flushed a little,
Saying, "It's probably as well, Josiah."
He looked at her a moment. I saw him make
The effort of his next remark: he twisted
His great broad shoulders as if he were lifting
An unaccustomed weight, and spoke: "Maria,

69

I know that Walter would be pleased to have you.
The house is large. There won't be many there."
Mother said, "Oh!"
          "Tom would be glad to have you."
"Oh yes," I said, "do come!"
              She looked at Father
With a remote expression. "I always thought
There were no women wanted by dear Walter."
"Mothers don't count," he said, "a race apart."
"Will there be other women?"
              "I don't know."
His voice had changed again. "I didn't ask.
Sometimes there are and sometimes there are not.
It all depends on whether Lucy comes."
"As on the yacht," she said.
          "She hates the yacht."
Then Mother laughed and said, "I know she does.
I had an idea Walter didn't always
Stick to stag parties there."
         He said, "I gather
That you don't want to come?"
          "I think, my dear,
I should have had a line from Lucy Moore.
Besides, how could I now? At this last minute?"
She turned to me. "I'd love to see you shoot,
Oh, more than anything! and be with you,
One solid week more of your company—
But it's impossible—Ethel Darnley's coming.
I can't arrange it—it's too difficult.
It's not that I don't want to, darling, truly."
"Yes, it's short notice," Father said. "But still,
Knowing that Tom was going, I just thought
You'd possibly be able—coming down,
Say in a day or so."
         She smiled at him.
"Thank you, Josiah. It was kind of you.
I thank you for the effort."
         Father rose.
"Come, Thomas, we'll be off. It's ten o'clock.
The cab must be here and we'll go aboard.
Good-bye, Maria, please remember me
To Ethel Darnley—but add the warmth I lack."
I said good-bye and kissed her. Out we went

Into the hall, where stood the bags and cases,
Symbols of pleasure. Agatha was there.
She helped us with our coats. The man came in
To take the bags down to the taxi-cab.
I said good-bye to Mother once again,
And Agatha cried, "I hope you've not forgot
The things you're needing. Remember, change your clothes
If you get wet, now."
                              "Send a telegram
When you are safely there or if you need
Anything left behind," my mother called
As we went down the steps into the dark
December night. "Good-bye," she called again,
"Good luck, good shooting."
                              Father called, "Good-bye.
I'll send some birds if anyone comes north,
Some birds for you, and some for Ethel, too,
And," here he laughed, "a few for Evelyn."
The front door shut.
                    "We're off at last," he said.

2

This was exciting: the rhythm of railroad wheels,
The long, torn whistle at night, the smell of smoke,
The endless snow in moonlight, familiar stations,
Trenton and Philadelphia and Baltimore,
Washington, symbol of head and centre, the high
Clean simplicity of the shaft, the curving
Elegance of the dome, the snow on the trees,
Sense of the south to come; Richmond, and voices
Calling the long-drawn words with the soft and singing
Virginia tones and negro's dropping inflection,
Little black coffee at breakfast, the unfamiliar
Names of fishes, snow that had vanished away,
The endless broom-sedge. This was exciting.

The South unfolding: Virginia, North Carolina,
South Carolina's border, the endless pine trees,
Pompano for lunch and the name of Charleston,
Voices, on platforms, that said 'Har'ya big boy?'
Sumter seen from a carriage, the colour of water,
Houses full of a sadness married to beauty,

Hot breads eaten, the endless face of the negro,
Voices soft as plush and the sound of wheels
Over the cobble-stones. This was exciting.

Everything different: Georgia, the name Savannah,
Languid and easy voices, the endless pine trees,
Flat brown fields and the tangled green of swamp edge,
Jessup and change your train and go on to Waycross,
Colour of grass in the evening, the grey and tumbling
Village outskirts, the music of negro laughter,
Smell of the pines and the soft-coal smoke and the dust,
The huge live-oaks, Valdosta, the nasal voices,
Warmth of the sun and the sharp and cutting winds,
Flat plains gone and the country rolling, rolling
Under the great tall green waves of the pine trees,
Off at Thomasville. This was exciting.

Now the end in sight: the Rolls-Royce motor,
Rugs for the knees, the luggage to pile around you,
Streets of clay and the lines of pretty, white buildings,
Streets of grey clay and the grey shacks tumbling,
Crazily-leaning, the thick swarm of dark faces,
Soft dark voices against the shrill white voices,
Rush of the cutting air, sweep of the big fields,
Skid of the tires on the wet clay corners,
Green of the ground-growth on the tangled fences,
Florida, endless roll of the long-leaf pines,
Long grey beards of the moss on the live-oaks' spreading,
Fine high gate posts, the terminal sound of gravel,
Green-banked driveway, the towering, huge magnolias,
Unfamiliar trees and the looming white
Breadth of a great house with its tended lawns,
Shadowed, high porch, the sudden calling of voices
Tuned to the northern speech, the journey over,
Men's and women's names in a civilized jumble,
Bags borne up broad stairs, guns to a gun room.
We had arrived at last. That was exciting.

3

We found our bags unpacked, our clothes laid out,
In our adjoining rooms. My room was grey,
And small red vases flamed in bright carnations

72

Against sobriety. My father's room
Was twice the size of mine, a lovely shape,
The walls of pale blue and all the furniture
Of polished, dusky walnut: such a room
As I had never seen before, complete
In all its least detail. It had no flowers
Save only one wide, shining pewter plate
In which there floated on invisible water
Four red camellias. Folded by the side
Of this perfected beauty lay a note:
The superscription simply said *Josiah*.
I saw it before Father did. It seemed
Familiar writing though I could not place
Its elegance.
                    Then Father saw it, too.
"How like her!" he exclaimed and opened it,
Read it and yawned and tossed it to me. "Catch!
Simplex munditiis. There's a model for you."
I caught the paper and I read its lines—
And thought I heard him murmur as I read,
"Insatiable and persistent . . . so it goes!"—
Written on its white surface in the fine
And curiously familiar characters:

> *One is for your head,*
> *One is for your heart,*
> *One is for your hand that lives*
>   *A life apart.*
> *Three are for the simple things*
> *That all men share,—*
> *The last is for your memory*
>   *With love from*
>   *Clare.*

"It's nice," I said, and gave it back to him:
To hold it longer made me feel embarrassed,
Wishing I had not seen it.
                            "It's a model.
If you go on with poetry, I hope
You can condense like that. Now pop along,
Get dressed for dinner. We have half an hour."
I went to my room. Father shut the door,
And rattled at it, opening and shutting it.
He said, "I'll have to lock this door, my boy,

It won't stay shut and makes a horrid draught.
Just sing out if you need me." He closed the door
And I could hear the sharp and grating noise
The big lock made, and then his voice call out,
"Come in when you are dressed, Tom—we'll go down
Together, we two."
                          I began to dress.
My room was cool. A fire briskly burnt
In the small marble fireplace. I thought:
With love from Clare. And if my mother'd come?
Who's Clare?
                    But those I'd met had seemed so old,
They made me feel so young. I had not seen
More than one woman, Mrs. Walter Moore,
She was called Lucy, and her hair was white,
Although she was still pretty, in a way,
If you could overlook her years. The rest
Had both been men about my father's age
Or somewhat older, men with greying hair,
With dark-burned faces, faces over-red,
The man with the brown beard speckled in white
Smoking a small cigar, the man in boots
And riding breeches, whose head was like an egg
Save for one black and shining lock of hair
That marked its dome like a blank music stave.
There were no boys like me. There were no girls,
Or I'd not seen them; that was a relief.
With love from Clare. Camellias in a dish,
The last is for your memory. But why show
The poem to me unless—but unless what?
Just because I wrote poetry—but that poem!
It did not matter. But why did I remember
The writing as familiar? Not the poem:
The writing on the page was only vague
In power to recall—the name, Josiah,
So boldly written, dark blue ink on paper
Whiter than common.
                          Then my memory leaped
Back to the days long gone: I stood again
On a green lawn under a blazing sun
And saw my mother stoop to touch the white
Stain on the grass; and tremble suddenly;
And drop the letter to the grass again.

74

"Ready now, Tom?" His voice came through the door,
Muffled and pleasant.
                    "Yes. I'm ready now."
I left the room and joined him in the hall.
He said, "Your tie wants straightening." His long fingers
Twitched at the bow. "That's better. Come along.
We'll face the many-headed Midas there
Waiting to feed us. Heaven bless the rich!"
He laughed and I laughed too.
                              The hall was dark:
A voice, most clear and lovely said, "Josiah!
Are you corrupting youth?"
                          He said, "Hello.
I didn't see you. The camellias lay
Between my vision and reality.
Come here a moment." I turned to look and saw
A woman dressed in white come down the hall,
Striding and easy. At my father's side,
She laid her hand upon his arm and said,
"Which one, Josiah?"
                    "Tom, the younger one.
This is the lady of the camellias, Tom,
Lady Clare Lovering. She's the only one
Anywhere near your age."
                        "Oh no!" she said,
"I am a thousand—set against this child
In a man's splendid body. Do you shoot?"
"I do," I answered.
                   "How well do you shoot?"
I said, "Just middling. Why?"
                             "Are you so rich,
Or really, so much richer than your father
That you belong here?" Father laughed. She said,
"It is no laughing matter. You must have
A solid bank account of youth and wit,
Rich bonds of beauty, coupons of delight
To cut with golden scissors."
                             "Like you, Clare?"
I watched her face while Father spoke: she smiled,
And when she smiled her whole face lighted up,
Her straight nose wrinkled, her large eyes grew wider
(I could not tell their colour in the dusk).
"Oh me!" she said. "How silly! I am just

75

Movable decoration—the parlour-maid
Who dusts the conversation and provides
A polish to flat silver. Look," she said,
Turning to me, "I am the lure for men,
I lure great artists who can shoot and paint—
Isn't that true, Josiah?"

               "Easy, Clare,
You'll shock him into silence."

                    "Shock the child-man?
How old are you?
          "Eighteen."
              "Eighteen? Dear God,
How long do you Americans maintain
Your innocence? But I'll corrupt you, Tom.
Should you like that?"
             I said, "I guess I would."
"You guess? Dear lad, you really should have said
'I'd love it more than anything on earth'
And bowed to boot. But still, I'm satisfied.
I'll take you for my pupil for this course,
My charge is very reasonable: I demand
Only complete absorption, perfect love,
Constant attention, perpetual compliments,
Incessant jealousy. If I get all that,
Ungrudgingly, in full measure, then perhaps
I'll kiss you once before you take your train
To leave me; just to make the agony
Of parting unendurable."
              "Stop it, Clare."
"Stop it, Josiah? I hope he's jealous, Tom.
Come, take my arm, and lend me your support,
We're young together, aren't we, you and I?
While Father fumes behind us, wondering
If his young son has wiped his eye already."
She slipped her arm through mine, smiled up at me
And then at Father. But he laughed aloud,
Saying, "You do it wonderfully, Clare!
Shall I pop back and move the pewter dish
Into the room of youth?"
             She looked at him
A long time without speaking—then said, "No,"
Most softly.
     A door opened suddenly,

Flashing a yellow path across the hall
To light the three of us. A man came out,
His bald head shining in the light. He stopped
Outside his door and said, "Hello, you three,
What's this, a conference?" His voice was heavy,
Full of the weight of overburdened R's.
"Good evening, Clare. Hello to you, Josiah,
Hello, young man."

         She answered him, "Yes, George.
It is a conference. We plan, we three,
How we may make our wits as valuable
As all the power that such chaps as you
Have girded to you."

         "Good!" he said. "Come on.
Let's go to dinner. We can talk it over.
You sit by me and teach me to be clever."
"How much for just that privilege?" she said.
"My God!" he cried, "I'd hoped it was for love."
"Love? Nonsense! I'm expensive. Don't be close,
Come on, George Barstow, bid! But bid it high.
These men are rich in wit."

         She turned away
Saying, "Young Thomas, take me down to dinner,
Your youth enhances mine. We'll brave our elders.
I'll give you my superfluous years."

         We walked
Down the great staircase to the blaze of light
Below us, to the sound of many voices.
They frightened me: but I was most afraid
Of this slim, striding figure by my side
Whose touch was but confusion edged with fire.

4

Rustle of silk in the pause of night
Winds of night in the trees' leaves,
Flush of heat and the crumpled pillow:
Dark's discomfort,
Mind's unease in darkness,
Fractured images in the blackness:
Red camellias in a shining dish,
Soft camellias for your memory,

Night-born aspirations dwarfing me
Who lie beneath their tropic-towered growth.

Rustle of silk in the hush of night,
Locked door grating on the mind,
Soft sibilance: crept through a locked door,
Through a locked door in the dark's discomfort.

Rustle of night in the trees' leaves,
Flush of heat in a crumpled pillow,
Red camellias for your memory:
Fractured images troubling me
Who lie alone in tropic-towered night.
Shine of pewter in the dark's discomfort,
Mind's unease in the hush of night,
Silence fractured by soft sibilance
Through a locked door: from the trees' leaves:
Grated lock on a red camellia.

Banished sleep in the hush of night,
Locked door's image in the blackness,
Silken sibilance: through a locked door,
Through a locked door to the heart's unease.

Rustle of night in a tropic-towered growth,
Voices heard in the locked discomfort
Turn to winds in the trees' leaves,
Rustle heard in the crumpled pillow,
Rustle of silk in the trees' leaves.
Silken sleep in the hush of night,
Banished memory of camellias,
Banished sibilant silk in blackness:
The dark's sibilance,
The mind's unease in darkness.
Tropic-towered sleep in the hush of night:
Rustle of silk banished: the pause of night.

5

A soft breeze, a pale sun, the fresh air of morning caught in
        the shadows of tall pines.
We ride over the sweep of gently bending grasses in the long
        fields dipping down to the close tangles,

The green tangles of swamp-edges, the graceful strands of
  bull-briar armed with needles.
Green of holly leaf, deep green of magnolia, hot green of
  pine-tufts swinging and singing softly,
Brown water swirling in slow spirals past small steep grey
  banks seamed into deep, sharp wrinkles;
Lavender shadows on yellow grasses.
Two mules pull a high-wheeled cart, black, strong mules;
One big black man driving, one little old black man beside
  him, saying 'Shush now!' to the white, shining setters
Caged in the cart, crouching eagerly, tense on the bumping
  floor,
A dozen white setters, silky, waiting, whining a little—Shush
  you!
Creak of the cart-wheels over hummocks.
Two negroes, wearing blue dungarees, on horseback, each with
  a gun in a scabbard.
One strong expectant mood common to all of us:
Lucy Moore's white hair under a grey hat; soft, plump curves
  in a fine grey habit, side-saddle, bumping a little,
Looking uneasy, smiling a little uneasily, whispering, self-con-
  scious.
Two white setters ranging in and out of the lavender shadows,
  flashes of white in the pale sun.
Walter Moore, brown beard speckled in white, a white linen
  hat, a canvas jacket, riding a big bay pony,
Riding beside George Barstow, bald head hidden now in a
  plaid cap, sporting a loud tweed coat.
Guns in scabbards and clump of the horses' hooves, and whis-
  pers.
Long thin nose of the tanned man in the white coat, Lowden
  Grainger, riding a piebald pony, calling out softly,
'Those dogs is making game;'
Sharp shrill whistle through yellow teeth; yes sir, no sir, should
  be here, sir, in a voice like a cheap fiddle,
To Walter Moore: placid man, heavy, kindly, smiling, spec-
  tacles flashing, sitting comfortably
On the bay pony, white hat with lavender shadows.
Breeze on the ruffled grasses, soft jingle of bit and bridle.
Flap of scabbards against the horses' flanks,
Flat voice of George Barstow, flat as a dog's cough.
Clare and Father and I, riding together:

Father in whipcord breeches, a soft tweed coat, a felt hat, look-
ing like part of his horse, back like a board,
Full lips smiling, silent, eye on the ranging dogs,
Shoulders square and easy, perfection of grace, model of form.
Clare, the match for Father, the half of a pair.
I don't remember what she was wearing, for her clothes were
always and ever part of herself, inseparable.
I can recall her face for you: small, fine-cut features, insolent
mouth, changeable brown eyes,
Eyes for laughter; or for a blank stare; or for a melting
Glance like the sun's surrender to the blue dusk.
So the soft breeze blows, the pale sun shines, and the fresh air
of morning creeps from the shadows of dark pines
Over the great fields of the yellow grasses, swinging and sing-
ing softly,
While the thump and the clump of the muffled hoof-beats
sounds on the sod-drums, beats on the Florida clay.

CLARE: How beautifully the dogs move!
FATHER: Don't they? Watch them.
              The left hand dog is making game. Do you see,
              Tom?
TOM: I can just see him moving.
FATHER: He's moving slowly.
CLARE: They're jolly graceful!
MOORE: Well, Grainger, how about it?
GRAINGER: Jem's on 'em now, Mr. Moore.

Whistle through yellow teeth, shrill and piercing. One setter
motionless,
Tail held straight, whole body tense in stillness,
The other dog rounds on his tracks and moves, slow step by
step, toward his companion: freezes:
Two dogs leashed on the yards of moving air, their instincts
bent to the way of man's remote intention. The wind
Ripples the yellow grasses in the pale sun.

GRAINGER: Pat's backed. Who's shooting?
MOORE: Want to start, George?
BARSTOW: No, my cigar's not finished.
              I began yesterday. Your turn.
CLARE: No, let the Cottrells,
              Father and son begin.

80

LUCY:	Yes, do!
MOORE:	All right.

Start it off, Josiah, and take your son.

CLARE: You're quite forgetting me. Must I be forgot?

FATHER: Come along, Tom. Will you come too?

CLARE: No, I'll stop here.
Two's enough and I expect he's nervous.

TOM: No, I'm not.

CLARE: You will be. Do get on with it:
The birds won't wait all day.

The little old negro hops down out of the cart, and runs to
    our horses' heads to hold them.
We dismount, pull guns out of scabbards, load them,
Walking slowly up on the dogs. Grainger follows.
The dogs have almost disappeared now in long, billowing
    yellow grasses: the curve of the land
Seen from afoot. The noise of dry-rustling footsteps
Drowns the song of the wind. The tense excitement grows.

FATHER: Remember, Tom,
Shoot straight, boy, straight, and don't try to brown
the covey.
Pick one bird.

TOM: I wish they weren't all watching.

FATHER: Think of the birds. Forget them. They can't shoot,
Save for Clare.

TOM: She shoots well?

FATHER: That among other things,
She's very practised, Tom—persistent, too.

Watch her? to see the possessive stare?
Hand on the arm in the dark flight,
Deep discomfort. I hate your Clare:
Rustle of silk in the hush of night.
Rustle of steps in the dry grasses—
    The image passes.

GRAINGER: Now, Mr. Cottrell. Hope your boy shoots like you,
We'll get some birds then.

FATHER: Hope so. Steadily, Tom,
Steady's the word.

81

Sharp whir, terrifying, the heart turns over, the lead bird
        rises,
Brown dart flung glinting in the sun.
Crack of a gun, the bird drops, tumbling over and over,
Roar of the covey rise as the quail scatter, brown bodies,
Dark speed over the yellow grasses,
Over the lavender shadows toward the green, cool, deep
Tangles of low land.
                            Shot. Shot. Shot again.
One bird tumbles and one bird flutters down, leg dropped,
        into the grasses,
The dogs stir slightly and are still once more.
Grainger looses the leash of air with a word. They run rapidly,
White heads lifted, questing the currents of scent;
Soon they find and retrieve the three quail,
Proud heads high, soft mouths full of the triumph of brown
        feathers.
We go after the singles then: some have settled down
Along the edge of bramble patch swamping an old fence.
One dog's at heel to Grainger, now; one dog hunting,
Hunting and pointing.
                        Barstow and Moore and even Clare
        are forgotten.
This is exciting: shooting and watching Father shoot, the in-
    credible skill
So sure and easy, missing nothing.
My shooting rises above its average by competition with him.
Then it is over, suddenly.

GRAINGER: I reckon we'd better get back now.
                Most of the covey has gone into yonder swamp,
                Mighty poor going. Your boy shoots fine, Mr. Cot-
                trell.
                He'll shoot like you do, soon.
FATHER: I hope he'll be better.
                All right, Thomas. Back to the horses, boy.
                I'm glad you didn't disgrace me.
TOM: Oh, so am I!
                But I missed lots of shots.
FATHER: Not enough to matter.
GRAINGER: This wind's going to blow some more. It sure is
                rising.
                Birds'll be wild as hawks by the end of day.
                Maybe 'twill drop by evening.

82

FATHER:	Yes, I hope so.

Spoil the doves. Are there many doves this year?

GRAINGER: Plenty of doves, but nobody can shoot them,
Savin' for Lady Clare and once in a while
Mr. Moore, he bangs one down. They're easy—
Seems so anyway, or so it seems to me.

FATHER: They're not used to the high shot.

GRAINGER: No sir, I guess not.
I reckon that that's the way.

We mount and ride again. We can feel the wind blow now,
See the trees bend and the long tufts of pine needles sway.
Patter of words from the waiting ones. Now the setters,
Jem and Pat, are ranging the fields again,
Off toward the sun, over the endless field, white grace running and leaping and suddenly hidden.
Sense of accomplishment: something well done.

LUCY: Good work, Josiah,
Good work, Tom, you're a credit to your father.
We wouldn't know what to do if he didn't come.
He shoots so wonderfully well. Far better than most.

BARSTOW: I never had time to learn.

CLARE: Then, why do you do it?

LUCY: Clare! you're awful!

CLARE: It's a natural question.

BARSTOW: I like it, you know that.

CLARE: You'd like it much better
If you'd just practise at it.

MOORE: Each to his own taste.
I'm a duffer at shooting.

CLARE: You're a dear duffer,
Isn't he, Lucy? Oh blast this wind! It's rising.

FATHER: One of those dogs is trailing.

GRAINGER: It's Jem again.

MOORE: Go on, Clare. You take George Barstow with you,
Show him how to do it.

CLARE: You see? I knew it.
I draw George and you go off with son Tom.

FATHER: You suggested it.

CLARE: Penalty for a Christian
Act that I did before I thought it out.
You've got to be jolly nice to me, young Tom,
To make up for my kindness. Come along, then.

83

Down from the saddle in one quick swing; takes her gun
    from the negro.
Barstow slowly dismounts; receives his gun. The little old
    negro takes the horses' heads,
Their tails blow in the breeze.

CLARE: Where are my cartridges?
MOORE: Grainger's got them for you.
GRAINGER: Right here, Miss. I got 'em right here for you.
CLARE: Thank you. And do stay handy by, please, will
            you?
            I wish you could turn the wind off, Grainger.
GRAINGER: Yes, ma'am.
            I wish I could. Pat's on 'em now, Mr. Barstow.
BARSTOW: I bet he is, and something's jammed in my gun.
            The damned thing's stuck.
LUCY: Oh, George dear, but how awful!
CLARE: He should be given a good gun at his age.
BARSTOW: Good? It's a Holland!
CLARE: Do you ever clean it?

Barstow looks up at her, his face a dull red, patently angry.
Clare laughs. The wind ripples her hair.

CLARE: Good-bye, George. I'm sorry that I can't stop.
            Come along, Grainger.
BARSTOW: There! There was lint stuck in it.
            I'll give my man the devil for leaving that there.
CLARE: Come on then! The birds will be over in Georgia
            Before we get to them. Blast this wind!
FATHER: Good luck.
CLARE: Want to come with us, Tom?
TOM: No, I'll stay here, thank you.
CLARE: Pity. You'd bust with laughing to see us shoot.
BARSTOW: Do lay off it, do!

They are walking now, through the grasses swung in the tide
    of the wind,
Their voices lost soon, Barstow talking rapidly, Lady Clare
    laughing, Grainger following.

FATHER: You might have gone then.
TOM: Why?

84

FATHER: To watch her shoot.
TOM: She makes me feel uncomfortable.
FATHER: You're not the first one.
MOORE: Poor George!
LUCY: He's so devoted. I do wish Clare
          Would make up her mind to marry him and not
          keep him
          Dangling forever. What are you laughing at?
FATHER: Hope springs eternal, Lucy.

The sound of four swift shots comes back on the wind,
The two close figures dark against the sun, the white coat
Standing a little distant, blue in the strong light.
So the day begins and the morning wanes and the shadows
      shorten,
The wind blows fresh and piercing cold, always more strongly,
The white dogs cover the yellow fields of broom straw,
The white dogs frozen to statues with rippling hair,
The yellow, endless fields silky in the flood of the wind;
Coveys found and the singles hunted and shot,
The swift precision of my father, the careless ease and the
      clean shooting of Clare,
The excitement growing when Father and I draw near, alone,
      we two, to the pointing dogs.
The excitement ebbing after, discomfort growing as we return
      to:
The voice of Clare, soft, musical, the biting words, the incred-
      ible smile, the red discomfort of Barstow,
Father's aloof, detached, and faintly bored amusement—the un-
      easy
Puttering words of Lucy Moore, forever bridging over the
      crises
Of George Barstow's fury and his captivity;
The kind, steady, observant Walter Moore, his beard blown in
      the wind to make his face look naked.
Lunch by a deep stream in a windy gully, soft clay banks,
      sluggish grey-brown water:

CLARE: Never mind, George. You know you did hit some.
          Pass me a bun, please.
BARSTOW: I hit some. Oh, yes.
          But think of the ones I missed!
CLARE: We haven't the time.
          I'd shoot much better myself, if I got some sleep.

85

BARSTOW: You went to bed quite early. You wouldn't play
                bridge,
                What made you short on sleep?
CLARE: Thinking of you, dear.
                Just couldn't close an eye. Did you sleep well, Tom?
TOM: Yes, I did, thank you.
CLARE: Good.
LUCY: Was the bed all right?
                We had those beds made over this year.
FATHER: They're wonderful.
                Soft and firm.
MOORE: Like Lucy.
FATHER: Are you so firm?
LUCY: Good gracious, no!
CLARE: I hope you're firm with the cook
                And tell him to give us food like this tomorrow.
BARSTOW: Wonderful food today.
CLARE: Unlike yesterday?
BARSTOW: I didn't mean that.
CLARE: Then do say what you mean.
                There's no excuse for you on the score of food:
                There you're an expert.
BARSTOW: I?
CLARE: Just look at your figure.
                Look at Josiah, George.
FATHER: Don't look at me, George.
                Look at Clare. It really repays you more.
BARSTOW: I can't help my figure. I exercise.
CLARE: Oh, do you really? Blast it! My napkin, Tom,
                It's blown away in the wind.
TOM: Yes. There you are.
CLARE: Thank you. Sit down here by me, here's a place,
                And act as a wind-screen, do, there's a good chap.
FATHER: You might better use George for that.
LUCY: Who'll have some coffee?
                Whisky for anyone?
FATHER: Please.
BARSTOW: Can you drink whisky?
                And then shoot anything?
FATHER: Surely. It's good for your eye—
                If you don't drink too much.
CLARE: Do you ever, Josiah?
                Do you ever do anything too much?

86

BARSTOW: Thank Goodness!
She's shifted to him for a change.

CLARE: I'll be back soon.

FATHER: My only excesses are carefully concealed,
I'm a bedroom drunkard. You'd really never guess it.

CLARE: What do you drink there?

FATHER: Nectar.

CLARE: Is that true, Tom?
Look, children, the boy is blushing!

LUCY: Coffee, Tom?

TOM: Please.

LUCY: And sugar?

CLARE: No sugar, I'll be his sweet.

TOM: Two lumps, please, Mrs. Moore.

BARSTOW: There's one for you, Clare.

CLARE: He's one for me. Have you turned against me, George?

MOORE: Leave him alone, Clare.

CLARE: Why?

FATHER: Ah, don't be stupid.

BARSTOW: All right, Cottrell, I can look after myself.

FATHER: Surely.

CLARE: Surely? And please to let me know
When that interesting process starts. Oh, can't we move?
Isn't there some place where the wind blows less?
It blows my hair in my food and the crumbs in my eyes
And the pepper goes up my nose.

FATHER: And comes out of your mouth.

CLARE: Have I been awful?

LUCY: Oh, darling, no!

CLARE: I'm sorry, George.
I love you with a deep and abiding passion.

BARSTOW: Like hell you do!

MOORE: Pass me the whisky, someone,
Nothing can hurt my shooting.

CLARE: You stop your swing.
I saw it many times.

MOORE: I know I do that,
But I'm trying hard to correct it.

BARSTOW: Is that my trouble?

87

CLARE: Oh, yes, among other things. You've never learnt
              form.
              Has he, Jo?
FATHER: I never have really noticed.
CLARE: Nonsense! you notice everything.
FATHER: Mm, what fun!
              The rip in your skirt, for instance?
CLARE: Lord, is it ripped?
              Will your maid mend it, Lucy?
LUCY: Of course, my dear.
CLARE: Can you see it, Tom?
TOM: I did, but you're sitting on it.
BARSTOW: That's the stuff to give her!
CLARE: Why don't you, then?
              Or give me a maiden, George?
BARSTOW: Do you need one?
FATHER: To make up for the maiden she lost, perhaps.
CLARE: You dirty dog! Isn't it bad enough
              For me to have George against me?
BARSTOW: I'm not, I'm not!
CLARE: You're not?
                          He's blushing now. Tom, you've a partner.
              We'll let the two great blushers shoot together,
              While the two cynical and worldly guns,
              Clare and Josiah, brave the winter winds,
              Profane but pallid.
MOORE: Come on, let's be off.
              We'll do a bit more and then try the doves.
              They're coming into Melden's Wood.
CLARE: Oh, splendid!
              You'll lend your father, Tom?
TOM: Why yes, of course,
              If Mr. Barstow doesn't mind me.
BARSTOW: Hell!
              You are a devil, Clare.
CLARE: But dear George, why?
              The boy shoots beautifully.
LUCY: All napkins, please,
              Just pass them over. And let me have the spoons.

Moore rises, his large hands brushing crumbs from his coat.
We all rise up. I am glad that the lunch is over and done,
That we shall now have shooting and less talking, less of the
      voice of Clare,

88

Less of the sense of strain and unease,
Less of the disturbing quality of her presence near me
Conjoined to dislike in a close pattern of feeling.
Moore and his wife are mounted, so is George Barstow, smok-
    ing a cigar, as though he had set part of his face on fire.
I feel a sense of being cast off, unwanted, separated from the
    rock of my father, flung on the discomfort of Barstow.
Father mounts. Clare speaks to the old negro holding her
    horse, and runs toward me, where I stand, uncertain,
    waiting.

CLARE: I do hope you don't mind my bagging him?
TOM: Your what?
CLARE: My sneaking off with your nice father.
            I want to talk—and watch him shoot, of course—
            I couldn't stand it, Barstow, all the day,
            You do see what I mean?
TOM: I guess I do.
CLARE: Your voice sounds patient and distressed.
TOM: Oh no.
CLARE: But yes, it does. Look here, you take him on,
            And shoot for two— you do shoot jolly well—
            And when we do the doves, we'll pair, we two.
            Is that all right?
TOM: But surely.
CLARE: How I love
            Your sweet American way of saying things!
            Surely. You say it as your father does.
            Till the doves, then. Thanks for the loan of father,
            I'll treat him properly.
TOM: Surely.
CLARE: Oh, you're sweet!
            Shoot straight. Don't shoot poor George. It isn't
            sporting—
            He never learnt to fly.

She turns and runs back to her horse and mounts it:
Graceful and supple movement. She is laughing, her head
    turned, looking up at Father.
One can hear then her clear voice saying, 'Damn this curséd
    wind!'
We all ride off together, saving only Barstow:
He rides behind, sulky, talking to Lowden Grainger, who
    picks his teeth with a grass stem.

89

I ride beside Lucy Moore, who chatters on endlessly about
    nothing, about not shooting,
While I pretend to listen, but think:
I never heard anyone call him Jo before, not even Mother.
How does she dare to do it? Does he really like it? How long
    has she done that? Since the letter?
White on the green grass, Mother trembles and drops it,
Why did she tremble?
Did she know then? Did she know?
This knowing and not knowing, this guessing,
All these relationshps jumbled up in the darkness of not
    knowing—
Was this always the way of the world?

So the wind blows and the grasses bend, and the shadows
    creep out of hiding;
The birds are harder to find now, and wilder,
They are more difficult to shoot, blown in the eddies of air,
Over the rippling rivers of broom-sedge,
Our speech is blown from our lips into severed small sounds,
    twisted
Into annoyance, the *what?* shot like the left barrel after the
    right barrel *what?*
The horses fidget and fuss and wish to stand with their tails
    to the wind's sharp speed.
Barstow misses and misses again and curses, and I shoot less
    well now,
And for each miss there is an edged word from Clare
Flung to Barstow, and no word at all to me, only glances
Saying nothing that I can comprehend.

Then the shadows grow bolder, an army of shadows
Out from this patch of briar, this grove of trees, this clump of
    bushes, hiding and increasing in hollows,
And the enemy wind gives way before them, dropping,
Ceasing its cold attack, till finally
The long shadows cover the low places in a blue peace,
And the wind has become a small and chilly movement of
    restless air,
Tipping the plumed tops of the yellow grasses turned golden
In the retreat of the sun.
We ride now, voices dropped, fingers chilly, tired but at length
    easily, toward Melden's Wood,

Quietly skirting a vast field of corn stubble pricked into sharp
    accents, sharp little shadow pricks, blue and unaccented
    hollows,
In the slanting light of the low sun, making a red prophecy
    of the morrow;
Down through a long swale to the edge of the big pine wood.
There we dismount, the horses are led off together into a
    neighbouring field.
Clare comes to me, takes my arm. Grainger posts us
Under the soft music of the big branches, in a clearing,
One here, one there, an irregular line, Clare and I together,
The sun on her face, the last of the breeze in her hair, her
    voice dropped to a soft, intimate whisper,
No noise, no shouting against the wind now.
So we wait in the nave of the pines, while the sun grows
    level through the clerestory branches above us,
And the great shadows spread into a blue veil between the
    hard day and the close presence of evening,
Rustle of silken grass in the pause of evening,
Soft sibilance of Clare's whisper, my own discomfort.

CLARE: They come in high and fast.
TOM: Where do they come from?
CLARE: They come from the stubble, they make for the tall
    pines,
    You've got to lead them.
TOM: How do we find the birds?
CLARE: Mark them as well as you can. But the dogs will
    find them.
    They come in singly at first. Then more and more.
    You take those on the right of this tree, Tom,
    I'll take those to its left. All right?
TOM: All right.
CLARE: Glad I can't see Barstow. Poor chap, he'll muck it,
    Always does. He may hit one or two, though,
    Since I'm not near to bother him.
TOM: Oh.
CLARE: Poor George!
    You noticed how he was bothered?
TOM: He seemed uncomfortable.
CLARE: Makes him angry that I shoot better than him,
    He thinks he should be able to shoot as easily
    As he makes money. See here, if you were me,
    You wouldn't marry a man like him?

91

TOM: Oh, I suppose not.
CLARE: For all his money?
TOM: I'd only marry for love.
CLARE: For love? We all thought that once on a time—
            Illusions pass.
TOM: Illusions?
CLARE: All illusions—
            Everything dies and passes—watch it! they're com-
            ing.
TOM: Who's coming?
CLARE: Illusions, birds—not Barstow, silly!

            She raises her gun and aims above her. She shoots.
            I see the bird only as it begins to tumble down, over
            and over.

TOM: Good shot, Lady Clare!
CLARE: Watch out now, they'll be coming.
            For God's sake call me Clare. You will, Tom, won't
            you?
TOM: Yes, if you wish me to.
CLARE: Your enthusiasm
            Quite overcomes me. You must be like your father.

The shots begin to ring out now, doubled in volume by the
      echoing trees and the wall of evening:
They are the echo of action, the tongue of the pointed gun,
The sharp, remote shots, lapping and crossing each other.
I can see the birds come, now: small, swift, planing in to the
      trees,
Incredibly rapid change of direction, bright-glancing bodies in
      the red-gold sunlight at the trees' tops.
The shots come breathlessly from the line of guns. We shoot,
Clare and I, rapidly. I have not time to notice now
Whether she hits or not. I cannot find the birds, at first: they
      escape me, it is like shooting at air or a blown leaf.
Then it becomes easy, suddenly: the birds drop,
There is the heartening sound of the soft plump as the body
      lands on the ground from its high fall,
My fingers are warm now, the gun is warm to my fingers,
One cannot load fast enough. This is exciting.
Then—Clare's voice repeating something, till I hear the small
      words, through my excitement.

92

CLARE: Tom, look here, do look here, Tom, do look,
            Stop for a minute, do look here.
TOM: What is it?
CLARE: Look, it's that bird there.
TOM: Where?
CLARE: Here, here—oh stupid!
            Right at my feet here.
TOM: Yes, but . . .
CLARE: Look, it's crippled,
            Stop it, do—do something.
TOM: Why yes, it's wounded.
CLARE: Oh, for God's sake, kill it, it's looking at me,
            Stop it fluttering.
TOM: Surely.
CLARE: Do be quick, Tom.

The bird flutters and flutters on the dry pine needles, soft
     blue-grey on the brown needles.
It is only a matter of seconds to pick up its velvet body,
Fold the fluttering wings and deal
Merciful quick death, lost from the stinging shot.
Clare is standing with her back turned to me. The doves
Flash in the last light of the lost sun. The hollow shots echo
Through the dark wood.

TOM: All right. It's done now.
CLARE: Thank you. Go on.
TOM: Go on what?
CLARE: Go on shooting.
TOM: But you?
CLARE: I'm done with shooting.
            Done for the day, child.
TOM: Why?
CLARE: Don't talk, just shoot.
TOM: You're not crying, are you?
CLARE: Suppose I am?
            It's none of your business, is it?
TOM: I'm awfully sorry.
CLARE: Don't be sorry. You're sweet. I'm just a fool.
            I didn't mean to be cross.
TOM: That's nothing.
CLARE: Horrible!
            Turns me up when I see a bird so . . . so . . .

93

Her voice breaks and she seats herself by the trunk of a big
　　　tree,
Facing me now, the tears in her brown eyes: beautiful.
This is another woman?
Some power beyond me sends me to her, she holds her hand
　　　up,
Seizing the hand I offer. She rises slowly,
She stands close to me, her hand laid flat against my shoul-
　　　der,
I see her gun on the ground, something to notice: something
To keep my eyes from hers, to help me cover
The fierce discomfort of her near presence. So her hand
Rises and touches my face, once, softly, sending
A long vibration through me.

The shots come singly now. The tops of the trees are green
　　　again, the red glow vanished,
The day is over. The voices begin. The moment of being
　　　alone is past.
This is Father; this is Mr. Walter Moore and his wife, Mrs.
　　　Moore, whom they call Lucy, with the white hair, the
　　　sweet vacuous expression;
This is Mr. George Barstow, his face reddened by anger and
　　　the incessant wind of the long day;
These are the white dogs, there is the heap of wonderfully
　　　coloured doves;
This is the little old and the big young negro, and these are
　　　the horses, their breath steaming in the blue air against
　　　the dull yellow of grasses;
This is the scabbard for my gun.
That is Lady Clare Lovering, sitting gaily on her pony,
Something to somebody, surely? To my father? The lady of
　　　the camellias,
The lady of the sharp words,
The girl in the pine woods, the possessor of a hand
Of fire upon my face.

6

It was a curious week: the shooting was splendid,
New and exciting. While we were off in the daytime,
Riding and walking and shooting, I could nearly
Lose myself in the joy of the sport, forgetting

All the personalities closely linked
In an uncomfortable mesh by the soft lamplight,
The house walls, the stairs, the carefully closed doors,
The drawn shades closing the day out, harbouring night.
I used to sit as long as I dared at tea-time
Still in my shooting clothes and my riding boots,
Clutching the good day to me, reluctant to move.
At the last moment I would dash up the stairs,
Fling my clothes off in an untidy muddle,
Bathe in a violent hurry and dress as quickly,
No pause for thinking, but only the sense of fleeting
Time that will not attend on a wish or a will;
Then down to dinner, feeling the separate entities
Move together in a close, hard group,
This one set against that one in a battle
Not of words, but of glance and pose and spirit.
You could take their words apart: they were harmless words—
The voice gave meaning, the stress was the pleading sound,
The accent cut or soothed, the laughter rippled
Over the stones of feeling, stones submerged,
Sharp stones cutting the course of flowing laughter,
Turning the rippled sound to a deeper tone.

Father laughed at everything, softly, gently,
Played bridge better than anyone save Barstow,
Moved with ease through the tangled situations,
Seemed to be happy to be with Clare or without her,
Drew a dozen pictures of Clare by lamplight,
Eyeing her coolly in a detached, observant
Manner of looking. They were brilliant drawings.
He drew them all in turn, in his odd moments,
Wonderful likenesses, always a little cruel,
Except for Walter Moore's. Then he'd destroy them,
Ripping the paper in his fine, strong fingers,
Throwing the pieces into the flames while they
Begged him not to. He'd say, "It's only for practice,
I'm just keeping my hand in."
                                        Clare would answer,
"Talk to me then, Jo."
                                "My bridge is rusty."
"Your bridge is perfect, damn you."
                                        "Let's play bridge."
"Good!" from Barstow, and, "Curse your cards!" from Clare.

She seemed to hate the evenings as much as I did;
She was at ease by day, her swift tongue turning
Words to her need, sharp, gentle, or amusing;
She was too sharp at night and only sharp,
But always clever. She kept the whole group talking
Wouldn't allow two people to talk together,
Throve on the words the others said, destroying
Sentences they had made with a swift, short phrase,
Sometimes witty and nearly always cruel.
Barstow followed her round like a country swain,
Forcing attentions on her, fetching and carrying,
Grumbling because she hurt him, angry and sullen,
Patient and choleric by turns and always
Coming back to Clare, and over and over
Laying himself wide open for her to hurt him.
She used to ask incessant attention of him,
Fetch me this or that, do this, don't play bridge,
Light me a cigarette. While he was playing
She would insist on talking to him eagerly,
Spoiling his game. She was like a thing on a wire,
Tensely moved by an incessant current.

So my week past. I wondered (in new excitement)
Why the door stood now unlocked between
Father's room and mine.
                        Had I heard the rustle,
Whisper of voices in that distant first night,
Or was it but the wind in the trees of darkness,
Something imagined?
                        Clare wasn't sharp with me:
Sometimes I found that I was wishing she would be,
Treating me as an equal of all the others.
Then I'd catch myself thinking, She doesn't see me,
She doesn't consider me.
                        There'd be a strange excitement,
New to my blood, when she was near.
                        Her words,
Barbed with the look of her eyes, at first could pierce me,
Make me feel naked and helpless—I did not mind,
After a short while, for it was soon transmuted
Into a quickening of the heart-beats strongly felt
Through gathering warmth, as though the world would open
Wide on its axis and display Elysium.

She was the key, or the Sesame—or the earthquake
Holding power to split my world asunder,
Then when the moment came and Clare's attention
Focussed upon me, I was bereft of words,
Lost in a sense of youth, and a tight, embarrassed
Emptiness of sensation.
                              Then she'd be off—
Turned to my father, perhaps—and all my void
Filled with a whirlpool of inrushing thoughts.

See, here is Clare. She sits in a chair by the fire,
One leg crossed on the other, her blue silk dress
Softly defining her. The lamp's light throws
Sparks in her dark hair, shadows under her eyes,
A crescent of light, cut by the chins curved shadow,
Lies on her chest.
                              Father is making a drawing,
Pad on his knee, pencil in delicate fingers.
Father says, "Does this bore you?"
                              "No."
                                   "To have me draw you?"
"No, Josiah, you always draw me."
                                   "Hush, child!"
"Hush, child, because of the child?"
                                   "I think I'm done now."
"Done, Jo, done?"
                         "It's been a long while, Clare."
"Not too long—for me—could have gone on longer.
Everything passes."
                         "That's cynical."
                                   "Cynical? yes.
True and cynical. But it renews again,
In a different form—or should I say body?"
"Don't say anything."
                         "No? But this drawing is finished."
"Yes, it's finished."
                         "But men must always look, Jo,
And looking has been fatal—for ever so long."
"Tom!" says Father.
                    "Yes?"
                              "Take a good look at her.
Here's a dangerous woman." She laughs and moves,
Stands and looks into the fire and says, "Medusa

97

Hides her glance in the flames, Tom. Are you afraid?"
I say, "Oh, not a bit." She says, "That's right.
Better to be afraid of him. He's ruthless.
Better yet if he feared for himself some time
Because of ruthlessness."
                              "Why?" says Father, softly.
"Why?" she echoes him. "Some day someone will kill you—
Not for what you have done—for what you may do—
A sort of panic, seeing your iron ego
Move irresistibly forward. It won't be me.
I'll solace myself with Tom." But Barstow enters,
Heavy tread sounding. So the scene is over—
I am aware that for me it has never begun.

7

Then the last night came, and I could not sleep.
Because it was the last? I did not know:
The last of shooting, or the last of Clare—
But what was Clare, whose face I could not see
In this unlighted living of no sleep?
I tuned my ears to hear the rustle creep
Through the near door, but knew it would not come—
To torture? Why to torture? Who was she
That I should trouble if my father took
Or did not take, or that his words and smile
Betrayed the bed of an old river dried
In later seasons?
                              So the pillow turned
To fire against my face, and all my nerves
Wove taut discomfort to the circling mind.
Should I be witness, silent and content,
To this strange robbery of my mother's life?
But this was an old robbery—had she found
Her stolen goods again with Evelyn?
Oh, hateful thought! it could not be, not he,
Not that crass smile and those unsmiling eyes—
Had she not cried out *There is no tomorrow?*
Why was the thought of Evelyn so harsh
And so unwelcome while the nearer view
Of this new Clare was—welcome? no, nor good,
Nor understood, nor wanted, nor denied,

Nor terrible, nor sweet—but what?
                              I turned
In slow discomfort in a bed grown small,
Become a prison that confined my spirit
A..d jailed my mind.
                         Why was this Clare so strange,
So different from the women I had known,
The girls at dances, the friends at Mother's house?
I did not know. I saw her quality
But could not yet define it—and I'd seen
Her beauty as a weapon.
                         So my thoughts
Swept round the circle of her being, confused
By the near mist of sleep that would not swathe
Its veils about my thinking.
                              I rose at last
And looked for cigarettes. But there was none.
My case was empty and the little box
Beside my bed was empty too. This looking
By the brief flame of matches made me want
Tobacco ardently. I could not lie
Longer upon that bed and feel my mind
Tossed in the ravellings of its tangled web
Whose warp was but discomfort and whose woof
Contained the colours of the unexpressed
Harsh threads of my desire.
                              Were these the nerves
That strung their filaments to perceivable
And tensive pitch?
                    Again I did not know—
I did not know, I did not know! How often
Did life force situations to arise
That had no answers, or whose answers lay
Beyond the forests of experience?
And must experience be forever grown
Out of a rank and disagreeable soil?
Enough, enough!
                    Still with the weight of these
Night-leaded queries hung upon my mind,
I opened the grey door with scarce a sound
Beyond its cricket-like small creaking noise,
Closed it behind me (why, I did not think,
Save that the air of a strange house by night

99

Should not invade the sanctuary room
Where one's own vapours harbour), set my feet
To a soft exploration of the way
That led below stairs.
                              I could hear the trees
Rustle their reminiscence of the day
Beyond the great glass window in the hall
And presently my eyes began to grasp
The shape of objects without colour stood
In half-familiar groups. I felt my toes
Press air upon the top step of the stairs,
And slid my hand along the polished rail
That led me downward to a deeper dark.
The stairs creaked slightly to my barefoot tread,
And whined most faintly as the lifted weight
Restored their placing: making little voices
Crying my presence as though I were guilty
Of some untoward and rather shameful act.
But I said, I'm alone—I do no harm,
And comforted myself, until there swept
The hot thought through my mind, so clear, so new:
I wish that I were not alone!
                              I paused,
My foot upon the last step of the stair,
And heard my heart thump loudly in my breast
With an unknown anticipation.
                                        Where
Should I find company and, dear Lord, with whom?
But there was no one here.
                              A newer sound
Grew from the night. I listened. It was rain,
Doubling the volume of the whispering trees,
A sad and lonely music, liquid wires
That led the current of the heaven's grief
Down to attendant earth. It made the house
Seem curiously less hostile, sheltering me
Against the winter's weeping.
                                  Then I moved
On to the drawing room, across cold boards,
Again the warmth of carpets. There the glow
Of the last embers in the fireplace
Seemed pleasant and welcoming. There were cigarettes
And matches on a table near its glow.

The struck match hurt my eyes as it drew near
The cigarette. I blew it quickly out
And sat upon a sofa, looking in
To the deep richness of the embers' changing
Play of live colours. Now I was at peace,
For smoking gave surcease to uneasy thought,
And made night tolerable and the lifted hand
A near companion.
                        I listened to the sounds
All houses make by night; I heard the rain
Mix with the wind beyond the sheltering walls;
Small dull explosions as fat embers cracked
To scarlet halves.
                        But then I heard a sound
That was not one of these, but like soft steps
Descending the great stairs. I held my breath
To listen still more closely. It was true,
The steps continued, steadily. I felt
Bereft of power to move, I could but sit
And wait in fear that seemed ridiculous
And real at the same time.
                                Why should I seem
Guilty in being here, guilty to myself?
I did not wish these steps to find me out,
I did not want to be disturbed—except—
Except? I did not want and wanted too,
Detested and was eager—could it be
That this was Tom who sat in darkness here
Motionless in a complex of his mind's
Wild indecision?
                        So the steps approached.
My eyes had grown accustomed to the dark
And saw the pale and colourless figure come
Out of the blackness of the door to stand
Within this room. It stopped.
                                    But still I heard
Rustle of silk in the dark hush of night,
Soft silken sibilance.
                        I ought to speak,
I must say something, make some sort of sound—
But my inept tongue could not find a word
To utter toward relief. The figure stood
A second longer motionless. Then a whisper

Cut through the darkness, saying: "Who is that?"
I said, "It's only me, it's Tom," and rose.
"I was just smoking." I did not need to ask
Whose whisper this one.
                    "Oh. You frightened me.
I thought . . ." she paused.
                        "You thought it was a thief?"
"No, not a thief, I thought . . . ." she paused again.
Some courage or some daring not my own
(Bred of the night, perhaps, or of the wind
Beyond this silence) opened my mouth for me
And said, "Oh no, my father is asleep."
She moved, came swiftly to me, till she stood
A foot away. "What made you say that, Tom?"
I said, "Oh, I don't know. Perhaps you seemed—
You sounded disappointed."
                        "Did I?"
                            "Yes."
"Suppose that were not so, what then?"
                            I found
My speech had gone again—what could one answer
To such a thing as that?
                    "No answer, Tom?
Does silence cover up as much distaste
As sounded in your speaking?"
                        Still I stood
Helpless before her. Then she reached her hand
Up from her side and laid it on my arm
And I began to tremble, but within me,
Hoping she would not notice. Then she said,
"Must I interpret this as well?" I moved
A step away, dislodging that warm hand.
"Interpret what?"
                    "Good night," she said, "I'm sorry
That I disturbed your quiet. I could not sleep,
My mind was like a squirrel in its cage
And rattled round incessantly. Good night."
She turned away and started for the door,
Not moving swiftly, but so steadily
That I became aware of it as speed
Most cruel and disastrous and my heart
Turned over once in a fierce spasm within me,
And I cried out (a whisper, but it rang

Loud as a shout in that enclosing dusk),
"Clare!"
            But she did not pause. I spoke again:
"Clare, stay a little."
                        She was at the door,
But paused within its frame, remote and grey,
For just the length of time it took to say
"Good night to you, Josiah's son," and then
She'd disappeared in darkness.
                              So I stood,
Torn with emotions that I'd never known,
And listened for her steps. I could not hear them:
The pounding of my heart was still too loud
And jerked its drum beats in my listening ears.

I remained motionless within that room
Until I felt the cigarette grow hot
Between my fingers. I cast it in the fire.
The motion broke the spell of stillness laid
By Clare's departure.
                    I heard her words again
Sound in my mind. *Suppose that were not so,
What then?* Not disappointed? Not, with me?
Does silence cover up as much distaste . . . .
But there was no distaste now—had there been?
Had it been panic, fear? The trembling, fear?
Must I interpret this as well? The trembling—
So she had felt me tremble?
                          She was gone,
And gone in anger, too. *Josiah's son* . . . .
Did that fling back at him, as well?
                                  But gone,
Gone in the instant when I first began
To wish that I had wished her presence sooner
And dared to see it clearly.
                          She was gone,
Something was gone as well, a chance, a moment,
A space of living filled up to the brim
With great excitement.
            Gone.
                  I moved again,
Thinking, I'd best go up. The room is cold
And more is cold than just the room. Would life

103

Snatch life away as quickly, always, always,
As she had vanished then?
                                    So I began
Reluctant progress of my dark return
Toward an unwelcome room that now would hold
Hazardous thoughts bereft of their last power
To turn to doing.
                              Here the boards were cold,
This was the hallway, then. The carpeting
Was warm beneath my feet once more. I reached
My hand to find the newel, and found Clare
Motionless, silent at the stair's beginning.

Rustle of silk in the pause of night,
Rain by night in the trees' leaves,
Flush of heat and the crumpled pillow:
The dark's comfort,
Tongue's new ease in darkness,
Fractured images in the blackness:
Red camellias brush against my lips,
Fierce camellias for my memory,
Night-born aspirations clothing me
Who lie beneath their tropic-towered growth.

Rustle of silk in the rain of night,
Bolted door closing in the mind,
Soft sibilance: closed by a bolted door,
By a locked door in the dark's comfort.

Rustle of rain in the trees' leaves,
Flush of heat in a shared pillow,
Red camellias for my memory:
Fractured words disclosing us
Who lie together in the towering night.
Touch of fire in the dark's comfort,
Tongue's new ease in the hush of night,
Silence fractured by soft sibilance
Within a bolted room: from the trees' leaves:
Lock of dark on a red camellia.

Vanished sleep in the hush of night,
Locked door's image in the blackness,
Silken sibilance: closed by a bolted door,
Caught by a locked door to the heart's ease.

Rustle of night in a tropic-towered growth,
Passion woven in a locked comfort—
Turn to rain in the trees' leaves,
Rustle heard in the lonely pillow,
Rustle of silk in the trees' leaves.
Silken sleep in the hush of dawn,
Vanished memory of camellias,
Vanished sibilant silk in blackness:
The dark's sibilance,
The tongue's new ease in darkness.
Tropic-towered sleep in loneliness:
Rustle of silk vanished: the pause of dawn.

THIS creep, creep, inching forward of old sly Time!
Now it's a foot, a yard—yet we saw none move:
Time nor his shadow? No, but on his high climb
Into the noon you cannot see the sun move.
You see the motion—Sun and Time—as great, lean
Hills cleave them sharply in hot descent to breed night:
Night, and his shadow, Sleep, to wipe the slate clean—
There is no time in dark sleep: the hours need light.
So shall our memories vanish, night, sleep, day-torn,
All sensuous images that once poor youth wove,
Ravel to discard—yet once were gay, worn
Like a bright scarf at the sweet throat of love.
This creep, creep, inching forward shall erase youth:
Man's but his knowing shadow in the day's truth.

EXPERIENCE does not always concentrate
Its essence in one day where hours are burnt
To the fine ash of knowledge. If that could be
We'd change our custom and our way of life,
Turn habits inside out until the seams
Were piped with wisdom and our hearts could walk
Down the too-peopled pathways clad in grace.

Experience most often is a sharp wound:
There is no pain at first, but only shock
Dulling the senses till the pain removes
Into the narrow harbour of the mind;
Then the dull opiate of the shock wears thin
And ten long fingers of living pain can pluck
Strung nerves to bitter music whose harsh tune
Forever and forevermore shall fling
Discordant echo from planes of memory.
Oh, from such feeding we draw nourishment,
Eating our passion at the board of life,
And all the long, drab days of simple living
Are framed for slow digestion.

The Easter following my shooting trip
I spent with Joss at home. New York was fun,
As were the Cambridge days—where then as now
The short and chilly days bred lighted nights,
And all the music and the dancing dulled
The furious memory of distant Clare.
I yearned and did not yearn. I wanted her,
And hoped, against a hot and vivid fear,
I'd never see her more. I felt ashamed,
And shame was so diluted by the surge
Of masculine triumph that shame and triumph both
Turned to discomfort's lingering sense of loss.
My home became a place where my unease
Took weight and body, becoming actual,
Made terrible by the thought of Father knowing,
Made shameful by my mother's candid love
And most undoubting pride, which framed in words
Image of me I knew to be the false
Erection of her heart.
                              And over all
There sounded always the discordant note
Of two untuned and warring elements.
Now to my eyes my mother seemed to be
Filled with a strange excess of energy,
Not wholly nervous: unable to sit down
In peaceful, wonted occupation, once
The measure of her soft-drawn way of life;
She was forever moving here and there
As though the room she sat in had become

Impossible, or as though some voice were calling
Urgently through the escape of every door
(Whose hinge was freedom and whose lock was but
Unbearable closeting with imprisoned thought).
She made irrelevant remarks and heard,
Seemingly, their irrelevance, as if
Some other person spoke within the deep
And carrying music of her stolen voice.
Then she'd look startled and afraid, her eyes
Puzzled to understand how this could be.
Such nervous quality sat ill on her
Who was so amply made, the Juno-kind,
Born to stand firmly and to sit enthroned
Even on grass.
                    She sought for quarrels now,
Saying the things she knew would rouse my father
Most surely to respond. But curiously
He was more gentle and more considerate
Than we had ever seen him, though his tongue
Would prove ungovernable from time to time,
When irresistible sharp words would leap
Out from the sheath of lips.
                              Both puzzled me.
I could not understand her change of mood:
I didn't yet comprehend the inactive mind
Turned desperate by activity's close need,
The unchanging heart caught in the web of change,
The generous spirit swept to pettiness
By new demands to a new side of her.
These matters are clear now: I see my mother
Forced to a run who could but slowly walk,
Turned to a hate who throve on sympathy,
To pagan rancour who clutched at martyrdom
Too long for sense or reason to remain
Dulled to such spirit-promptings: instinct-holds
On matters better to subject to all
The worldly lights lest they at last currupt
From Christian preservation in their dark.
I was not old enough.
                        But in one day
I saw enough to feed my grasping mind
With thorny and unpalatable truth
For everlasting, and the food was life

And turned to blood and bone and of this feeding
I am the richer and the stronger now:
Pity the man who has not swallowed down
His peck of dirt before the dirt and he
Make earth for tillage of their unity.

That day we lunched at home, just five of us:
My father and my mother and her friend
The short and stocky Ethel Darnley, she
Who always seemed to back my mother up
As though her strength were needed by her friend.
She was a woman with an eager eye:
Joss said he liked her, but she frightened me
With unremitting interest, as though she shared
A right to half one's soul and half one's mind
Because of long association. Still,
I did not really mind her—was amused
To see her try to exercise this claim
Over and over on my father's life
And always stand rebuffed—and try again.
Joss had a gift for letting questions glance
From his poised spirit; Father diverted them.
I stumbled lamely in a poor attempt
To say a little, but not say too much,
Being forever at a loss for words
And yet bedevilled by a common fear
That I might seem unkind.
                              My mother said:
"We have had no spring yet, but still I feel
As though it waited close around the corner.
Some quality in the air?"
                              Miss Darnley answered,
Saying, "How true! I felt that way myself.
You must be yearning now for Cottrellton
After the winter." Mother went on eating,
And did not answer. Miss Darnley turned to Father.
"You should be moving soon. Tell me, Josiah,
You plan to open up the place this spring?"
"Perhaps," he said. "Maria knows the dates."
"But for the fishing?"
                              "Fishing? I'm at work."
"Come now, don't say you ever work so hard
That fishing is forgotten—does he, Joss?"

Joss laughed and said, "My mind is on the dance.
I'm but a dancing man."
                              "With whom?" she said,
Smiling and glancing sidewise at him.
                                        "Girls."
She said, "Oh, yes, but . . ." and then stopped a moment,
Reddening as she felt the implication.
"You haven't answered me, Josiah."
                                   "No.
I haven't, Ethel."
                    "You are most annoying,
All of you. For you turn a simple question
Into a puzzle. Come now, Tom, you're kind,
Tell me your plans." I said, "I have no plans.
We go back down to Cambridge in a week,
Joss and I do. I don't know when we move.
It hasn't been discussed."
                           Then through my mind
Ran the swift realization that this year
For the first time we'd come to Easter-tide
Without a word of Cottrellton. Father's work?
What work? Why did my mother sit and stare
So hard at bread she crumbled in her fingers?
My father's ease and silence, Joss's boredom,
Mother's dark looks. The sudden flash of Clare
Like needles in the veins. A sense of life
Hung dangerously balanced.
                            "No, not discussed."
Mother's deep voice took up the words I'd said.
"We've made no plans—as yet." And Father murmured:
"Here endeth the first question," and Joss laughed.
"This afternoon," said Father, "I've got two men
Coming to see my job. Come over then,
You boys, if you're not busy. You might hear
Some good talk, Murray's coming and old Flett."
Joss said, "I'll come with you right after lunch,
I must be uptown about half-past four."
"You, Tom?"
            "Yes, rather."
                           "Is the painting done?"
I was surprised then—Mother rarely asked
A question on his work. He said, "It's done
If ever any work of art is done."

"Oh please, do tell me, what's it of, about?"
Cried Ethel Darnley. "Could I see it, too?"
"Oh yes, of course," he said, "I'll hang it soon,
When I have my next show."

                       "Oh dear, I meant . . ."
"Yes, surely"; he smiled and interrupted her.
"Oh!" But she'd never learn. "Maria, listen,
Please make him ask us, too. I love to hear
The real artistic people talk, discuss
In studios and places. Make him do it!"
"Make him?" said Mother, dully. Then suddenly
She straightened up and raised her head and spoke,
Quite normally and loudly in her fine
And ringing voice. "Who's home for dinner? Joss?
You, Tom?"

            "Yes, I'll be here."

                       "Not I," said Joss,
"I'll just pop in to change. I'm dining out,"
And turned his head to Ethel Darnley's place
And spoke to her: "With Mrs. Ross, John Ross,
One hundred thirty-seven east thirty-nine,
At half-past eight exactly, a white tie,
In honour of Miss Mary Manly Ross,
I'm not quite certain of her age, she's dark,
And really not too pretty." Father smiled
And ran his tongue along his upper lip.
Miss Darnley blushed.

               "He's learnt from you, Josiah.
It's just your manner. Shall I order dinner
For you as well as Tom tonight?"

                           He said,
"I don't think Ethel minded. No, I'm out."
"Oh no," she said, "I didn't mind at all,
I thought it most amusing—and you see,
I did find out."

          "You did?"

                   "Yes, did I not?"
"Find what, Miss Darnley?" Joss looked serious.
"Oh, about dancing—what I asked you first."
"Oh, to be sure," he said. Then Father laughed,
And said, "Don't be impertinent. Come along."
He rose. "Good-bye. It's only men, dear Ethel,
Or you might join us, and Maria, too,

If she were interested. Good-bye, Maria,
Lunch was delicious in more ways than one."
Mother rose up and pushed her chair away;
Her white hand carried to her throat and touched it.
"Good-bye," she said, and turning swiftly, walked
Out of the room and closed the door behind her.
We heard her footsteps going up the stairs.
There was a silence of this awkwardness,
Broken by Ethel Darnley who cried out:
"Oh dear, perhaps it's something I have done."
She turned to follow, but the fast-closed door
Seemed to pierce through her flurry to her mind,
And she stood fidgetting before its blank
And final surface while we remained in silence.
"I'll see you out," said Father. He stirred, and moved
Out of the room. Miss Darnley followed him.

"Joss, she was crying!"
                    "Was she?"
                              "Yes, I saw her."
"For God's sake, what about?"
                              I didn't know,
Nor could I answer him. "Well, God Almighty,
If Mother'd only not be quite so touchy—
Gosh! you can't speak now without hurting her—
What's come to her, Tom?"
                              "I don't know," I said.
"Oh well, I guess she'd best be left alone.
So long. I'll see you later."
                              I said, "Yes."
"You going up to see her?"
                              "I don't know."
"I'd leave her be. Come on with me and Father.
She's better left alone. She's mad at us."
I wanted to go up and comfort her
And tell her something to divert her sorrow
So curious and so obvious, but I felt
Awkward and foolish, not knowing what to say
If I should go. He said, "Come on!" again,
And his age pulled my lesser years along
Against my inner feelings, to my relief,
Surrendering to his voice.
                              I shall remember

Always the scene and the round table's shine,
The crumpled napkins, the red stain of fruit
On yellow plates and the small voice that cried
Vainly within me, *Go, go up to her!*

2

We came at length out of the bright spring day, to the old
        building,
Climbed up four flights of talking stairs in semi-darkness,
Into a big grey room, with a huge, north-slanting skylight
Pale blue now, a luminous rippled heaven of glass.
There was a Japanese screen of many folds, bearing
The lines of its singular harmony over the hazard of angles.
There was a huge, carved, dark and shining cabinet, shut and
        withholding,
There was a long, thin green rug, its pattern showing
The path of many goings; it made a hush
In the urgent sound of our feet on the bare, stained boards.
One whole wall was crazy with pinned papers,
Flimsy fragments whose living, leaping lines made
Motion in immobility.
There were ugly, useful, flat-topped tables, criss-crossed by
        brushes,
Enamelled surfaces dotted over with pigment fires waiting
The brush to fan them to flame;
The simple stools worn into expression of use and function.
We found the dais set beneath the skylight,
Covered and draped with a blue brocade, its folds retaining
The light and the shadow of use.
We brought into this room the crossing currents of our living
        selves,
Joss interested; I, eager, feeling as always the familiar essence
        of this work-shop;
Father proceeding as usual, knowing just what he wanted.
Under his orders we moved the big easel and its covered
        canvas
To the south side of the studio, arranged chairs,
Brought out a sofa from behnd the big screen, from the
        corner stacked
With rolls of paper, where hung the polychrome brocades and
        textiles
In a rich jumble. Joss asked: "Can we see the painting?"

"Not now, no. Wait. You, Tom, bring the glasses out.
They're on a shelf in the corner. Whisky! Curse it!"
He gave his purse to Joss and said, "Run to Sixth Avenue,
Buy me a couple of bottles of Johnnie Walker.
Sorry, old man, I thought I had had some here."
Joss went out on his errand.
                              I said, "Shall I pick this up,
This blue brocade on the stand?"
                              "No, please don't touch it,
I'm going to have just one more final check-up,
Model's coming this evening."
                              "I thought you'd finished."
"It is finished—but there's always one place, one corner, one
            little passage, always
Waiting for one touch more."
                              He picked up a zinc pail,
Its dull, grey surface surrounding the brief rainbows
Caught in the flaws of the ice, and he vanished with it
Behind the big screen. I heard him chopping the ice up
With crisp and crackling blows and the music of metal.
He came back soon with a shining bowl in his hands,
Full of the jewels of ice shards.
                              "Look here, Tom,
I hate to unveil a picture when anyone's looking—
An idiosyncracy, or a superstition—
Or a combination. Run out to Rauscher's grocery,
Over on Lafayette Street—buy me cigars,
Corona Perfectos—I should have made Joss do it.
You can be back before he comes. The painting
Will be uncovered and set for you to see it.
Be quick and you'll be here first."
                              "Shan't I wait for Joss?"
"No, don't wait. I like to receive some kindness
When I show a new picture—you'll be kindly,
You have a warm spot, Tom. Joss is like me.
Have you got some money?"
                              "Yes."
                              "Be off then, quickly."
I ran down the steep stairs, ran all the way to Rauscher's,
Ran for the sake of the warmth that grew within me,
Ran for the words he had said, not understanding,
Not bothering yet to understand them, not caring,
Save for the warmth they bred, and the sense of passing

Joss in a race at last, though a queerly run one.
I to be first, and be first because I was wanted!
My breath was short when I reached the stairs again.

I climbed the last flight slowly. I must have come
More quietly than I realized. I paused to breathe
On the dark landing, in front of the open door.
The light from the studio window caught on the paint
Of the rabbet about the frame—so I recalled,
Suddenly, seeing a sunlit scene through a door's frame
In the days of childhood. Here but a faint resemblance,
Yet it had power to recreate a strong mood holding the grown
    boy
Motionless and distressed.
                              The frame directed
Eyes to the opposite wall. The wall was covered
By a huge, stencilled curtain, a Persian pattern,
Blue and green and orange against grey-blue ground.
It was pulled back now, showing an open door,
A door that was hidden, a secret door, disclosing
The shell pink of a small room, with a white rug,
Turquoise curtains at a far, small-paned window,
The back of a deep chair, the foot of a wooden bed
Covered in turquoise cloth with a silver design.
Father was standing, looking about this room,
Finger to chin.
                    I knew that I should not see this:
The frame of the near door warned me, the recollection
Made vivid my sense of intrusion.
                                    I drew back slowly,
Crept down the stairs to the next flight, turned and whistled,
Clumped up the stairs now, slow and loud, still whistling,
Clumsily, jerkily whistling through the short breath
Lent by the labouring heart. I entered the room,
There was Father standing, the bowl of ice
Glittering in his hands. The far door was once more hidden
        by deep folds, barely stirring, the faint and failing mo-
        tion
Of a stencilled curtain: the untranslated whisper
Too faint for hearing.
                        Then I saw the painting.
I stood still:

Silk brocade of a deep blue,
Luminous flesh of alive curves,
Motion in stillness,
Poise and shadow of the bent knee's hollow,
Luminous body lifted from its reclining,
Breast that is caught between a breath and a breath,
Back and elbow and strain of the lifting fingers,
Face and lips and eyes all told in the curve of one cheek,
In the dark hair and the white nape of a neck,
The hidden face;
Balance of passion: body strung to lifting
For the near proof of love.

Light of candles on a woman's body,
Yellow softness on a fierce desire,
Tuned and tensile pose of vital shadows,
Pause in action: the heart's tumult.

Silken softness under a knee's hollow,
Face and lips and eyes within the mind,
Memory's body tense in its reclining,
Light of a fire on a woman's body,
Shock of a lifted hand on the dark stair,
Passion in stillness;
Balance of passion: memory strung to lifting
In the heart's tumult:
Face and lips and eyes in the dark mind.

A clear voice inside me said, Keep silent, keep silent,
Publish your heart to your heart's pain. Speak, but keep silent;
Move and speak and let the small words of day
Cover the words of the night, the syllables of this provoked
    and mind-trapped tumult.
My tongue trembled to say: *Where are the camellias?*
I moved, a little. He turned.
He looked at me, now for the first time defenceless,
A new and naked look, a clear, appealing,
Questioning, begging look that took shape in words: "Do you
    like it? Tom?"
I drew a breath and said, "It's wonderful. It's amazing."
So the look on his face slowly vanished; there stood Josiah
    Cottrell

115

Smiling, at ease, pleased, not remote but removed
Into the sphere of his own way and his own life.
He said, "It's the best I've ever done. A wonderful model."
I looked, but said nothing.
"The candle-light was exciting. I'd never tried it —
At least, I never did with a nude before.
Did you ever see such skin?"
I looked and said nothing, but the awkward silence
Broke with the sound of Joss's steps returning,
Tap-tap-tap on the stairs, click-tap on the landings,
The world brought in to the rescue, the air now
Rushing into the separate chamber-void
That a body had emptied, a void to surround me, all warmth
     gone,
Breathless and stirred and troubled, anger and envy
Beating about my mind in a new conflict.
Tap-tap-tap on the stairs and . . .
                 "Here's your whisky!
Lord, Mr. Cottrell, Lord my Lord! it's ripping!"
Suddenly through his eyes I saw it again:
It was a painting, a picture, a piece of canvas
Covered with beauty and life and living colour,
Passion in stillness—but this was not my passion,
This was an old and a cultivated passion
Grown in the bed of knowledge from seeds of knowing.

"Wonderful!" said Joss, "with two young fools,
One bearing gifts of drink and one of smoke,
As a libation to your deity."
                  "Deity?"
"Well, a goddess—or visited by a God,
Or by a bad old Chinaman knowing too much."
Father threw back his head and laughed aloud.
"You know too much for your age. I suspect you, son.
But still you like it?"
            Nothing defenceless here—
This was the mind—the heart was covered again.
"Like it? It's marvellous! God, what a colour blue
Under the yellow light—and the flesh, the flesh!"
"Glad you like it. Tom, do you realize, boy,
You were the first to see it?"
               "I was?"
                     "You were."

He stood looking at the picture, now, eyes half-closed,
Hands still holding the bowl with jewels of ice.
First to see it? Except the subject? Or not the subject for a
　　　while yet, this evening?
Was this the reason for the barriers falling? Fallen,—how
　　　swiftly mended!
That was a new man. How many men lived in us?
Were we a house that harboured a group of tenants
In the dark rooms of body and flesh and bone,
In the queer corridors of veins, behind the windows
Of our thin-curtained eyes?
　　　　　　　　　But Father moved then,
Breaking the thread of thinking.
　　　　　　　　　"Let's put these down.
Here we stand, we three, each clutching something.
My hands are nearly frozen."
　　　　　　　　　We put down our parcels
On a big wooden table, opened the box,
Opened a bottle of whisky, collected glasses.
Through our bustle we heard light steps ascending.
"You don't need a bell here," Joss said, "You hear them com-
　　　ing."
"May not be for us—though it sounds like Flett.
Hope it is, for I want his fine opinion."
"How could he help liking it?" Joss said. Father smiled.
"Never can tell, boy. And he tells the truth—
Truth that is worth its weight in human hearts.
Only a few will tell you. Only a few.
Hang to them like grim death, when you find them.
Flett's my truth teller."
　　　　　　　　　We turned to watch the door.
The man who entered it was both tall and thin,
Holding himself erect, a monocle to his dark eye,
Black hair brushed smoothly in a perfect parting,
Black short coat and elegant grey, striped trousers,
Tip of handkerchief out of the breast pocket, shining black
　　　shoes,
Thin and delicate lips under flaring nostrils
Terminating a straight and prominent nose,
Malacca cane and a black soft hat in a grey-gloved hand.
He stood a second and said, "It's a devilish climb.
Hello, Cottrell, how's the art business coming?
I hope you've got something really decent to show me

After this Alpine work. Are these your boys?"
"Yes, this is Joss, the elder, and Tom, the younger.
You look as though you'd been to a wedding breakfast."
"Never!" he said. "I studiously avoid them.
Marriage is nonsense, rigged for inheritance taxes,
The single state is blessed. How do you do,
Legitimate Joss and younger legitimate Tom?
You might have been bastards if you'd a sensible father,
And never have known a worry about your parents
As they crawled into their dotage." He peeled his gloves,
Put them neatly into his hat and tossed it
With excellent aim into a nearby chair.
"Now," he said, removing his monocle,
And strolling into the room, "having cleared the eye
Of this affected impediment, let's have a look."
He stood with his hands on his stick and stared at the paint-
      ing.
We stood behind him, for a long space of silence.
The silence was broken again by the sound of footsteps
Scurrying up the stairs.
                        "That's Murray," said Father.
"It's Murray," said Flett, "or a Western Union boy."
Father walked over to the door and through it,
Stood on the landing and called out, "Hi there, Ferdinand,
Hurry or you'll be late!"
                        A rich voice answered
Over the drum of feet, a musical voice,
Full of laughter, "Hello! is old Flett afire?"
I heard Flett mutter, "It's not too far from the truth."
A small, stout man bounced into the studio,
A man in a brown and sloppy suit, with a brown beard,
Extraordinary pink cheeks, a bulbous butt of a nose,
A pair of close-set blue and shining eyes,
And a round head covered over with rigid brown bristles
Of clipped hair.
                  "Well, well," he said, "quite a party.
Where's your glass eye, Flett? I hardly knew you."
"I'm looking at something, you fool. Why make it harder?"
"To be sure!" cried Murray. "Josiah, fellow, master!
I'm glad to see you. This your get?"
                                    "It is.
Joss and Tom."
                  "Hello boys. Where's the painting?

118

Ah, oh, well, well, for God's sake! Mm, here's something.
Give us a drink, boys. Give us a good strong drink."
"You can take this neat," said Flett. "It needs no whisky."
"I need the whisky."
                    "You shall have it," said Father.
He turned his back to the painting, stood at the table,
And poured a drink. I saw that his hands were trembling.
"Now!" said Murray. He seized a chair and pulled it
First this way, then that, sat on it, rose again,
Moved it a foot to the left, and again was seated.
"Ah, that's better. You better sit down, old Flett,
Take the weight off your feet and give it back to the—mind."
"If I ran around New York like an eager Boy Scout,
I'd be tired and have to sit, too. But, as it is—"
He paused.
           "As it is?" said Father. He gave the glass
To the seated Murray.
                      "I hoped someday you'd do this."
"Yes," added Murray, and clinked the ice in his glass.
"He's been a long time coming," Flett continued.
"First the drawing and then the battle for colour—
Too much shooting. Too much monkey-business.
I always thought that Cottrell's gentility,
Hedged by an egocentric and ruthless mind,
Added to masculine charms and sporting proclivities,
Would stop him short of the mark. I see I was wrong."
Father flushed a little: I don't think Joss saw it,
He was watching Flett.
                       "Out of the monkey business, the self-
ishness, this—this marvel, this amazement!"
Murray giggled and said, "It comes down to this:
The burnt child turns to ashes and then plays Phoenix."
Joss turned and looked at Father, who laughed and said:
"What's your verdict, Ferdinand? What's your verdict?"
"Great! without any possible reservation.
Perfect! But where in hell did you find the model?"
"I like your judgment," said Flett, "but you have no manners.
You also don't exercise the eyes God gave you,
Or you'd see that Cottrell turned her face to the wall."
"Because of her beautiful behind," said Murray.
"I'll have a drink, now," Flett said, "and a cigar.
Also a chair, you boys." He stuck his monocle
Back in his left eye. "Come, let's all sit down.

119

We can talk, and Murray can make his vulgar
Comments from time to time."
                              "Me vulgar?"
                                    "Yes, you, most vulgar.
It's probably the reason you paint so well."
"Your own gentility hasn't seemed to stop you,"
Murray chimed in. "You act as cold as a fish
And harbour the waifs and strays, thinking to hide them
Under your cutaway."
                        "Each to his weakness," said Flett.
"Fishing versus philanthropy," cried Murray.
"Well, don't stop fishing before our next trip, Josiah—
Fishing or anything else that Flett implies now
In his cultivated and nasty-polite sort of way.
You've a nasty mind, Flett. It must be your poetry.
I hope that none of your boys write poetry?"
Joss said, "Tom writes poems. But he's nice about it."
"Do you?" said Flett. "You must show your poems to me."
"There!" cried Murray, "you can't resist the kind act—
You scoff at marriage and take it out in helping
People who have no claim. I may be vulgar,
But at least I follow my line in open country."
"Yes," said Flett, "you're open, so open you never close,
Like a saloon door."
                        Murray said, "Good!" and laughed.
"Let's sit down," said Father, "for I'm exhausted.
Talk, you fellows. I want to look at my painting.
I never saw it before this very moment."
"Father, you act like a prima donna," said Joss,
"I hadn't believed it of you."
                              "You're young," said Flett,
"And perhaps you haven't yet known the fear and the strain
At the ebb of the tide of art, when the flood's forgotten."

We sat then in a comfortable half of a circle
In front of the painting. I held a drink in my hand.
I heard their voices sounding around about me,
Word upon word. But my mind was off in a new space
Peopled with images, and I did not hear them,
Save as a beating of words against isolation.

I thought of the picture hung in our drawing room:
The small gold label below on the frame, black letters,

Maria Northrup. Blonde and young and lovely,
Little brown J.C. down in the left hand corner
Against the dark green of the velvet dress.
One peered to see it.
                              Stiff, correct—a portrait
Of a woman unknown to me. Had Josiah known her?
Stiff painting, yes. Beauty of young face, yes. It was not Maria
        Cottrell, today, this minute . . .
Was it the ancestor of this new painting? of her?
Who had laid the line between that and this?
The studio was grey; it was cold in colour, it gave
Warmth to the mind, the warm words beating about me,
Warm thoughts, finally this: a flame of paint
To scorch the spirit, to turn my world to excitement,
As though to burn and consume the pettiness of my small
        growth,
As though to burn and consume pity and envy and the little
Delicate hesitations of mind and body, the small regrets,
The image of sin and the guilt of re-desiring—
It left a Want and a Would.
Home was the colour of cushions, the massed objects, the deep
        red curtains, the candles
(Candle-light on a body and youth deriving
Strength from a burnt regret?);
Home was the music of a voice, the deep voice, the constant
        love, the dilemma of loving—
Home was the barren ground of small words, small doings,
Endlessly jigging against each other in confusion of pursuit
Of what object?
Home was the seed-bed. Was this the garden?
No, no! unfair thinking—and yet—an essence,
A distillation of knowing, a sense of the truth:
Here was living, there was existence.
                              The small things
Crowded and pushed and shuffled and covered you over . . .
As the snow covers the ground to a fertile silence?
The snow is beauty, you cannot divide the fallen
Snow to its flakes, it is one, it is unity,
Rest for the earth, the page for the wild story
Printed—and melted—and born again of a night wind
And a winter sky.
                              The small things, the little matters,
The matters that would not congeal to a great matter,

But remained little and crowding and overbearing,
Drops on the temple of the bound prisoner.
                                        What fusion
Led to a room that could harbour a flame in comfort?

What was Clare to me? The sign of the passing
Moment of youth when the shafted eccentric wheel
Turns to deliver its force that a force has lifted?
Happenings, happenings! This and that and the other,
Happen to me—and I? Do I just happen,
Is there a force to make, in me? Or always
Wait the event, and grudge it—and so use it,
Held in receptive hands, that the clean angles
Wear to the round and fit to the palm's pleasure?
Little by little by little—worn to a shape,
Worn to a mould, to a round that the winds will roll in the
        least effort
Of diverse breaths?
                        Pray for the strength of angles.

The light was dim now,
The painting glowed in the dim bluish light,
Skill rashly used, the pattern of a life hung
Precisely—so precisely in its due frame . . .
The evening star in a white tie? Not quite—
Venus removed from god-head, turned to flesh,
Fitted to life, to the day and the night of earth.

I did not see Joss leave. He stole away then, quietly, purpose-
        fully, on his own occasions.
I heard the voices beating about my ears, till I became aware
        of a voice,
Only one voice, fine, strong, mellow, a balanced voice,
Father's voice—the voice of the body that lifted
The hand to the brush, the brush to the canvas,
The voice that gave sound to the eyes that detected and fixed
Life in a curve of flesh, the flesh
That had made unrest for youth, for my years,
The life that turned away from my mother's life,
In cruelty, in understanding, in self-preservation?
What had she turned to? Had she too turned away?
From life or to life? Reality or its dream?
Tears on the stairs, and the presence of Ethel Darnley,

Little by little, Evelyn, body in candle-light
Strung to the lifting for the near presence of life . . .
Tears on the stairs, and a hand on the dark stair . . .

The words came in now, forcing the thoughts aside.

"Black and white—the line on the empty paper,
The line that exists to tempt you to disregard it.
Lines are abstractions, frames for a whole idea,
But the idea is the reality—no line lives
Independent of what it tries to contain
Even within its thickness. My art is a lens
Through which you see, but it's your special seeing
Brings it alive."
                    "For whom?"
                                   "For me," he said.
"That is but selfish."
                       "No, it is but essential.
What is a colour if I do not see it?
Colour is just abstraction, the re-creation
Of the pith and core of a mood through light and mass.
The colour is mine—not life's—and though it always
Lives in your eye beholding, my eye's the touchstone
To a reality rendered by the mind's heat
To its essential qualities—all superfluous
Stuff that adheres to life as we first see it,
Is condensed to a tone, to a line, to a single mass
Telling a single story, my story, mine only.
Though a thousand eyes retell it within the limits
Of their experience, they see it through my mind,
And only so."
              "You bar the emotions," said Flett.
"There speaks the poet. You mean but tears by emotion."
"No," said Flett, "I mean the love of the world,
The love of God, the anger, the true desires,
The satisfaction of passion harnessed to living
In a fine pattern of gift beyond reception,
Reception that doubles gift. These things are greater
Than the mind's span will stretch."
                                     "I harness passion."
"Only to ego, Cottrell."
                         "To ego, then—
What am I but an I? Shall I spread my ego

123

Thin on a world that it may but hurt and confuse
As much as help and clarify? Is my painting
Colder or less good because the ego forced it
Into the way of the flesh controlled and bounded
Always by that one instrument, the mind,
Which can still top it, harness it, control it,
Bend it and warp it till the final production
Is the synoptic of the mood and the manner
That first excited? Shall mood be our whipping master?
Leave it the upper hand and what becomes then
Of such a one as me? My passion spent
Here, there and everywhere on the evanescent
Business of living, business of mere existence?
No! let the world go on in its own damned folly—
Touch it and feel it, taste it for your knowledge,
Hold it and use it—it is warm and pleasant—
Turn off the light when eyes are craving darkness,
Turn off the passion when the mind needs only
Solace of loneliness. Can you touch passion
But to your hurt unless the mind is master
Always and strongly?"
                              "I don't understand you."
Murray's voice sounded deep and puzzled now:
"But you have made me see how you could do it:
Paint such a picture and remain outside it,
See it and understand it, and yet give it
Whole to the world without a reservation.
Can nothing scar the man whose eye permits him
Vision to see the heat and the spring of passion?
Have you then no religion beyond yourself?"
"God is his adjunct, the Church for resting, only—
That is my guess," said Flett.
                              "Oh—about," said Father.
"Only the fools deny the force of religion.
We need our strength—why should we struggle singly
When we have priest and canon to hold up our hand?
They have reduced the mystery of our living
To a perfected pandect that can embrace
Me and the man on the corner, the woman in sin,
The prince and the beggar, the Slav and the reasoning French-
        man.
Look at my father—what have the Protestants given
Him in his old age, now with his art behind him?

Has he not drawn on the wells of his own existence
For all the courage needed? It's energy wasted!
Turn your eyes to the Church and the Church gives visions,
Asks no return but the turning of eyes, the mutter
Of a prayer intended. I grasp at the true intention,
And in my failures, I draw on the strength they lend
Freely and willingly.
            You are the irreligious,
You who battle to fix the eccentric world
Into your own circumference, and not God's.
Who gave you the power to stand alone?
Am I being too personal?"
                "No," said Murray. "Your painting
Fades in the darkness but you grow somewhat clearer."
"Good! For you see, we're simpler than you—Flett and I.
We dress for dinner. We cultivate good manners.
We brush our hair and polish our finger nails.
I practise shooting before the season opens,
I go to the priest and confess all in due season,
I order champagne for the purposes of seduction,
And claret for taste and pleasure with men of taste.
I close my ears to the many discordant voices
That beat against my system, my way of living,
I follow along my path in water-proof shoes,
And keep my body in good condition for jumping
Brooks, and puddles of mud. And I turn my eyes
Away from the glances of those who say, 'Josiah!
Let us cling to your strength, let us jump with you!'
Flett's like my father, he draws on his capital,
Lends it to fools and weaklings—he'd lend to women
If they should touch him otherwise than through loving.
He's part way right there, marriage is not for poets,
A wife is the one charity he's forsworn.

That's the trouble with women, they go back and forth
On a man-moved shuttle of love and a narrowed interest,
Weaving a web of the small threads of small matters,
Seeing God in a flower and faith in a gesture,
Fearful of thunder and fierce clear blaze of the lightning,
Always dependent—yet with a strength for clinging
Would build a monument, properly directed.
What is a wife but a mother, what is a home
But a bed forever covered with stuff that musses?

What is a woman but negative to our positive?
Must we forever use up our current in contact?
This that you see, this piece of canvas painted,
This is a flame seen through the cool night window,
Flame that is fed on the logs of a tree cut down—
Cut down by man expressly to feed the flames.
You could call this selfish, if you should choose to.
I see a light at the end that is blinding bright—
Shall I be hindered in my progress toward it?
Shall I impede my progress by yielding, yielding
To soft demands, waste energy in revolt
Against the inessentials? against convention?
Against the matters that ease the road no man
Born to the vision of a bright light finds other
Than a long, rocky, terrible path, forever—
Forever! forever! to be travelled alone?"
"Go then, alone—with God," said Flett.
                                        "For me,"
Murray put in, "let me be going with Flett.
You are cold calculating devil, Josiah,
And someday someone will murder or wish to murder you.
I'd hate your guts if I didn't find you attractive,
And I'd hate your work if it wasn't so god-damned good.
You baffle me, fellow, and I don't like to be baffled.
You don't know women, and you don't know about marriage,
You've never known the surge of the blood arising
Hot from defeat and pain, from the daring failure,
And I don't believe that you even know your father,
Though they say that takes a wise son, wiser than you—
And yet—you balance like some damned cold equation."
He rose in the dusk of the room. "Come on," he said,
"Let's join the Catholics, Flett, and become great artists,
Eating our sweets and having them, all together."
I heard the delightful sound of father's laughter, echoing
Through the dark room. I saw Flett rise up slowly, his thin
          shape silhouetted
Against the blue of the skylight.
                          "Good-night, Cottrell, we're off now.
I'm grateful for what you've painted. Good-night, Tom."
I said, "Good-night."
                          "I'll light the light," said Father.
"You'll break the mood," said Flett. "We can see the door.

Sit till your light is ready to burn again."
                                        "Cold light!
Scientists looking for it for years," said Murray.
"Good-night, Josiah. The painting will live beyond you."
"Thanks," said Father, no more.
                                        We heard their feet
In broken rhythm descending the unseen stairs.

We sat in the darkness for a while in silence.
I felt a tension growing. Did he expect her?
When was she coming?
                        The prickles ran up my spine
And into my scalp. Suppose that I just stayed here,
Stayed till he sent me off, or waited below-stairs,
Caught her as she entered, and whispered, 'Clare!'
In the dark of the entrance?
                                The vision became so actual
That I could feel her arm with the tips of my fingers,
Hear her clear voice, see her in spite of the darkness . . .
Lying stretched out, taut on the lifted fingers?
Oh, no! . . . then it was over.
                                All life was as flat as the soda in
    my whisky, nearly finished.
There was no point to this, it was simply childish,
The idea vanished before it took flesh from action.
What should I do when I found her? What should I do?
To wait was to let it happen, merely, to place oneself
Blindly upon the path of the event.
                                No more of that! There'd been enough.
Happenings, happenings, the guessing, the unknowing,
The event of the unforeseen, undirected solution, the drifting
Into the way of happenings always beyond me. I said:
"I'll go now, Father. It's late."
                                "It was nice to have you.
I'd rather you left before the model came here.
I promised she'd be alone."
                                I said, "Remember me to her."
He didn't answer. I didn't look over toward him.
The pause grew horribly long.
                                "You've got eyes," he said.
"I'm blessed if I thought you'd know. Well done, my boy.
I'm grateful you didn't blab it."
                                "Oh no, I wouldn't."

"Bury it now, son." Silence again; so I rose up,
Put the unfinished glass on the table.
                                        He said,
"How did you know?" I had no answer. His voice
Came then softly, gently out of the darkness:
"Did she upset you? Stupid of me, that was.
I should have seen that happening. It's so clear now.
I wouldn't have had her hurt you."
                                        I stood there wondering,
Listening to this familiar voice grown strange
And strangely warm.
                        "So young! Oh, one forgets
The cardboard armour of youth! The flesh triumphant
Over the puzzled innocence of the spirit
Trapped into action. You give the wheel a push
And it spins without you. I wish that it had been Joss.
He was begun like me, full-grown, full-armoured,
His heart in a steel box and his soul already
Headed for the still reaches of the mind-made
World of self-seeking—beyond which lie the marshes
Of lonely sinking. You are beyond me already,
You are beyond the reach of a hand to touch you—
My hand to help you.
                        Father was strangely right.
He planted his tree in the thickets of man's living,
Bent his boughs to the neighbourhood of his fellows,
Saying the lone tree reached swiftly up to the heavens
To find an empty sky. The sky is empty.
Yet I must keep it, for that is the air I crave.
Poor Tom, the thicket's beginning. I might have spared you
Thorns for the sapling.
                        Ah well, the painting's there.
There'll be another and another painting,
Murray has said it, they live beyond my life,
My life is mine and must be for me only.
Write your poems, Tom, and write them from your being,
Not from your eyes and fingers. Show 'em to Flett,
He spends his years in helping a hundred others,
People who have no claim—just other people.
That's his life. Perhaps it nourishes him.
Time to be going, boy. Time to begin again, seize time,
Don't let it slip you, the hours are cheats and frauds,
They look so many and they're so few for living,

So few remain for redemption, for covering canvas
With life to outlive a life and excuse a living.
Be off, boy. Go now."

                    I stood for a second longer
Wishing at last that I could see the expression
His face was wearing. I felt a sudden flooding
Sense of well-being run through the veins of my body.
The bitterness moved in his voice like an autumn leaf
Pierced by an arrow of wind from the bow of winter,
It made my youth an eternity of fine years
All for my happy spending. Life was a deep purse
Full with the price of days.

                    I turned and departed.

3

So I went walking along the street,
The dusk flowed under my marching feet,
And I heard the sound that the city sends
With a beat and a roar and a rattle,
My heels clicked down and my toes made a shuffle
And a fellow went by with a nasty snuffle
And the trucks bumped
And the cars thumped
In the traffic battle.
The dark grew so deep
Between the watch that the buildings keep
Guarding the sky,
Their lights hung up in the night so high—
So my heart went up and my feet came down
For I was young in a living town.

As I went home by familiar ways
My head was full of the future days,
And I jumped ahead and I dodged my past
Like the trucks and the cars and the trolleys.
My heart was high with the things to be doing
And to hell with women and all their wooing,
So I'd get tight
And I'd go tonight
To the latest Follies.
For Spring, drunk on air,
She wrapped the streets in her amorous hair,

Filling the town
With the flicker of lights upon her gown—
So my heart kept time to the rattle and ring
For I was young in New York in spring.

4

I felt released and comforted then when I came home,
This was behind me, all the talk and the big, wide thoughts,
　Pressure of age and years and the fire of making,
　Praise for accomplishment creating but sadness.
I had a sense of an empty departed Clare, gone fully
Into the realm of past days, no longer shamefully shared,
　No more need to wonder about the sharing,
　No more need to puzzle relationships—
　　These were past things, these were clear.
I didn't want Clare now, it was too much trouble, too hard,
Leave her to pose in a studio lit by the flame of candles:
　She was a painting, she was not flesh, not blood,
　She was an image created by magical brushes,
She was removed by the mind that could no longer maintain
Effort of distant and dim re-creation, a lost mood holding
　Only the memory, not the touch nor the savour,
　Only the fact of its distance, only the dream fled,
　　Only a figure on the mind's canvas.
Life was a flood and a joy, youth was not for repining,
　Spirits are swift to descend and swifter to rise,
Here was the coming of night, the promise of pleasure for
　　seizing,
　Here was the first decision, deliberately taken:
　　I was a man—with the pulse of a boy.

So I mounted the stoop, in my happiness planning and think-
　　ing:
Maybe my mother will go to the Follies, we'll go together,
　I'll wear a white tie, then go on to the Ross dance,
　That will be fun and Joss will be there already.
I turned my key in the latch, the soft click opening my home.
The hall was webbed in darkness and quiet lay over the
　　house,
　No light showing above-stairs, curious, no light
　Welcoming through the open door to the parlour,

Darkness and muffled sounds of the city.
I called for mother then, but I heard no call in answer;
I called for Joss. No answer. I ran up the flight of steep stairs,
  Looked in our room and saw by the pallid street-lights
  Streaked through the window, his day clothes in confusion;
Turned the light on, looked at the clock: it was well past
  eight.
Then I ran downstairs and went in to the dark pantry,
  Called down the dumbwaiter, "Agatha, Agatha, hi there!"
"Agatha's out," cried the cook. "You're late for dinner,
  Agatha's day out, your mother's not home."
I said, "Just send my food on a tray, I won't wait for Mother."
Then I went upstairs again, to wash and get ready,
Peered into Mother's room to be sure she was out, not sleep-
  ing:
  Paper all over the floor, the signs of confusion,
  White bits of paper, ghosts in the dim light.

So I turned on the light which was like a voice to the room
  Lying choked with the words it could not utter:
  Everything helter-skelter here, tokens of hurry,
  Desk in a muddle, newspapers on the bed,
    Marble mantel bleakly denuded;
Bureau bare of its brushes, the host of little objects,
  Absence of silver, absence of the sharp gleams
  Born of the cut-glass bottles—the walnut wardrobe
  Standing agape and empty, mute where it sang once
    In the gay tongues of many dresses.
Set on the dark and polished surface of one table
  Were the grey warnings of three envelopes.
  They were the neat touch in disorder's middle:
  One said *Josiah,* one said *Joss,* and one
    Cried out aloud its single *Tom.*
Strange that I had a hand to grasp and open the letter,
  Yet that the hand should be so slow, reluctant,
  Dreading and wanting, timid and curious,
  Able and yet unwilling, the heart still lagging
    After the mind, fearful of sorrow.
Curiosity bred a courage. I seized it and slit it open,
  Looked at the dark words creeping across the grey page,
    Saw a beginning and an ending.

Dearest, it said, at last I have courage to leave and depart.
  You cannot find me. Please do not try to discover
  Where I am hiding, hiding alone in my anguish,
    Waiting for time and the healing of time.
This is your father's doing. I did not dare now to face him,
  He is so hard and so cold, ununderstanding.
  This is a wall between us. My sorrow has grown
    Too great a burden to carry forever.
Soon we shall meet, be happy again, you and I and dear Joss,
  This will be merged in the past then, dim in our minds.
  See, it is kinder to go and go swiftly, alone,
    Sparing the tears, the anguish of parting.
So you can think of me now as ever, a loving, devoted
  Mother who thinks of you, thinks of you always and always.
  If I had stayed you'd have seen me in sorrow, in anger:
    Anger and sorrow are never forgotten.
How could I stand the days and nights of your father's deser-
    tion?
  Where could I turn but to sin, where but to shame?
  Who shall be mine now with never a shadow between?
    Where is my God? Whence love, save from you?
Let me be hidden a space till my heart heals over. You only
  Know of the love I forswore—remember the love
    That I have borne you. In sorrow. Your Mother.

Echo on echo! her ghost was about in the room as I stood.
  Ghost of a day of rain, and the echo of hoof-beats,
  Stars on the pavement, scattered in points of fire,
  Tears in the darkness, anger in battering footsteps,
    Evelyn! Evelyn! I shall come down!
Echo of trials evaded, courage that failed in the rain,
  Death of Childhood the Deathless, the evanescent
  Trust in the strength of the tree that is cracked by frost;
  White letter held in the hand, its issue avoided.
    Whom did one turn to? Who knew the answers?
Telephone Father, tell him? I burned with the picture
    evoked:
  Clare on a blue brocade, the flutter of candles,
  Clare on a bed of blue and silver, a pink room,
  Warm as the skin of her body, her body lifting
    For the near proof . . . Shut the mind! shut the mind!
Jangle of telephone bell on a pause? or feet on the long steps,
  Warning, intruding, bearing what words on the tongue?

Mother is gone, she is vanished, a letter for you,
Mother is gone, she is hidden, your art is her exile,
  Room that is hidden, white letter on grass.
Who should be asked? Ethel Darnley? Publish your heart and
    shame?
  Who should be asked? even Evelyn? Anger and sorrow—
  Adding to sorrow out of memory?

So I called Joss from dinner. Servants . . . the waiting . . .
    waiting . . .
Footsteps that echo and leave . . . the shadow of distant
    laughter . . .
  Voice in annoyance at last: "Well, what's the trouble?"
  So is the story told, breathless, without an ending.
"What can I do? I'm here, I can't leave. We cannot find her.
  Why tell me now, you fool, there is nothing to do now,
    nothing,
  If she has left no address. Why spoil my party?
  Why in the name of God don't you call Father?"
    I said nothing. I couldn't answer.
He said then, "I'll be home, after the party, I'll come then.
Nothing to do. I suppose Father's working. Leave him alone.
  Wait for morning. Come on here, come to the party.
  Don't tell the world your troubles. Show a good front.
Don't be a damned fool, she is just angry, this is a gesture,
Wait and she'll come back home, and no one the wiser.
  Don't be so sensitive. No mountain, only a molehill.
  I must get back to dinner. Keep your head, Tom."
    Sharp click, the dead phone. I was alone.
He had not seen her room, the passion of its disorder,
  He had not seen the letters, on the neat table,
He had not heard her ghost, loud in the absent objects—
  He had not heard her cry, loud in the dark house,
    Evelyn! Evelyn! I shall come down!
  Evelyn! Evelyn! Tom's here! I dared not, alone!

These were the fruits sprung from the blossom of home, of
    marriage:
This was the father cut off by the wall of a shared passion,
  This was the brother to brother, no help in need,
  This was the mother to son—who did not go up to her.
Food sits untasted on a bright tray in a warm room
Under a portrait of youthful life in a green dress,

133

Face at peace, unaware, the stiffness of art
  Still unflexed of its youth, seed of the fluid
    Passion in candle-light building a wall.
Fundamentals of life—one tree can alter the whole last
Shape of another growing beside it, just by its shade,
  But the growth of neither need falter, they go on—
  Though in the final growing, their roots, interlocking,
Weaving together, suck the same moisture. Echo of rain:
She was content to let life's burden slip off her shoulders.
  Vision of Mother freed of her self-made bundle
  In the great sword of a lightning flash, while I . . .
    God is electric? E pur si muove!
Youth is forever a bright light, a gloom that the light refuses,
  A harmony unresolved, a separate discord—
This was the gloom and the discord, always to be remem-
    bered:
  Schism and strife and pain from the bed of marriage,
    Each to the other, cutting and tearing—
    Each to the other . . . E pur si muove?

PART THREE

FLOWERS are mine, and I am flowers' slave:
I prop their weakness, mine they can condone,
They bend before the wind, more wise than brave,
I cure their hurt and so they heal my own.
They seek the sun because I tucked the seed
Into the moist compassion of the ground,
Their search is but the answer to my need,
They cannot reach the sun: so am I bound.
Their blue is my reflection of the sky,
Their red, my anger, and their purple blooms
Reflect a glory that shall as surely die
As flowers and I shall seek our earthen tombs.
Friendship is but the flower I have raised
Through fearful care to make me stand amazed.

I'LL GIVE you now my room-mate, Samuel Allen,
Whose six foot one of solid flesh and bone
Was always near me. We were both large men,
Full of a Junior's pride, working together,
Eating each other's thoughts and quarrelling
Over the terms of matters past our grasp.
That was a queer time, surely, while we grew
Rapidly toward our manhood's final stature,
Growing like corn in a full field of corn,
Washed by a rain too steep and blown by winds:
The sons of summer usurping softer spring.
Sam was gentle and handsome, sometimes clever,
If cleverness was expected: he cut his cloth
To suit his situation; bent his ways
To the ways of those about him, yet kept intact
The sum of selves whose total's kindliness.

In February, nineteen-seventeen,
We made a slippery progress in Sam's Ford

From Dedham homeward. The uncertain snow
Was caught between the wish to melt or freeze,
But we progressed with an abandoned speed
In leaps and skiddings. The harsh and biting air
Was full of evening and the light was grey,
But we were armoured against the cold and dusk
By happy lunch and friendly alcohol.
Although the light was failing, yet the snow
Postponed the evening, and one saw the road
Stretching ahead, a maze of wavering ruts
Dark in its whiteness. The occasional trees,
Ribbed in the remnants of snow's skeleton,
Were black and white against the leaden sky,
And houses had but just begun to prick
Their sombre silhouettes with pallid lights.
We talked of our last visit to his place
Down in Virginia, and planned another trip
To see that lovely country in the spring.
We sang *Colombo* to the empty road,
Oh Nasty Fly to set the winter off
With a warm wall of words, and followed that
With lusty Limericks. In the midst of these
We saw a solitary figure walking
Along the road ahead.
                    "A girl," said Sam.
"Let's give the kid a lift."
                        "All right," I said,
"But see if she is pretty."
                        We drove past.
I turned to look at her. She looked at me:
A young and welcoming face in a red hat.
"O.K.," I said. "She'll do." Sam stopped the car.
"You want a lift?" we cried. She called, "Which way?"
"We're bound for Cambridge."
                        "Fine! You're on my way,
I live in Somerville." She hurried on.
I climbed out to the road. "Hop in," I said,
"We'll all be warmer three in the front seat."
"Why don't you get some curtains for your Lizzie?"
"Somebody pinched them, but we've got a rug.
Get in. I'll give it to you."
                        "Thanks." She climbed
In beside Sam. I tucked the rug around

Her knees and climbed in afterwards.
                                    "And you?
No rug for you?"
                        I said, "I'm warm enough."
"I'll share it with you." She smiled so prettily:
I felt a tingle run right up my back
At the look she gave me. "No," I said. "You keep it,
I like to stretch out with my great long legs,
The rug is cramping." We were moving now,
A rough and bumpy progress.
                                "Oh," she said.
She looked at Sam. "Some start in slow, some boys.
I thought the way the car came down the road
You boys were tight."
                        The car lurched suddenly
And flung her hard against me. "Ah!" she cried,
"That was my corner!" and looked up at me,
Smiling again.
                "She thought us tight," said Sam,
"And yet she came aboard. You're pretty young
To train with drunks."
                        "I know my way around.
You didn't look so tough. You're Harvard boys,
I know the type. You live in Randolph, don't you?
Or maybe Claverly—somewhere, anyway,
Along the Gold Coast."
                        Sam put back his head
And roared with laughter, and I laughed, but felt
Ashamed to be so ticketed. "Right!" said Sam.
"You know your oats, you do. What is your name?"
"You tell me yours," she said, "your truly names,
I won't believe it if you say it's Smith."
We laughed and told our names.
                                "So, Tom and Sam.
We'll get on faster without Mister, Miss,
Or anything like that."
                        "And yours?" I said.
"Rosemary Whittaker, Rosy to you boys,
Tom, Sam and Rosy—Bump!"
                            We'd hit a rut,
And as the car slewed, she threw up her arm
And caught me by the shoulder.
                                "God!" she said,

"She certainly takes the bumps." I laughed a little,
Feeling my body glow beneath my clothes.
My hands were clinging to the door's thin edge:
I kept them there. She looked at me again,
A curious look, and slowly dropped her arm
And settled in her place. She looked at Sam:
Both hands were fully occupied with the wheel;
He grinned one swift, malicious grin at me.
He said, "Where to in Somerville? What address?"
She stared ahead and answered sulkily,
"Just drop me off in Cambridge, I'll get home,
I wouldn't trouble you. I'll take the trolley."
"She's mad at you," Sam said. I grinned at this.
"I am not mad! You tell me why I'm mad?"
"Don't ask fool questions."
                              "Hey! that's rude," she said.
"Perhaps. I didn't mean it rudely, though."
We lapsed to silence. So we went awhile,
Her body stiffly held between our own.
But as the car drew near the Charles, she let
Her stiffness so relax that now she sat
Pressed close against me. Every now and then
She'd look up quickly at me, and half smile,
And drop her eyes, and sigh, and so repeat.
We crossed the Charles by Cottage Farm. The river
Lay static in its stolid icy state,
An uninhabited and silly-flat
Strip of rough field that held the failing day
And carried it far off to a grey death
In smoky distance. Now the factory lights
Were bright against the dullness of the west
And all the darker shapes were little squares
Enclosing people lost in half-way land
Between day's vigour and night's credulity,
While we were of all living souls the three
Whose lives were still in motion.
                                   "Well?" she said.
I looked at her. "You're cold?"
                                 "Not much, a little."
She snuggled closer. "Can you get the rug
Up and around me?" I tweaked and pulled at it.
Sam said, "You take good care of her, Tom, take care."
She bent her body forward and I tucked

140

The rug behind her. Then she suddenly
Sat back while still my arm was round her waist,
Imprisoning it. She did not look at me,
But moved her shoulders till I felt their weight.
I thought: this is the shadow of the substance,
I know the substance, and I like it more.
I pulled my arm back, gently, and she sighed
A vexed and shorter sigh.

                    We drove in silence
Until we'd passed through Cambridge and were near
The edge of Somerville. "Be guide," said Sam,
"The Gold Coast doesn't know these foreign lands."
"You wouldn't," she replied, and told the way.
"You don't know much of anything," she said,
Breaking the newer silence. "I bet you went
To Groton or St. Mark's." Sam laughed.

                                "It's true,
I know it's true. What do you know of life?
Just books and easy chairs and all the fat
Fine houses on the Hill, and stuffy dames,
And caviar and big cigars and cars,
And fancy dances. We sit at home and wait—
To see if Father has been fired again."
I said, "As bad as that?"

                          "As bad as what?
You think we don't have fun? No fun, you think?
You're crazy! I can find me lots of fun,
There's lots of boys will give a girl some fun
Without her asking."

                  She returned again
Into her sulky silence. I was sorry:
I had not meant to hurt her. Then I felt
A strong and subtle feeling creeping up,
Up through my legs and arms, along my back,
To settle in my loins. I could not stop it:
It fed upon the dusk and the dark streets,
The small and unavoidable soft touches
Of body against body, on my youth,
On pity, on the opportunity,
On all the long past of this winter's drive,
But most of all on Sam's half-mocking smile.
I sneaked my hand beneath the folding rug
To find her own that she had hidden there

Against the double cold, and finding it,
Found it was snatched away, quick, angrily,
And saw the pale flash of her scornful face
Turned toward me, saw her lips twitch and shut close,
Her face averted solidly.
                              The car
Drew to a halt before a little house,
Wood-framed, unpainted, bare and comfortless,
With an exposed and winter-speaking porch
That cried 'Keep off!' I thought: when summer comes
Perhaps the porch can harbour life and love
And speak less angrily.
                          "All right," she said,
"We have arrived, my lord." I jerked myself
Back to the present, took the rug from her,
Opened the door, got out and helped her down.
"Thank you. Good-bye," she said, and turned to Sam.
"Thanks for the lift. It was a lovely ride.
Good-night, Sam, call me up some other time,
We could have fun. Remember the address,
The number's in the book, Frank Whittaker."
"Good-night," said Sam. "But how about tonight,
I'm going in to Boston later on
To catch a movie. Want to come along?"
"Just you?"
              "Tom, too." He grinned.
                                          "No thanks," she cried,
And started for the house. "Some other time,
When you are free." She opened the front door,
Without a key, it seemed to have no lock,
And disappeared in darkness and the door
Shut in the twilight of the street's pale lamp.
I stood and stared: my eyes took in the house
In singular detail.
                      I heard Sam laugh.
"So snubs to you, my handsome lad," he said,
"Come on, let's go, I'm cold, I want a drink."
I climbed in quickly. As I slammed the door
I closed the moment out into the past,
And laughed with Sam.
                        "You made a hit," I said.
We started back for Cambridge.
                                  "Don't be silly,

She used me as a stalking-horse, you fool,
She thought you dandy, but you wouldn't play.
Why didn't you, Tom?"
                              "Because," I said, "because."
"Come on!" he said, "That's different. Oh, I know
We gave up all that well-planned sort of work,
The parties with the chorus girls, all that,
A long time back. But this was unexpected,
She dropped right in your lap and she was pretty,
Young, with red hair. I bet you she could love:
She's been there and come back."
                              "Oh, love!" I said.
"That sort of loving, kisses in a cab,
Excitement carried to the breaking point—
And then—'Good-night. I'll call you up again'—
Oh yes, that sort of mean, unsatisfied,
And dirty sort of loving without love,
The rotten sense of doing but not done—
Better to sleep with them."
                              "Why not?" he asked.
"You could with that one, or I miss my guess."
"You'd miss your guess," I said. "They kiss for fun,
They pay for parties in the taxi home—
With reservations. Ask to sleep with them,
And they go up in smoke."
                              "You've asked them that?"
"You have too, damn you—when tight—half-heartedly,
Under the stress of that excitement, hoping
It wouldn't happen, frightened, throat all dry,
Acting outside yourself. It's not our dish."
"I know, but why? I know the why for me,
What stops me—but for you?"
                              "I'm not quite sure.
I sometimes wonder if we'll feel regret,
As we grow older, that we have passed it up
For some vague standard that we can't define."
"I can define it."
                    "Can you, Sam?"
                                        "Of course.
I'm waiting till I marry. It's not fair
To ask the girl to be so good and pure
And not be pure ourselves."
                              "Why should you care?

Do you demand a virgin?"
                                    "Yes."
                                                "But why?"
"Because—oh, damn it, I don't know. I feel
It must be so, the children."
                                    "You're just tied
Into the old knot of convention, Sam."
"Perhaps. Why you, then?"
                                    "I shall wait until
I find me someone fairly of my sort,
To fit the mind and body, both."
                                                "Oh sure.
We all want that. What of it?"
                                        "You can waste
Your life away with little tarts like this,
Who neck for money."
                                "Yes, I know you can,
But after you have found this perfect girl,
This mind and body, after years have passed
And you've been married long, why won't you feel
What you just said to me a moment back:
You were a fool not to have satisfied
Your curiosity first?"
                                "Who said I'd marry?"
"You did."
            "Not I. I hope I never fall
Into the trap that makes men marry women."
"Not marry? Why?"
                            "They eat each other up,
And still stay hungry."
                                "Nonsense, you're a fool,
Marriage is not like that."
                                "The hell it isn't!
You don't know marriage, Sam. I've seen it fail.
I've seen two people use their tongues like knives
To cut and wound, by little, cuts that heal,
Small wounds that don't show, but they leave small scars,
People who look at one another sharply
As barriers, not as lovers. Love's all gone,
Gone down the drain of habit. Married love!
God, no! No marriage! Just stay single, single,
Pick 'em and have 'em and leave 'em when it's through,
Lap up the cream and leave the sour milk

144

For hungry cats. Be married to your work,
And let this loving business be the key
To knowing life."
                        "You're innocent," he said.
"Just young and innocent."
                                "Me, innocent?"
"Yes, you, you don't know anything. You're too young.
You're innocent as a babe. Do you suppose
A woman lets you take her and then leave
With just good-bye? She has no claim on you?
Will you be satisfied just with prostitutes?"
"Christ no!"
                "Well then! What makes you think that love
Is easier out of marriage? That your hat
Won't fit a peg and want to cling to it?"
I said, "I know because I've seen it done.
You take it and they like it and you leave—
Or maybe they do, it's no matter which—
Whenever you are finished."
                            "Can you be sure
That you won't fall in love?"
                                "You kill it, then.
It isn't difficult—it hurts a little,
But hurts far less than if you let it grow
Up to the mountain that lies heavily
On top of two poor mortals, crushing them
To bitterness and anger."
                            "Poet! poet!
You poetize your small experience
And blow it up to universal size.
Men love for life, all through their married lives.
Are you the only one who knows of marriage?"
"I've seen men live when love had died and gone,
Their lover dead. They did not die for it."
"But lived on it."
                    "No—lived in spite of it,
Made richness of their selves."
                                "I don't believe it.
They lived on love."
                    "You're a romantic fool."
"You're the romantic one," Sam said. "Your mind
Refuses logic. If you feel like this,
Why pass up Rosy, when she offered you

The chance to take her? Well? Are you afraid
You'd get involved?"

                        "No, not involved. Perhaps
I don't because it's cheap."

                        "By which you mean
It's cheap because it's easy?"

                        "There's no mind,
There's only body there."

                        "How do you know?
What do you know of her, compared to whom?
You say you must have life. Well, there is life,
A life so different that you've never touched it—
I know the type, you live in Randolph, don't you?
Poverty, ugliness—how do you know
She may not have a better mind than you
And twice the knowledge of what you call life?
You'd rather have a lady? Someone nice?
It's pleasanter in the Ritz than in a shack?
You'd learn more what? More tricks of love, perhaps,
But more of what else?"

                        "Shall we just turn round
And go right back and rape the girl?"

                        He laughed.
"No, life's too short. The chance is gone. It's dead."
"It's dead."

                        "And so shall we be."

                        "Happy thought!
Can you conceive yourself as dead? I can't."
"No. It's impossible. We say it, don't we?
'Some day we'll die.' It doesn't mean a thing.
Do older people see it, Sam?"

                        "Perhaps.
Let's get our loving, though, before we die.
And if we go to war, it brings that close."
"You think we will?"

                        "I do. We're on the edge."
"What shall we do, enlist?"

                        "You bet we will."
"Do you believe in war?"

                        "No, it's the bunk.
But once we're in, we're stuck with it."

                        "Perhaps.
I guess we are. It seems a fearful waste,

146

It frightens me," I said.

                    "Does it?" said Sam.
"It doesn't frighten me. I'm only scared
Of what might happen if I lost my nerve."
"Sometimes I dream of horrible small wounds,"
I answered. "That's what scares. I wish I had
The courage to keep out of war, to say
To hell with war, it's just a madman's game,
I will not fight. I know I haven't though.
The thought of those wet, slimy trenches turns
My stomach in the night. And all the horrors
The Huns have perpetrated make me feel
Only a little anger."

                "Look," said Sam,
"Do you believe those stories?"

                        "I don't know,
They seem to be official. Why, do you?"
"I guess they're savages for all their music.
What shall we do, Tom, if we have to fight?
I'd hate the infantry, it's filthy work."
"Let's fly," I said. "That's a clean, sudden death."
"Oh, death!" said Sam. "The hell with it, my boy.
Somebody else, perhaps, uh-uh, not me.
We'll fly and live."

              "O.K., we'll live," I said.
"We'll join together, what?"

                    "You bet," he said.
"Let's stick together."

                  The light car rocked on,
Its wheels creating peace with a crisp sound
Of freezing snow beneath them; so we drove
Silent a space through dark streets, following
The thin outriders of our wavering lights,
And in our silence I thought of flying high
Up in the triumph of more brilliant skies,
Through tall, tumultuous clouds; I thought of Clare,
And felt the shoulders of young Rosy press
Their provocation on me.

                    "Listen, Tom,
I didn't mean to heckle you just now—
About that chicken."

                  "That's all right," I said,
"I don't give one good god-damn what you say.

Perhaps I don't mean all I said of marriage.
I'll be your best man, boy."
                              "You will," he said.
"We'll stick together."
                      "Yes, we'll stick," I said.
"To hell with love. We're friends, we are. Come on
Let's get back quick and then get stinking drunk
And go in to a movie."
                          "Good!" he said,
"Eyeless in Gaza at the mill with slaves."
"What made you say that, Sam?"
                                  "Oh, I don't know.
If love makes blind, can friendship really see?"
"I see you, you old fool, and that's enough."
"I see you too," he said.
                      We laughed. But why,
I cannot answer now: I knew more then
Than I shall, haply, ever know again.

NOW at the timid first-flare of true love,
Go warily: for here confined in it
Is power that can so strive and shake and move
That souls are sundered once the fuse is lit.
Here but a little tremor of the heart,
Flutter of pleasure, the pursuing eye?
Softly, go softly—from these tremors start
Such seismic cleavage as shall split your sky.
The flush soon mounted shall the sooner fade?
Its red shall vanish to the hidden vein?
One is a fire not to be allayed,
One is a virus mounting to the brain:
Love is a virus, passion, and a strife
I would not part with for eternal life.

ONCE on the thin edge of a winter's noon, I took
Leave of the over-many Cambridge days and nights

And fled by train to Providence to visit
Mother on ice-bound, steep-laid Angell Street.
I can remember how, as the steel wheels clattered and clicked
Sounding the syncopated metronome to time thoughts,
    Resentment rose at this strange house, not home,
    Harbouring Mother in another's strange air:
        Not a home, not home, not ever home again?
So one thought caught in the wheel's compelling rhythm
Circles the wall of a mind grown hollow, clings as it circles,
    Making the undertone for the surface thoughts
    That flicker and pass like the poles past the window glass,
The beat of the wheels, the bare trees, Gorton's Boneless Cod-
    fish,
Carter's Little Liver Pills, white letters on a barn roof,
    Snow on the fields in furrows of blue shadow,
    Drifts on the north of the snow-capped grey stone walls:
        Not a home, not home, not ever home again?
These are the quick moods of the young mind shifting and
    turning,
    Subject to change without notice, like railroad schedules;
Nevertheless they possess, and possessing, print on the mind
    Mood of a time past, indelible diction of wheels:
        Not a home, not home, not ever home again.

Why was I going? How much was habit, how much affec-
    tion?
I was but just beginning to judge my people, to rate them—
    Love was a sturdy habit, planted and tended
    Over the tender years, the major memory.
So I loved and I judged, but the one balanced the other,
Something warm and happy alongside something resentful,
    Love for the soft voice and the big kind eyes,
    Love for the love demanded, the love given,
    Love for affection, the split, severed love.
Why was I going? I didn't know, I thought, not clearly:
Was it because of the dance, the fun, the excitement of
    strangeness,
    Or because Mother wanted me there, beside her,
    Wanted the son for the new house, old love, the new place?
Not a home, not home? Why not? Mother was there, her
    presence
Stirred in the rooms—but the rooms were not hers, not yet—
    What did it take to make a house receive you,

Bear your image—years? or the force of objects,
  Little things, big things? Little by little?
Voices of men or women, or voices blended, or silence
  Wrought of the voice at rest, the thoughts resting?
Restive sounds of a woman's feet, forever on errands,
  Sounds that were undirected, purposeless, single—
    Single sounds have singular echoes.

Not a home, not home, not ever home again, clatter bang
    switch points,
Punctual rhythm of roar, stop, roar, stop, cars passing by,
  Brakes scream, cars jerk, Providence, train to a slow halt,
  Jerk and a stop. Get out, to the acrid, cold air.
So the thoughts dissolve in the need for pleasant action,
Shuffle of feet, and the bag's weight gravely shifted over,
  Down the dark steps, passage, and up the dark steps,
  Out to the cold air past the incurious, watchful,
    Suspended vision of those still waiting.
Now my thoughts had turned at last to the simple pleasures:
Seeing Mother, and lunch, not being at Harvard, being here,
  Dance tonight, new girls, old things to say
  Over again, as new things to new ears.
I took a taxi, sat and shivered happily, bumping
Over the uncleaned streets, so through the struggling traffic,
  Happily hearing the chains that flailed at the fenders,
  Out of the roar, up past a white-spired church,
    Crawling progress up a steep hill,
Wheels that slipped and suddenly gripped the sanded ice-
    slopes,
  Jerk of the brake and the cab, the sudden stopping,
Here was the brick house, set back from the steep pavement,
  Elms in the front yard reached for the city sky,
    Cold sky, cold air, run for the warm house.

The front door opened under the hand of a neat maid with a
    new face.
I put my bag down. "Where is my mother, is she at home?"
  She said, "Right in the parlour. Will you go in?"
  I heard the sound of voices, of voices blended,
Suddenly stop, and the rich, warm voice of Mother calling,
"Is that you, Tom, my darling? How lovely! Do come in!"
  I entered to find Miss Darnley standing with Mother,
  Mother smiling and waiting, back to the window

In that dim light, young and lovely.
"Bless the Babcocks, Tom, their party has brought you down
    here,
I'm so glad to see you. You must be famished with hunger.
   Lunch is ready, Ethel and I have waited.
   Wash up and come down quickly and we'll begin."
I had hoped half-heartedly that perhaps Ethel Darnley
Would be away for a day or so, leave me alone with Mother:
   Not that I disliked her, but somehow resented
   This established right to be always present,
     Half the house hers, half my mother's.
Woman and woman, the part and the curious counterpart:
   This was my fourth time here, I was not yet accustomed.
Here I had found my mother, found her sad, with a woman,
   Men forsworn, Father and home forsworn,
     Peace bought dearly, cost not reckoned.

I went up to the pretty green room saved for me always:
It had the unlived air of the comfortable, well-stocked guest
      room
   Though on the mantel, resting as if for a moment,
   Stood a familiar picture of me and Joss,
Picture of Mother, young and lovely and proud in her wed-
    ding dress,
   Train in a swirl like the tide of life controlled to a pattern,
   Picture of Father, youth on a great proud horse—
   What had it cost to place that there for my pleasure?
     Feather pounds equal the pounds of lead.
So I wondered, and looked at the room's familiar strangeness,
Weighing the worth of women, measuring man in my wis-
    dom;
   Washed and unpacked my bag and returned to Mother,
   Mother and Ethel Darnley, waiting together.
Once on a day I had clumped downstairs in an empty house,
Brushing against the darkness, toward two figures standing,
   Waiting in silence for me. What could make me
   Think of that now, when the cheerful voices
     Happily blended, women's voices?
There a possessive love had had scope, yet turned to anger;
   Turned to denial as the cock of love crowed—
Here was affection lived in possessive voices calling
   Each to the other across the day's small orbit,
     Each to the other and, each voice to me.

Lunch was pleasant, being composed of familiar dishes;
Mother would say, "I ordered this specially, this is for you,
    Tom."
  Ethel remarked, "Your mother's a wonderful woman,
  She runs the house and the meals, while I do nothing."
"Nonsense," said Mother, "don't you believe her, Tom, she's
    busy
Running the hospital, running her wonderful, competent
    Art League,
  I have nothing to do but to make the house function.
  So we divide the labour, but my part's easy,
    I keep the home to receive the worker."
"She just says that, you and I know better," said Ethel,
"All the detail of a house, day in, day out, incessant."
  "Nothing!" said Mother. "No, nothing," echoed Ethel,
  "If you do it so generously and so kindly."
"Keeping a house for two? Child's play! We don't entertain
    much."
"No," said Ethel, "we must. We've been slack about it, Maria,
  We must have young ones in, to mix with the elders,
    Dinners—how stupid of me! not to have thought
    Of a dinner for this dance—dinner for Tom."
Mother said, "Darling Ethel! In spite of your wonderful ef-
    forts,
  It takes time to establish oneself in a new place,
I never really lived in Providence. I'm still a stranger.
  I don't know the answers, the Providence answers."
    Ethel said, "Nonsense, lovely Maria!"

I noticed then how dark the moustache had grown on her lip,
More than a shadow now—so plain beside Mother's beauty,
  Woman and woman, the part and the counterpart,
  Nervous strength against a lovely softness.
When we arose from lunch, Ethel said, "Now Maria,
Do go up and rest, you need it, I'll talk to Tom."
  "What? and miss the company of my son?"
  "Make her go, Tom—she has not been sleeping,
    Every night I hear her, restless."
I said, "Surely, rest now, Mother, rest for an hour."
"I'll be gone then, Maria, you'll have Tom all to yourself."
  "Oh, don't go," said Mother. "Must you go out?
  I had thought, what fun we'd have, we three."
I was not sure but I thought I heard the echo of panic,

Saw the flicker of fear reflect in her tired eyes:
   Fear of me? Of being alone with me?
   Habit of love grown timid, from whose refusal?
     Turning from me? turning to Ethel?
"I shall be back for tea, you'll hardly have time to miss me,"
   Dark upper lip in a smile; strong, assuring voice.
"Rest now, Maria." Mother smiled, sighed. "Yes, I need rest,
   That is the truth, but an hour can be a chasm."
     Chasm between us? Between her and Ethel?

After my mother had left us we sat and chatted warily,
   Sparring each other off, postponing the moment
   When we should turn to the one subject possible:
   Speak of Mother: her shadow lay there between us.
I had a feeling Ethel had carefully planned this moment
   Hoping to draw me out. I didn't want it.
   Where were the words to weigh the worth of a mother?
   Measure a mother wisely? Measure in wisdom,
     Speak of the split, the once severed love?
Friendship—but not with me—a snow that covers to silence:
   Words were the swift betrayers, the traps and dangers—
   Separate snow to its feathery pattern of flakes:
   What have you left but the isolation of crystals?
What did she want of me? support for her way of living?
   What was her way? I knew it was not my way.
   Mother and she, in a house that was not a home:
   Did she want words from a son to make it a home,
     Woman and woman: permanent words?
Here was energy locked in the box of a strong friendship:
   Open the box and out would swarm what words
Winged to trouble me, stir me, drive to the dangerous surface
   Thoughts now wrapped in the cocoon of habit,
     Waiting for new wings for an old love?

Ethel began it: "How do you think that your mother's look-
    ing?"
   I said, "She's looking well, but a little weary.
   Has she been sleeping badly?" "Badly, and dreaming,
   Says she's been having nightmares, just like a child."
Then she added, "But I am sure that Maria's happy."
   "Yes," I said, "I suppose so." Ethel reddened,
   Ever so faintly, I could scarcely discern it,
   Cried, "She's happier than she has been for years,

Rid of the burden of . . . " there she paused.
Rid of the burden of me and of Joss and of Father, I thought,
  Burdens are meant for wearing, they're like the words
  Spread on the page's surface, each meaning little,
  Parts of a whole on the indivisible page.
Ethel continued: "We have a happy life, here together,
  We have divided everything, work and play,
  We understand each other—oh, it's splendid!
  She is so good for me, I am happier with her
    Than I ever was, living alone.
She was afraid of people, afraid of—well, the demanding,
  Admiration of men, Maria tells me.
You know what she suffered, what she so bravely renounced."
  I said, "Yes. But why did Mother renounce it?"
    Ethel stared at me, looked with horror.

"You would never say that to her, Tom, would you, truly?"
  I didn't want to discuss this with Ethel Darnley,
  I didn't know what she knew, where it all led;
  These were affairs of ours: she had made them hers.
Once more she said, "You'd never say that to your mother,
    would you?
  It would upset her terribly, she who already
  Suffers so much because of renunciation."
  Did she mean Joss or me, home or her husband,
    Did she mean Evelyn? was he renounced?
"It will depend, Miss Darnley, whether my mother speaks of
    it."
  "No," she cried, "no, believe me, leave it alone,
  This is a battle won, but the wounds are healing,
  This is an old war, never speak of it more."
Here was a love loud in possessive voice, calling, calling:
  Here was a trespass, heel-marks upon my lawn,
  Scarring the surface; here was protection's habit,
  Habit of love grown fierce for a pledged refusal,
    Woman the part and the counterpart.
Man and woman, the balance had trembled, finally tipped
    down,
  Pound of shadows against the pound of flesh.
Here was a new lawn, snow-covered, guarded against my foot-
    steps
  Printed, and melted—to come again of a spring wind?
    Ethel would guard against me? against Evelyn?

Something about my silence, perhaps the anger that lay then
  Warm in my heart, or the arrogant, unsaid answers
  Formed in my mind, must have been shown in my eyes,
  So that she looked hard at me and then came close.
"See," she said, "we love her, we two, we want to protect her.
  Think what her love has meant, the love of a mother,
  Think what it still can mean, love for the years,
  Love unbargaining, warm, and yours for always,
    Mine, too—but yours forever greater.
Think, Tom, think! The sacrifice, the devotion, the patience,
  Love for the great times, love for the day's small orbit,
  Think! she has left her base, the home she builded.
  Oh, be just! Her home? Would you have stood it?
Would you have had the courage to tear your roots up boldly,
  Risk the sneer of the world, destroy the habits
  Grown in the patient years—just for a principle?
  How can you ask me, 'Why the renunciation?'
    Do you, Tom, not know the answer?"
I held my breath then and kept silent, wondering, waiting,
  Would she dare to state the reason to me?
"Cast her lot with a single woman, knowing my need,
  Keeping her love intact, giving affection,
    Love for affection, the split, severed love."

So she avoided the point again. I had a sudden impulse,
Wanted to cry out 'Bosh! you're talking nonsense!
  What do you know about it, know about Evelyn?
  Why should she live here? Isn't it just from fear?'
I suppose I showed what I thought in my face again clearly,
For she turned away and her voice changed and she said,
  "Dear me, Tom, I'm sorry, I'm keeping you standing,
  Do sit down here, here on the sofa, comfortably,
    You don't need to stand for your figure."
She sat down in a big chair, gestured me to the sofa;
Thus we sat in silence a moment, but only a moment.
  "Tell me now," she said, "all about Josiah."
  I said, "Father was well, when I last saw him."
Ethel laughed. "You used to answer my questions, once—
Joss would never do it, nor would your father, ever.
  Now you have learned their trick of evading me."
  Then she added, suddenly quite serious,
    "I am asking to spare Maria."
I said, "Yes, I see. But what do you want to know?"

"What are his plans," she cried, "what will he do?
What does he feel? We hear no word, never a word,
   Tell me, what are his plans, is he happy, unhappy?"
      I just laughed and Ethel grew angry.

"You can laugh, Tom? I didn't think that you were so heart-
      less.
   This is a matter that worries your mother, daily.
   She but rarely speaks of it, yet I see it
   Printed—and melted—and born in a new expression
I can hear her asking herself, 'What of Josiah?
   Is he unhappy, does he miss my presence?'
   She was so tortured by his single letter.
   Did you know he had asked for a divorce,
      Did you know, Tom? Why did he want it?"
"Yes, I knew," I said, "but I don't know the reason.
   Maybe he wants to make the final gesture,
   Father is logical: marriage or no marriage—
   Separation—an inch that is like a chasm."
Then I found I was angry, angry at her, at myself.
   Why should I discuss it with Ethel Darnley,
   Why not with Mother? What was Ethel? I cried:
   "This is their problem, it is theirs to settle,
      It is their problem, it is not ours."
Ethel said, "All her problems are mine because of friendship,
   She is too sensitive to ask, to question.
Yet the question's a thorn in her mind, shifting and turning,
   Wondering always: what is Josiah doing—
      Does he still love her, does he love someone?"

I was confused now. There was a genuine emotion sounding
Deep in her voice: it was not curiosity, merely.
   Nevertheless I did not want to explain to her,
   Though I knew the answers, the arrogant answers.
There was one matter I did not know: where did Ethel stand?
Was she the one to counsel separation, not divorce?
   She was staring at me, her lips still moving,
   Framing the questions in a voiceless query:
      Voiceless questions have singular echoes.
So I waited uneasily, lacking the simple usage
That will turn a trend in the talk to a new channel.
   Suddenly she spoke: "I am disappointed,
   Hurt and disappointed, I wanted your help, Tom.

This has been for me a long, slow battle—Maria
Sank to the depths, she is but now slowly emerging:
   This is the privilege, the duty of friendship,
   Friendship is love moved to its highest power,
      This is my power, this my duty.
You will see these things. Youth is preoccupied, selfish,
   Moved by its own needs, only. Now I shall leave you.
She will be here soon. Love her, and treat her gently and
      warmly,
   There is no strength within her now to combat,
      Give her support, Tom. Give her your love."

I could have answered, 'My love is a split love, severed love,
She can have half my love, the whole was cloven long ago.
   I was silent: words were the beat of wings
   Soaring about the mind; the tongue, a broken wing.
Then she arose and smiled, and said, "It will happen in time.
Mine is the long slow job. Yours is the quick one, the swift
      salve.
   You have a medicine of old love to give her.
   Now I am off, Tom. Work, for the night is coming
      Wherein no man shall work—nor woman."
Then she went to the door, but paused there, a brief mo-
      ment—
Paused and turned to me; said, "One thing, Tom, one surely:
   Never believe I grudge you the power you have,
   Never believe me jealous. Your mother loves you
More than the rest of the whole great hard world put together,
I am a part of the world—nothing I do can change that.
   You are a part of her, her life lives in your life,
   I am not jealous of you—I am jealous only
      Lest you withhold love that can heal her."
So she turned and went to the door, opened it slowly,
   Passed from my sight and was gone, and the door shut
      softly.
I thought, You speak of love too eagerly, much too often.
   Why do you wear a moustache. Why not a razor?
      I'm glad you are gone. I do not like you.

Then I dismissed her from my mind: youth does that, simply,
Grasping the present strongly, letting the future be only
   Warm dream of the moment of half-waking
   When the will first flutters behind closed eyelids.

I explored around the room in my curiosity.
Here were a number of objects, half of them were familiar:
  Here a lacquer box, an old friend, mated
  With a brocade I did not know, whose pattern
    Flowed with the box's pattern, happily;
Here was a blue vase set on a dark teakwood stand
(Once it was set in a crowded jumble of many others)
  Solitary upon a walnut table,
  Full of the soft white flowering of freesia:
Here was a shelf of books, but the backs made lovely patterns,
Some were Mother's, but some were leather-bound, gilt-edged
    strangers—
  Mother had never arranged them so—and yet
  Here was the value of their size and colour
    Mixed with an air of use and pleasure.
How could Ethel Darnley, who dressed and looked like a
    frump,
  How could she so mix these manifold objects
Into the beauty of use, the clear directed arrangement?
  This was an oddly beautiful room. And here—
    Snuff-box of silver: Evelyn gave it.

Gave it a long time back? I couldn't remember exactly.
How many things that I knew here had once been given by
    Father?
  When did the giving evaporate, leaving the gift
  Wrapped in the stronger atmosphere of the owner?
I heard voices, a soft laugh, Mother speaking to someone,
Saying, "Serve tea at five, Miss Darnley will be home then."
  I put the snuff-box hurriedly back on the table,
  Crossed to the window, semblance of occupation,
    I heard the door creak, Mother enter.
"Well, Tom, Ethel is gone? Left you alone a long time?"
I said, "No, she only left a few minutes ago."
  Mother came over to me and kissed me warmly:
  Just for a moment the touch of her lips dispelled
All the questioning mood of the young mind, shifting
    and turning,
Banished the weighing of worth, the measure of woman's wis-
    dom,
  Left me free for a space, alone with my mother,
  Wrapped now in the manifest and moving love
    Flowing from her, love with affection.

158

So we stood for a moment, the mood preserved by silence,
  Held in suspense by the hand's touch, silence of tongues,
Mother and son, balanced in love of the unspoken words,
  Mother and son—the balance trembled and tipped,
    Wavered and fell, overweighted with words.

"Look!" she said, "It's snowing again, isn't it lovely!"
  I peered through the window: the feathery pattern of flakes
Fell without sound like the lapse of invisible seconds
Adding to hours till time be as deep as a drift.
"The snow is friendly: it covers the streets to a heavenly si-
    lence.
  But come, Tom, come. We haven't time to be silent.
  How does the work go? Did you bring me some poems?
  What have you heard from Joss, he never writes me,
    Never a word—how is your father?"
I said, "So many questions!" She smiled and patted my shoul-
    der,
  Turned and left me and sat her down by the window,
  Yellow hair like a pale flame in the grey light,
  Yellow against the white of the gathering snow.
"So many questions? Yes, and so few answers. It's difficult.
  Tell me of Joss." I answered, "I hear nothing,
  Save that he's well and still at his job in Wall Street."
  "I am so glad," she said, "his work makes me happy,
    I was afraid he'd be an artist."
"Are you afraid for me?" "Yes, in a measure I am, Tom.
  I am afraid for stability lost, for the drain
Made on the mind and the heart, the eye turned always in-
    ward,
  Art is selfish work, the heart grows selfish,
    Everything measured only in its terms."

"Joss has been trying to join with an ambulance unit in
    France."
  "Has he? How awful! Why was I not told, then?"
  "It is not done," I said, "it's merely a plan."
  "Yes, but I should have been consulted beforehand—
    Not be told, after it's settled."
"Would you forbid it, Mother? Would he accept your forbid-
    ding?"
  She made no answer but clasped her hands together,
  Letting them lie so, tense but still on her lap.

I could see the thoughts that showed in her eyes:
  'Who am I now? Oh, who am I?'
What could I do to divert her mind? I said, "War's coming.
  What would you have us do?" She gave a great sigh,
  Swept the room with her eyes, like someone waking,
  Lifted her hand to her face and said, "War's coming.
    War for the men, waiting for women.
England and France and Belgium—the gross, barbarian Germans,
  Spoilers of civilization. God is against them,
  God will speak for the right side—if He calls you,
  You will go, and Joss, and God will arm you,
    God is nearer now, is near me.
Heaven was distant, the door was slowly closing: it opens
  Through the pain of the heart and the soul's confusion.
    God is near now. Josiah blinded me."

I felt a wave of embarrassment, knew that its flush was
    mounting.
  Up to my cheeks: I turned and walked to the table,
  Fingered the objects on it, saying nothing,
  Picked up the silver snuff-box in distant fingers.
The silence lengthened. She cried, "We are drawing slowly
    apart!
  Nobody understands me save only Ethel.
  Why do you mind the truth? I can see you mind it.
  Have I hurt you? Why do you blush and leave me,
    Just because I say 'Josiah'?"
I said nothing, but I turned back slowly toward her.
  "It is the truth, your father blinded and bound me,
  Where was I, Maria? Left and neglected!
  Still he'd leave me, more, he is not done yet."
I said nothing. I stood and fingered the glittering snuff-box.
  "Why should we divorce? Is he in love, Tom?
  Tom! can I ask you nothing, is love departed?
  You and I so close—must one be lonely,
    Single and lonely to hear God's voice?"
I said nothing, I could not, though I loved her—nothing.
  "Evelyn gave me that, the box you're holding.
Evelyn gave love, would have given life, I would not permit it.
  I was faithful—and faithfulness met with coldness,
    Selfishness, coldness. Shall I give more now?"

'Shall I give more now?' The sounds had a singular echo, I
thought.
Shall I give more—a puzzle. What was she withholding?
How could I ask what hope remained for the future,
Father's and Mother's future—each of them single?
Single sounds have singular echoes.
"Look," I said, feeling the pressure of youth to be able to an-
swer,
"Have you a term in mind? This is not permanent?
Would you go back?" She cried, "How can you believe it!
This is the end, the end! It's over and done with."
I said, "Will you not make it final?"
"What do you mean?" She gazed at me with great, wide eyes.
"Tell me, Mother—or not, as you please. Why not Evelyn?"
"What about Evelyn? What do you mean, Tom? Say it!"
"Marriage," I said. "Isn't that why you left Father?
Not for dislike alone, not for Miss Darnley?"
Mother leaned forward and spoke, her voice was the merest
whisper:
"Never," she said, "it's over, I never shall see him.
How could I know—perhaps we'd run the same circle,
Come to an ending, love of a man for a woman,
Make a home—break home, break home again.
Man and woman, the meeting and joining, the terrible parting,
God is banished, the flesh corrupts the spirit,
Men are so terrible—things that they want."

There was a pause then full of a hundred words unspoken.
I didn't want to look at Mother. I turned.
Then her voice came full, the deep sound slowly
Growing in volume, rich in its resonant beauty.
"That is enough now. Leave it. It is not fair to burden
Your young shoulders with what's beyond your mending.
These are the crosses carried by all poor women,
Love and affection, war, the madness of men,
Weakness and strength, joined to each other.
It is not yours to settle, not yours, my darling, my dear Tom.
Come sit near me. We'll talk of the pleasant things,
Put the devils behind us . . . . " Her voice faltered.
"Talk of the good things." But her voice was weeping.
So I moved to her side and knelt down by her, holding
Her hands within my own. Her tears were falling,

161

There were no tears for me: I felt too empty,
  Empty and troubled, as though the current of anger
    Swept below the ripples of love.
Thus we remained, in silence. I heard a door shut loudly,
  Heard the clear and commanding voice of Ethel,
"Tea directly." The rattle of hand on door-knob, door opening,
  Swift and firm. She paused: hope, for a second—
    Useless! She entered, crying, "How lovely!"

"Mother and son!" she said. "Ah me, what a lovely picture!
Don't move, don't stir!" She came close; peered; her voice
    changed then:
  "You have been crying, Maria, you have been crying.
  Tom, oh Tom! I begged you to be gentle."
Mother said, "He's been lovely, we cried for love together,
I have been silly, he comforted me, as always and ever.
  Turn on the lights, dear. It is dark and gloomy.
  Now we can laugh and chat, the crying's over,
    We three together, happy and gay."
I rose up from her side then, awkward, ashamed, uncomfort-
    able,
Ethel looked at me, lips pursed; slowly she looked at Mother,
  Dark upper lip lifted and turned to smiling,
  Back to me, smiling now. "Turn on the lights, Tom."
Bustle of tea—the maid—it is all gone now, all gone—
Fragments of words, the thoughtless words, thoughts roving
    elsewhere,
  Tea to the chatter of women, the clatter of cups,
  Cheerful thin voice strong in its own direction,
    Beautiful deep tones, undirected.
So to my room and the thoughts, the postponing of thought
    in dressing,
  Always the undercurrent of unexpressed anger,
Echo of Ethel's voice, the dominant—thoughts of the future,
  Pitying men who were caught in the strands of women,
    Woman and woman, each to the other.

These were the quick moods of the young mind, shifting and
    turning:
Weighing the worth of women, measuring man in his wisdom,
  Knowing the answers then, the arrogant answers,
  Close to the truth—but an inch can be a chasm.
Here the possessive love had scope and yet turned inward:

Here was a love lived in possessive voices, calling
  Each to the other across the day's small orbit,
  Habit of love grown kind in a fierce refusal:
    Not a home, not home, not ever home again.
Man and woman, the balance trembled, trembled and tipped;
Woman and woman, the part and the perilous counterpart,
  Weight of feathers, equivalent weight of lead,
  Pound of shadows against the pound of flesh.
Friendship is snow that covers the soul to a fertile silence:
Can you separate snow to its feathery pattern of fallen flakes?
  Impossible! This is the indivisible page
  Printed and melted—and born again of a new wind:
    Love for affection, the split, severed love.
So on the thin edge of a winter's night I took
  Leave of the women's voices, the voices blended,
I took a taxi, sat and shivered, half-happily, hearing
  Echoes beyond the chain that flailed at the fender:
    Single sounds have singular echoes.

2

(THIS is a still pond: it is steel under the moon;
The pretty trees hang upside-down:
The mirror is ravishing: stillness is doubled.)

Music all over the house. Thin music upstairs,
Tempting the feet to move; fingers at the white tie,
The hair to brush again. Brush to music:
Shuffle the feet with the brushes, you must—
No one is looking.
The air is music, breathe the good notes:
The drum is a heart and the violin is the flesh,
And the horns are your lungs. Angell Street is distant.
So. Go down the stairs—they are used to it:
There have been dancing feet upon these stairs
Over and over again. The walls say so.
The bannister says so. The mahogany doors,
Rich with wax, say: Dine and Dance and Conversation
And Bow and Good Evening, Gentlemen,
Good Evening, Ladies. Ladies! Pretty young ladies!
The floor was for skirts to brush and slippers to polish.
The music is new music caught in the walls,
In the wax of the old music on the dark doors.

(The water is still: there is no breeze.
The moon is perfect in a romantic mirror:
So charming!
No breeze, only the mirror for still life.)

This is delightful: the music, thicker and thicker.
Good evening, Mrs. Babcock. This is delightful.
Good evening, Maude. Good evening, Caroline.
Good evening, This and That.
Oh, yes, good evening! The music
Feeds you and nourishes you and cures your thirst:
You need not think now,
The music is your brain, it is in your mind;
The walls go round you, it is Maude,
Yes, in the pink, fluffy dress;
The walls go round you, the sound of the horn surrounds you,
The green taffeta number, Caroline, words:
The floor is good: the floor is better, is best,
The music is fine, compare it, conjugate dance,
This is the present, but it is not tense—
Laugh, Caroline, Maude, Tom, This or That.
Ah, Mrs. Babcock!
The music has coloured your walls if I dared to say so,
But, you see, you only say: *May I have this dance, Mrs. Bab-*
   cock?
For the music speaks for you.
Is the music young?
Were you young? are the walls old? Did they see
Fun forever?
Good evening, Mr. Waterman.
So? his family owned the musical walls
And the Maudes and Carolines and the thin breathing
Of the notes in the upper rooms . . .
And Mister Babcock . . .
Whisper! Hand by the fine mouth and the bridged nose:
Made his money the day before yesterday,
It hasn't had time to accumulate wax and music,
But she was a Sargent. Good evening to you, Miss Brown,
You're as pretty as Billy-be-damned.

(There is a cat's-paw riffle. The light deceives,
Part is polished and part is frosted silver,
The images of the trees are drowned in silver:

164

This is a pond? The light is so deceitful:
The far shore may be clouds in the shape of night trees.)

Oh, you are so pretty, you dance so well,
Miss Brown, you are so pretty, your little pink mouth,
Your pretty fair hair—Mother's asleep now,
Or isn't asleep, or Ethel hears her restless . . .
Sh! the music is now and that is other,
The music is called Miss Brown in a bright blue dress,
With a hand that clings a little,
And champagne in a tall thin waiter who pours
Himself into crystal and bubbles and glowers at you,
If only you'd tell Miss Brown. Perhaps she'd laugh?
You say, *The floor is fine, the music is fine,*
You hear the other black long-tailed, white-tied tongues
Clicking and clacking and laughing but you say nothing:
The music is speaking, your tongue is a silent one,
And a hundred bright blue images called Miss Brown
Have dashed their reflection against the wax of the doors,
The wax of the floors, the silver on the tables,
To make the room so rich for yesterday's Babcock.
Yes, Miss Brown, or No, as the case may be,
My feet are talking, my feet speak,
Let's just dance—no?
The big white hand that clutches and interferes,
Oh, thank you ever so much,
I'll join the music, or Caroline—Maude's in pink—
Or the black and swaying island that floats in the sea
Of the rainbow dancing waters, the male island
Lost in the wash of the waves of the men and women.
The champagne bubbles. The tendons of your arches:
They are the strings of the cello:
They speak the time, the clock of pleasure, music:
Notes are the seconds, the dancers are the minutes,
The girls are hours, sand of the running hours.
Oh, yes, Mrs. Babcock, it is a splendid party!

(This is a breeze, the cat's-paws all are joined:
There is no double shore now, all is single:
It is a night wind. Can you feel it?)

You are alone? In the midst of many Carolines?
There are two Toms in the wax of every door.

What is the matter, music?
What is the matter? You are of the island,
The black and white and moving, floating island,
The many-legged island in the sea of dancers,
Women and men waves.
The champagne is music, drink the notes down,
Leave the island, the air is close, is cloying:
The music is like the scent of a gardenia—
Hello John and Henry and Felton and Hammersmith,
Hello Fred, and *How are you, Mr. Beckwith,*
Sorry, oops! Can I get past, the music
Caught my heart in your eyes . . . if I could say so . . .
Instead of *Sorry, my sleeve caught in your dress.*
You're pretty, Caroline—maybe it wasn't Caroline,
Somebody else in green, it doesn't matter . . .
You just looked the words, the violins spoke for you,
Pour a drink from the waiter with the eyebrows,
It costs five dollars a night to have such eyebrows.
This is a door, a door is meant to open,
This is a room, go softly, the music is very thin here,
Here is the scent of kings and queens and deuces,
This is the colour of red and of black, double-faced:
These are the mute fours:
These are the music thinned to the slap of cards:
The walls are spades and clubs and the flowers are hearts,
The long, tall glasses gleam with the bubble of diamonds,
The wax on the doors reflects the music of cards,
Trumps for a trumpet: but the music is thin, go softly.
Good evening, excuse me, good evening, Mr. Hallowell,
This is the way to the porch? it is cold on the porch?
There is air on the porch. There is music left in the darkness?
The violins can creep through the spades and diamonds?
Think it, think it, the champagne thinks and the music,
Simply say, *Excuse me, Mrs. Frobisher*:
The face is flat with the echo of slapping cards.

(There is a breeze, the waters are disturbed,
There is no shore now, there is distance wind-filled:
It is a night wind.)

Softly, go softly, this is a place for lovers,
The music is only the echo of music:
A sound that fled from a window,

Crept through the night and is tapping against the glass
That keeps the night out and the winter out.
This is a place for lovers: there are no lovers:
Only the dim light, and soft flowers come to the party,
Moistening air with the scent of unbidden spring.
There are no lovers: there is no one.
Stand in the centre and breathe the air of the flowers,
Hear the faint tapping of the exiled music.
Stand in the centre, breathe relief:
No need to say *good evening* to the flowers
Or to the darkness.
Breathe relief; say: Jesus!
Swear you're alone, declare yourself alone
By your swearing. You say it:
Jesus!
Swiftness of echo: sibilant silk
Rustles and moves in the dim light.
Look, fool, look, a woman, a girl,
Standing alone: she heard you. Can you see her?
Here is the dark hair and the slim back.
Can you not trace the carriage: shoulder and neck
In dark's discomfort?
Cry out *Clare!* and your heart turns over—
Bubbles of champagne vanished, gone,
Slap of the cards is silent: music is silent:
You hear only the one word *Clare!*
One word cutting among the flowers,
Sweeping soft scents suddenly upward.
Hear your heart pound: it is a hidden drum:
Blood is music, in the flutes of the veins:
In a hard music.

(This is a wind of night, over an ocean,
There is no shore but the shore of the moving wind,
And the rising sound of a growing wind.)

The back is no longer there to be stared at:
This is a face in the dim light,
Staring and smiling. You hear the word *Mistaken.*
The face would be pretty except that serenity
Lifts it to beauty.
No Clare? Who is this,
Owning a back like that, in dusk, with a silken sheathing,

A silken sibilance and a proud, dark head?
Why, boy, manners, manners! the seconds are growing
To an intolerable heap, like ants on a floor
Shedding their silly wings in the sudden scent of flowers.
Manners: *I'm sorry. I thought I was alone.*
This should be over, get out:
You do not belong here: this belongs
To somebody else: you should be off, be going—
Excuse me, please—and after that why stand
Frozen in movement's intention like music writ on paper?
Why does the heart not cease its drum?
Why does the blood flute in the hollow veins?
Did you come out for air?
I was waiting for someone.
Manners: just for the moment's peace, the music is loud,
Please don't look at me, please don't look the question:
Where did you find the voice that cried out 'Clare'?
But you say, *oh just for the air, I'm sorry,*
I didn't see you. I am going now. Sorry.
Look down hard at the hard cement floor:
Why do your feet move where there is no music?
Why do the feet move off, why does the hand move?
This is a door? A door is meant for opening,
Open the door, this door is meant for closing.
The music is thin, *Excuse me, Mrs. Frobisher,*
Why does the heart make music in the caverns
Of all my hollow being, why am I empty?
Back to dance, Mr. Hallowell,
The flowers are hearts, but they do not beat like mine,
There is a wind that blows through the long bones of my
      body
With a wonderful, terrible sound,
The sound of eyes, the sound of a face not pretty:
The sound of beauty seen in the dusk and the moist air,
Standing like music,
Excuse me, Mr. Hallowell,
I am not crazy: I'm blown by a new wind.

(This is the mother of wind, it bears strong waves:
The waves are born out of the wind's womb,
They are the well-born children: their crest is power,
They carry the flame of foam, their voice is thunder,
The deep green thunder.)

Come, you must meet Miss Carpenter.
Who's Miss Carpenter?
Judith Carpenter. Boy! she's a dandy dancer!
The hand compels, the reluctant feet follow,
And there is a lavender dress with a silken sound,
And the music is gone, you cannot hear the music:
You hear the blood sing and the drums beat,
And you say, the music is gone, you stole the music,
You've hidden it in you: keep it: I give it to you:
You do not need it: you are become the music—
How do you do, Miss Carpenter;
I'm sorry I cursed, it was dark . . . it was dark . . .
And the words go lamely,
The feet go clumsily dancing, the cursèd feet,
The Judas-feet, the Benedict-Arnold-feet,
Betrayers, traitors.
She floats, but you are sinking—
Into the grey eyes, into the trap of words,
But the big white hand clutches and interferes,
The lavender leaves with a rustle, black and white with her,
Oops! I'm sorry, can I get past, the music
Caught in my heart and tripped me.
Wait and attend!
So once again, many times again:
How do you do it, Miss Carpenter, look so beautiful,
Why do you feel like the blown wind, the terror of light-
        ning?
Why do you make my veins like a flute at evening
Over the dark waters?
The music is splendid.
When shall I see you ever again—Miss Carpenter—
Miss Judith Carpenter—Judith—beauty in lavender:
Music for my blood: wind in the forests of me . . .
Yes, Mrs. Babcock's giving a splendid party.
Always the white hand in the black sleeve, seizing,
Terminating, snatching, robbing: cutting in half.
Don't look now, it's Caroline: looking daggers;
Don't look, now it's Maude—or perhaps Miss Brown—
Dancing a long time with the selfsame segment
Torn from the black of the island. Don't look: go home!
Go home? Go back, go back to Angell Street,
Good night, Mrs. Babcock, it was a wonderful party—
I've left my hat . . . or I've left my heart . . . I gave it

169

Over to some young woman: they call her Judith;
The air is cold, the night is deep and sorry . . .
Fly through the night:
Judith has lent you wings.

3

Next morning I awoke to a false spring:
Warm air charged with the moisture of old snow
Turned wet and porous.
                        To my waking mind
There was some overwhelming misty joy
That blew about my brain as this air blew
Through billowing curtains, bringing scents of earth
And promises too vague to be fulfilled.
I rose and dressed. The house was very still.
The stairs were empty; so, the dining room,
With breakfast on a heater, and one place
Set at the table. Must one always eat?
Whence came this appetite when my thoughts were food
So rich and filling?
                      If one telephoned:
Would one be overheard?
                          I closed the door.
I swung the pantry door and peered within:
A Sunday silence, and the instrument
Black and inviting on the clean-scrubbed wood;
The thin book on a string, its pages curled
With airy hanging. C for Carpenter.
But many Carpenters. Shut your eyes and guess?
John, Henry, Isaac, Samuel and William,
Mister and Mrs, Inc. and Co. and Bros.,
Hardware and Grocery and Woolen Mills—
Ah, look: here's Isaac, business, residence,
Westminster, Hope Street, Dexter 209,
A pencil to scratch it on an envelope—
But do not call it up, it may be late,
It may be early, what's the earthly use?
I sat upon the dresser. What should I say?
But I had better do it quickly, now—
Might they not come? Was Ethel out or in?
Was Mother still asleep or up or where?

Be quick! Be brave! She couldn't eat you up.
She can say No. All people can say No . . .
Excepting me, whose heart is crying Yes
In a strange passion.
                    Dexter 209.
It rings and rings. Will no one answer it?
Is this the right house?
                         But a voice: "Hello."
"Miss Carpenter at home?"
                         "No, she is out."
A deep dark well of misery steyned in words:
A pause for falling to such deeps.
                              "Miss Cora's out,
She won't be back till dinner."
                         Such relief!
Hope liberated, rises, bringing courage:
"Miss Judith Carpenter, I meant."
                         "Oh, her!"
The Irish voice grows friendlier. "Sure, she's here.
She may be in her bed yet, wait awhile,
I'll take a look at her. What name, sir, please?"
"It's Cottrell, Mr. Cottrell."
                         "Spell it, please."
I spelled it. Every letter seemed too long,
There were too many T's, too many L's.
The R gave trouble: I gave it Barstow's roll,
It sounded silly in my New England mouth.
She said, "All right, I'll tell her. Cartwell, is it?
Hold on a minute." She was gone. The line
Hummed softly, emptily.
                         How would she know—
Cartwell or Cottrell—among so many men?
But had she even heard my name last night?
And if she hadn't, how identify?
By speaking of the dimness where the flowers
Woke to the name that cut the silence down?
Interminable wait! Do heart-beats sound
As fierce and throbbing down the buried wires,
Turning the current to a pulse like drums?
The house was still. I listened for a sound.
Why did I care? What harm to call a girl?
Why should I mind if Mother knew of this?
Was I afraid she'd look the question at me

That I was frightened of?
                                      All this secrecy
To hide from Mother, or to hide from Tom?
Interminable wait.
                            The clicking sound
As of loose slippers on a wooden floor.
I heard a fresh, girl's voice. "Hello, who's this?"
"It's Thomas Cottrell."
                                "Who?"
                                              "You might remember.
I met you last night at the Babcocks' dance."
A pause. "Oh—yes. You are the man who came
Out to the porch."
                            What could I say, but 'Yes'?
There was an awful interval. My mind
Groped for some words, oh! any words at all,
Just something. Suddenly I said, "Hello,
Are you still there?"
                            She laughed and said, "I am."
"Would you have tea with me—some place or other?
I don't know Providence. Anywhere you'd say.
I'd like to see you." Silence. I went on,
Less nervous, curiously enough: "You see,
One never gets a chance to talk to you,
So many men cut in—each dance with you
Was just 'Hello—Good-bye'."
                                        "As bad as that?"
I didn't know an answer so I said:
"Will you have tea?"
                            "I can't." She paused again,
Just for a second. "We have people coming.
Why don't you come here then?"
                                        "Oh no," I said,
"I didn't mean—I mean—I didn't know."
"Of course you didn't. Come along, at five.
We'd love to have you. Will you come?"
                                                    "Oh, thanks,
I'd like it, if you're sure I don't butt in."
"No, not at all. Good-bye. I must go now.
I'll see you later." She rang off suddenly.
I held the dead receiver in my hand
As though it had grown strange. I hung it up

Slowly and carefully.
                    Tea.
                              A lot of people.
No chance to talk alone. Unless she chose . . .
Why should she choose?
                         And not to tell them here,
Not tell, pack up the bag, have lunch and leave,
Leave and deceive . . . and have them find you out?
Tell half the truth . . . but would they guess the whole?
Miss Darnley and her questions, Mother's eye
Turned softly, sadly on me. Better risk
Than now confess, confessing interest grown
Just overnight to this.
                        So it was done:
It was so easy, and so natural.
They'd asked no questions, for I'd told enough:
Where I was going, to a tea at five,
The Carpenters.
                    The Isaac Carpenters?
My dear, they're awfully nice, two pretty daughters,
Two sons, about your age, how nice, indeed,
We knew them well, her name was Cranston, Rose,
Her sister, Rachel, went to school with me . . .
So natural . . . and so suitable . . . no questions.
One kisses and says thank you, and departs,
The chugging taxi and the melting snow,
The evening sky of a metallic blue
Pierced with the barbs of stars. My mother waved,
I waved and left her, Ethel by her side,
Two women, single.
                    I'm a man, I thought,
How lucky to be single and a man,
And on one's way to Judith Carpenter,
Whose mother was a Cranston.

4

This house, a home: sidewalk to steps to door;
Black iron leaps from white paint: a knocker to thunder;
Hall with manifold objects strewn
In the disordered arrangement of use:
Leather leash, greatcoats, hats, gloves,

Empty parcel: shell of a wrapped excitement.
Black dress, white apron: maid with a use for guests;
Voices and laughter and open doors.
There was Judith. There was a host of people,
Barriers: reefs and shoals, no channel to harbour,
Old men, young men, faces,
Clatter of voices, pretty girls' voices, Judith's voice:
This is my mother.
How do you do, Mrs. Carpenter?
How do you do, Mr. Cottrell?
Mr. Carpenter . . .
This is my sister, Cora Carpenter . . .
This is and this is and this is and that is. . .
Mr. and Mrs. and Miss . . .
And Cora's a flame of beauty . . . and Judith is . . . Judith is?

So it began: the strange faces, all new,
The sense of confusion, the words lacking as ever.
I didn't know a soul there—saving Judith,
And didn't know her, by rights.

              (But I did know her,
Something within me knew, as though my being
Were as a hazel wand bending to deep water
Without my willing.)

              Now I began to sort them:
Mrs. Carpenter at the tea things, saying,
"One lump, two lumps, cream or lemon, Arthur,
Ring for some more hot water, did you play squash?
Who won? Tell me, oh, here's your tea, Isaac,
Edward has won his squash match, isn't it nice?
Cora, be careful, you'll dump the whole tea-table,
Oh, Mr. Cottrell, this is my sister, Rachel,
Mrs. Standeven, she used to know your mother.
Judith has been out hunting, do you like hunting?
She's mad for it—risky—Judith, open the window,
You all talk so, you've used up all my air,
Let in the winter, poor thing! it'll perish, Isaac! dear,
Tea, it's stone cold, would anyone like a whisky,
Cora, do keep that flimsy dress from the fire."
Mrs. Standeven said, "Are you Maria's son?
H'm. We went to school, ten thousand years back.
Pity you couldn't bring her."

              I said, "I really

Asked myself, I wasn't invited, really."
"Of course," she said, "that's right, they're crazy here,
They have these scrambles and do it all of a sudden
And everyone comes except the ones whose feelings
Would get most hurt by not having been invited—
Two months ahead. They're crazy. I am crazy.
It runs in the family. We all like a noise.
I daresay, now, that your mother's house is quiet
And decently run?" I blushed. She said, "Ah, yes,
It must be . . . oh, dear me, she's living here, isn't she?
Living with that Miss Darnley, admirable! admirable!
Rose, I forgot his mother's with Ethel Darnley,
I've put my foot in it."
                          "Yes, dear, cream or lemon?
She says the most terrible things, we all do, all of us.
Isaac, take Mr. Cottrell away from Rachel,
She's stamping upon his tenderest spots."
                                            A small, thin
Man with a priestly tonsure, a long, hooked nose,
The biggest eyes that I'd ever seen in a man,
Moved up and said, "Hello there, you must like pictures,
I'll show you one of your father's." We moved slowly
Off through the crowded room. He said, "It's that one,
Look at it well, it's a beauty, I'll leave you to it.
Then you can find your way back to Cora or Judith,
Whichever one you're in love with."
                                      I said "Oh, goodness!"
He cut me off and said, "Everyone is, this whole room
Teems with young men panting with fiery passion,
If you can reconcile passion with Providence parlours—
It ruins the tea. I wish they'd both get married.
We'd have some peace and they could have some babies:
Better than always having two Penelopes—
You're not Odysseus, are you, by any chance?"
I laughed and felt at ease. His enormous eyes
Were full of humour.
                       He left me. I looked at the painting.
Big sheer cliffs that dropped to blue-ruffled water,
Black stone cliffs. Down in the right hand corner
The little *J. C.* and *Norway nineteen-six.*
That must have been the time when . . . the yacht . . . the
    letter,
Walter Moore . . . Lucy who didn't like boats . . .

You ran away from a wife to practise an art,
You ran to . . . wonderful painting! The cliffs were wrapped
In a veil of air that was not American air,
Not the clear biting of our sun, our shadow . . .
The painting had no heart, it had no passion,
It had a fineness, a quality of the truth,
(A woman astride a horse in the pride of excellence)
A sharp, cold breeze that blew a tangible air
To wrap dark cliffs . . . a dove in the rustled leaves . . .
Voice at my shoulder: "You like it? We all love it.
What is he like, your father? As perfect as this?"
I didn't turn, I knew it was Judith. I said,
"That was long ago—his painting's different, changed,
I think you'd like it better. It still is distant."
"What do you mean?"
           I said (for I wished to hold her),
"Triumph of mind over matter, standing apart—
I can't explain it." I gulped. "It was nice of you
To ask me today." She said, "Oh no, we're lucky,
Nice to get you. Have you met all these people?"
"No, not yet—but must I? I came to see you."
She smiled at me; she said, "Well, now you see me."
I drew a breath and I said, through my surprise,
"Yes, like a picture veiled by a strange air, new air,
You are so distant."
          She said, "Time shortens distance."
"Time? and the waiting and waiting. Sometimes I think
I must wait until I am dead. But it seems so long—
I must simply say Miss Carpenter—oh, if only
I could call you Judith—to shorten time—
My name is Holophernes, I've lost my head."
"Your head?"
         "Or perhaps my heart, it is all the same."
She said, "You're mad, Mr. Cottrell—I must go,
My guests . . . "
         "Oh no, don't leave me, no, please stay,
I'll stop, and I won't offend again, I promise."
She said, "Your words have a rather practised flow—
Did you say all this to—who was it? was it—Clare?"
Then she laughed and left me.
         I turned my back to the room
And stared at the picture: bitter that words should rise
Suddenly, swiftly—to raise an echo again

That was only hurtful—hard—and the thoughts
Grew to a huge size and I said,
I shall leave. And then,
There was a loud scream, someone
Shouted, "Cora, look out! Cora, look out!"
And I turned and I saw
Cora, her dress afire, there, beating with bare hands
At the flaming fabric, and others
Beat with their bare hands and I smelled
The stench of the smoke, and I looked
Quickly around me, and I saw the long rug, lying
Under the table, and bending
I wrenched it away, and the table fell, and the silver
Crashed but the rug came free, and I ran
And I wrapped it around her swiftly and held it, and so
We fell, tripped by its length and I lay
On top of her, clinging, clutching, and my nose
Was full of the acrid smell. And so
For a long time, or a short time, we lay there, but the time
Was beyond counting.
And then,
I do not remember then: clearly: but perhaps
I rose up and they lifted her and she
Had fainted and they bore her off, many hands, until soon
There was no one there—that I remember, because
I was alone, standing, hearing
Voices and feet moving, and the sounds
Of feet on the floor above me, and I thought,
I shall go now, I shall go because—because—
But I want air now, and I do not want
Anything else now, but the night air, except—
But these thoughts stopped there, and I moved
Out of the house to the porch, and there
It was night and I saw the stars, and the cold
Air came into my lungs, stinging, and I stood
Undecided, thinking:
Why do you go, and why
Did you think of the rug, and why
Did nobody act, and why
Does a man act, and oh, how, how
Does one ever know of a speech or an act
Before it is said or is done? And I descended the steps, going,
But a voice cried, "Wait!" and I turned

And it was Judith.
She came to me, running, and she said,
"You were going?" I answered
"Yes, it is better, I wanted, you see, only . . .
Only the air." And I said, "Is she hurt?"
"No, she is not hurt, only a little burned, nothing,
But thanks to you, and we thank you, and oh,
Isn't there something we can do for you now?"
But I said, "No, nothing," knowing
Many things that I wanted. And she said,
"Good night, then" and she smiled, but then
She swayed, suddenly, and she laid
Her hand on my arm, and she said,
"I am dizzy—silly—I'm dizzy," and I knew
It was true, this, and not as with Clare, and I held her,
My arm under hers, and I took
The fingers of her hand and I raised them, and kissed them,
And she looked at me, saying nothing and then
I fled, in the dark, fled
From my love, yes—
For I dared not remain.

PART FOUR

E SHALL not soon forget? But we have laid
Dust covers on the memory's hidden seats,
White sheets that in the dusty years are greyed
With deep precipitation from long streets.
You who were once the intolerable price
We paid for dressing hate in glittering metal,
Are now the tolerated dust that twice
Covers the loathing that we dare not fettle.
Oh, see the slick and polished face of life!
Its lips are framing words that will atone,
Its tongue is glazing glory over strife:
These were your lips: this tongue was once your own.
We shall not soon forget? We must, we must!
It was forgot before your flesh was dust.

NOW IT IS hateful: all that speaks of war.
The years that wore the livery of its hate
Are all detached: strong pictures, but their face
Is varnished in malignant chemicals.
Now it is hateful: I did not see this then:
These thoughts arise and speak long afterward,
Reflection's children, from parentage of peace.
I've watched the shortening cycles of man's hate
Aroused and sated and aroused again.
We stir the beast, and kill and burn the beast,
We stir the ashes and he's there once more
Shouting his war-cry of a different word:
Democracy, Totalitarian Statehood,
Marxian Utopia, Greed, or Colonies:
No matter: all the syllables resound
With trumpet tones and the hot beat of drums
Till hosts are moving in hypnotic hate

For one more shibboleth.
                              Such years as these
Grow false in retrospect: it was not I,
Not Tom who lived then, but another being
Bearing my name, using my fingers strangely,
Clothing my body in a uniform,
Seeing through these my later and grown eyes,
But adding nothing to the stranded brain
Save images such as fever in the night
Flings up through wakefulness or frantic sleep.
Try to add love and friendship to this brew:
It is unpalatable, bitter stuff
To feed young mouths.
                         There's Martin and there's Sam,
There's Judith unacknowledged. It's all gone
Down the neap tide of war years. I should tell
In crazy words of crazy hours that filled
Months of this sickness of my mortal self.
It is not, nor it never will be clear,
Nor is there clarity to explain the wild
Seeking and striving of one human soul
Torn into separate entities of being,
Pricked by his devil, tortured by his love
That seemed so dangerous, pouring out his will
To master time the masterless, bridle haste,
Kill passion in the manual of arms,
Reconcile death with the remembered grace
Of dear and living movement, and become
One part of many and remain as one.

2

Grandfather said: "All right. Get a commission.
You were born so, take the unpleasant way.
It's easy to enlist, to join the ranks,
To sink into obedience and lie back
Against strict orders always from above you.
Restful. But if you give commands, remember
Though they are only words come down to you
From some superior mouth, you are become
Particeps criminis in the last result.
I know. I did it. I learned to hate the whole
Insane invention. Maybe in the high air

182

You'll ride alone as nearly as any war
Will ever permit. Be hard. Be just, but hard:
Justice and kindness must walk side by side
Where killing's legal.
                                    There's no good in this
Or any war. I know. I understand
More than is comfortable. You must go to war.
Shoot straight. Be mercifully merciless.
Be a good murderer, and record your heart
Before you change it in the heat of war.
You must grow old, and soon. Good luck to you.
Stay single till it's over."
                                    I said quickly,
"I'll never marry."
                                    "Nonsense. Bosh and slop!
You have it in your eye. But wait, but wait,
The days of war are alien days to love
And rear confusion's children. Let her wait.
Let her knit socks while you are knitting death
With your winged needles. Go ahead and fly.
You'll break your silly neck and men will cry
'The glory of it!' Go and break your neck.
But don't break someone's heart as well.
                                    Too young,
Marriage is for the adult, you're not grown,
You'd fancy flesh was paramount. Well, it is,
But as a spring-board helps you to a dive
Into deep water. You haven't learnt to swim.
Go ahead, learn to fly. Keep off the tarts,
Don't waste your energy to get diseased.
If by some happy accident you survive war,
You might as well be healthy.
                                    Take my blessing.
It's but a biblical gesture, but a good one.
There's much fine common sense in the old Bible.
Be blessed. I'm fond of you. Be a good soldier.
Be a good flier. Shoot the Germans down—
But save your hatred for the men who made
The Germans enemies."

3

My father said:
"Yes, yes, of course. An excellent idea.

183

Flying is skilful. Seems a pity, Tom,
Joss didn't think of that. Still, he'll be good
In any branch: the infantry will do.
Will you need money?"
                              "No, not much, I think—
If you can help me at the start."
                                    "Of course.
I'll keep the allowance going. Seems a bother
We shan't be able to go shooting now,
Nor fishing even. Well, I'll paint instead.
You've told your mother?"
                              "No."
                                    "But you must do it."
"I thought I'd tell her after I'd enlisted."
"H'm. Yes. The accomplished fact. Perhaps you're wise.
Wise, but a little cowardly. Isn't it?"
"I hadn't thought so."
                        "Yet it is. Not fair
To cut a mother off from all her power
Too suddenly. You ease the break by giving
A chance for protest."
                        "She is sad," I said.
"I didn't wish to bother her too much
With my decisions."
                        "On top of all her own?
Decisions are so hateful. Drift and drift,
And life makes up your mind. I'm sorry, Tom,
I didn't mean to say that. Go ahead.
You've my permission. You've my approval, too,
Whatever that is worth to you. I've followed
My own way long enough to wish to give you
The same disastrous opportunity.
War! What a pickle! What a silly pickle!
My sons at war! The artist sends his boys
To inartistic strife. Well, try to be
A credit to my capacity to shoot birds
When you shoot other fliers. Right and left,
And pick the high ones. Tell your mother, Tom,
And let her howl a little."

4

Mother wrote
Six anguished letters. I destroyed them all.

They were not all germane to this, and yet
Some phrases cling to memory.
                    Ethel   says
She knows a man in Washington, a General,
Staff work, he needs intelligent young men . . .
Isn't it quite enough to have Joss gone
Into the Infantry . . . so many people
Feel that one son's enough.
                    Barbarians
Clutching   the   throat   of   France . . . poor, war-torn Bel-
     gium . . .
What Viviani said: "Forever secure
Existence of a world in which our children
Shall draw free breath in undisturbed full peace . . ."
And yet my children go . . .
                    As Ethel says,
It is our duty . . . women wait and wait,
The terrible dry waiting, without motion,
We are so useless . . . Flying frightens me,
Must you take double risks . . . already Joss
Headed for the deep trenches . . . one's enough.
I'm sure your father prompted this . . . all flying
So lonely . . . if you're hurt and no one's near . . .
Ethel, like me, is proud of your intention,
Your wish to serve . . . the cruel submarines . . .
The Aztec sunk off Brest, you saw, at night,
No warning—terror on the land and sea
And now the air . . . Consider . . . God is with us,
But cannot want you both . . . our Enemy
Crucifies prisoners, it terrifies me so,
The babies slaughtered . . . Just a little while,
You are so young . . . and Ethel says you're young,
There is no hurry, there are many others . . .
We all must do our part . . . we serve in small
And womanly ways . . . write soon . . . as Ethel says . . .
Braver to wait, wiser to wait, and harder,
The harder way . . . or drive an ambulance . . .
You are so young . . . this flying . . . Ethel says . . .
The Germans have not changed since Attila
Whipped on his Huns . . . your father does approve?
Oh, I'm so distant . . . can't you hear me, too?
God will hear prayers, my prayers . . .

And Judith wrote.

That's the first letter that I had from her.
I'd written many.
    The knife cut the flap;
A voice within me spoke to me and said:
Read it.
   I must, but let me breathe, once, twice,
Let me have time!
     Read, coward!
       I am not.
Why should I fear?
    *Why do your fingers sweat
Against the paper? Are you . . .*
      No! I'll read it,
Be quiet, be quiet, some things are left unsaid.
I'll read:
    'Dear Tom: Thanks for your note. Of course,
I meant to tell you you could call me Judith
At Mrs. Preston's party. I felt shy.'
Shy? All that self-possession, that calm glance,
That ease with people? Shyness?
      *Never mind,
Read on. She has said 'Yes' for the first time.*
Be quiet!
   Read!
     I shall. 'You should have asked me,
I am no good at letters, but I like yours,
Will you write letters and forgive no answer?
Send me your station after you enlist,
I'll try to write, do you know where you'll be?
It seems so awful, Arthur has gone too,
My brother Edward is too young, it makes him
Fearfully angry, Arthur's gone from here
To join in Boston, he goes to Plattsburg next,
I shall go up and see him. Will you be there?
Do they train aviators too? I liked
The flowers ever so much, I cut the stems,
Took off the wire and popped them in a vase
They lasted days. When do you leave, how soon?
So many questions! but I'd like to know.
I think it's fine you want to fly, I wish

Women could fly. If you have time to waste
Come down and get some hunting. Cora's well,
She sends her best, Mother and Father both
Think you are splendid, I hope that pleases you,
It pleases me. Do write. I do love letters,
I'll try to answer. Good-bye. Judith C.'

Then I re-read it. And then read again.
Such a nice letter!
      Yes.
         Why did you write?
I don't know.
      But you do. And yet you claim
You have not fallen . . .
        Be quiet!
           But why write?
This is the path, your feet are on the path.
In truth, you're running toward her.
           I am not.
I shall not see her now.
        You'll write to her.
No.
  Yes, you will.
      Perhaps.
        But why, for fun?
For the excited leap of the free heart
As the thin letter slides out to the light,
All fresh from Judith?
        Oh, I do not know.
Life is so difficult!
    You make it so.
No, I'm uncertain.
     Of love?
         It is not sure!
Love: marriage: Judith!
       No! Remember Mother,
Remember the white letter, think of Clare,
Norway, and the stiff painting on the wall,
Maria Northrup, remember Ethel Darnley,
Remember these.
     But you are you, not they.
And this is Judith.
      Yes.
       I'll say her name

Softly: so: Judith. It is like a small
Fire in the veins, the sound goes through the brain
And echoes wonderfully and the blood responds.
There is a tremor that creeps around your ribs
And pricks the surface of your spine with pleasure.
Speak truly, what is that?
                              I do not know.
I must wait, all alone. The war, this flying,
Is made for waiting. There I can be free
To sift my thoughts.
                    There is no freedom, none.
You carry this about. You may not fly
Into oblivion, nor insulate your mind
Even with excitement, nor cut off your heart:
There is no switch to throw.
                              No freedom, none?
This has crept in: poor mortal Thomas Cottrell,
Run far, run hard!
                    I shall run hard and far.
But this is you: you may not with all speed
Outdistance Tom. Can you escape yourself?

6

So it was done. Sam Allen and Tom Cottrell
Left Harvard for Long Island, were examined
Naked before a lot of naked men,
Pounded and tested, whirled in a low chair,
Hopped on one leg, were prodded, asked to cough;
Accepted. That's all simple. That's Mineola,
That's in my papers. First Class Private Cottrell,
The Aviation section, Signal Corps,
United States. And First Class Private Allen,
Accepted. Wait. And wait. And wait some more,
For this is life, Privates, to wait and wait,
And not to know what you are waiting for
Save further orders.
                    But the rest?
                                   It takes
The form of spoken words, not images:
It was all told once, now it is not clear
Save as the memory recalls the words
That first recorded. The matrix is destroyed:

The cast is left me: a sharp sculptured frieze
I've coloured with the pigments of the years
Of stained remembering. But the figures on it,
They do not move, though I can feel their shape
Under my fingers.
                    Are they so embalmed
Because I let them petrify in words?
But there is love: and friendship: and affection.
Can these be static, like a painted flame,
And still give warmth? Is there a warmth in dreams
Remembered afterwards?
                        It is still real and warm,
I can still touch it, taste it, hear its sound,
See its firm colour; but it will not move.
Nor will death move: nor life that's frozen up
In the deep floes of discontinuous time.
I did not sweep into my stream of life,
Released to warmer movement, till those days
Were tacked like photographs upon the wall
Of a removed and seldom-entered room.
So must the shades remember us: as now
I see the dead days of my madness hung
In immaterial immobility.
I can remember anger and remorse,
I can remember the ambitious hopes
Centred on present doing; drunkenness;
Wild laughter that had neither pause nor stop
But was just laughter sounding in my ears;
I can remember women in a bed,
Their flesh in motion, neither past nor future,
But present so, forever, without names,
Equal in memory to the cylinders
We touched and handled and with skill replaced
To function further, to carry us again,
To fill an hour.
                  To fill an hour full!
What wild extravagance of the stuff of life,
These posturings upon an hour's flat
And anvil surface to hammer minutes out
Into the weapons of their use to kill!
So I remember them: but so absorbed
Into the fascination of their action,
That all life turned only upon the axis

189

Of action's sedative. Perhaps the love
I gave and got was but the safety valve
Of unused living.
                                        But the love remains,
The sadness is still there, this life goes on
Forever eagerly, excitingly—
And that remains in motionless suspense
Like an alarmed and gathered spider hung
On an invisible thread in the still air.

Perhaps these motionless, distant months of mine
Are so suspended on a thread I wove
And cannot longer see.
                                        Perhaps some day
This frightened little spider of my past
Will turn to motion and so weave again
A web for living.
                                        Now the embracing air
Gathers the leaves to motion on the trees,
And all the scarlet and the spotted gold
Says Life and Life: we droop, drop, grow again;
Continue, for the years will not attend
On the awakening of static memory.

THESE WERE direct and shafted words, their aim
To fly like arrows to the chosen clout:
They struck, but as they touched, the mark became
Only the circle of another doubt.
Those were the hiding, halting little phrases
That crept so slyly past the flat, uncouth
Door of a statement, yet their meaning grazes
The very centre of the essential truth.
Glancing, direct, we must be over-wise
To hide or to reveal as we desire,
To block the searching of men's curious eyes,
Or tell a tale, explicit and entire.

Conceal no longer, let the words betray:
They'll turn sweet darkness to the harder day.

↑   ↑

CHARLES looked the same as ever. He said, "Do you need
    help,
Or can you navigate by yourself? You look fine.
You seem a trifle pale. Mr. Cottrell's well.
He's waiting inside, these evenings are too chilly."
"No, I'm all right," I said. "You bring the bags in,
I haven't got my strength back altogether."
"Right in the living room, Mr. Tom, he's raging
With his excitement." He laughed.

         I stood in the doorway
Just for a moment to smell the salt-sea perfume.
Dark now so early, the quick November evening,
Everything hidden away in the cupboard of night's room:
All the good toys of sea and air and houses:
These were invisible, but the mind sees soon.
The wind blew softly, coldly, in from the ocean,
Rich with the scent of weeds and the sound of waves,
Stored with the stuff of love.

        The door stood open:
Out of it the yellow hall-light came gravely
Down on the green grass squared by the frame of night.
Grandfather heard my steps and he called out, "Hello!
Are you all right, have you got Charles there with you?
Come right in, there's a drink for you here, old fellow.
Hell and damnation, but I'm glad to have you!"
I entered the room and saw him. He looked unaltered,
Crouched in the wheel chair; his voice was large and ringing,
Strong as my memory, the great sound did not falter.
I said, "It's grand to see you. I'm glad to be back here,
The house looks nice and the air smells fine and salty."
He cried, "You didn't expect the blessed ocean
To smell like a damn fresh fish-pond, boy, now did you?
It leaves its blasted salt all over everything
And everything's damp and my rheumatism twitches.
Sit down, sit down. Or pour yourself some whisky,
And pour me one. Will you change?"

        I said, "I'd rather."

"Yes, you'll eat better if you wear clean linen.
John shot some duck. You'll have to be the carver,
My hand shakes now. And Burgundy. Charles!" he shouted.
Charles called "Yes, Mr. Cottrell?" from the doorway.
"I thought you were still outside. Did you get the wine
Up from the cellar?"
                              "Yessir. You want me more now,
You ring the bell, Mr. Cottrell, I'll be right handy,
I'll fix Mr. Tom's things."
                              I said, "On the second floor?"
Grandfather said, "The Blue Room. Do the stairs bother?"
I said, "It's just the dizziness, comes on the stairs.
It's rare now, don't you worry. Charles will police me
Just for a day or so. And I'd like to be there."
"You're sure?"
                  "I am."
                              "All right, Charles, in the Blue Room."
Charles disappeared and I poured us out our drinks.
"Sit, boy, sit. The journey down is fatiguing.
How is your father?" I said, "He's nicely, thanks,
He sent his love."
                    "He hasn't got love to send me.
Some admiration, because he still remembers
I could outride him once—and for my painting.
No love."
            "He has grown kinder and more tender."
"To you?"
            "To me."
                        "Yes, that might be. He's older.
There's no eternal flame but leaves some cinders:
He burnt his for himself. Well, here's your health.
Mud in your eye. By God! I'm glad to see you
Alive and well." "I'm lucky."
                              "You are, damned lucky.
Lucky more ways than one. You've got your freedom."
"I failed," I said.
                    "There's many a kind of failure
That breeds success. Drink up." We drank together.
"We'll talk of this tomorrow."
                              "Tonight," I said,
"If you're not too tired."
                              "Not me, I'm in fine feather.

192

What's the great hurry?"
                                    "It is a cowardly canker.
If I make it clear to you, it may help me cure it.
You are both wise and old."
                                    "I'm old," he said,
"But I grow less wise, more noisy, more of a nuisance,
Much more cantankerous, with the passing days.
I'm making a saint of Charles. If he don't lose it,
He has his martyrdom here in serving me.
Heaven's a-yawn for him." I laughed. He cried,
"Smile you my speeches as I were a fool, boy?"
We shouted out the tag lines side by side:
"Goose, if I had you upon Sarum plain,
I'd drive you cackling home to Camelot."
His laughter roared out till it rocked him there.
Charles came in smiling. He said, "Your bath is hot,
Is that right, Mr. Tom? You're all unpacked.
You want me with you?"
                                    I said, "Yes, the stairs,
Just see me to the room." I rose and walked
Out of the warm room, past the familiar chairs,
Up the steep steps (with Charles beside me then),
Full of a happiness exorcising fears.

                              2

Charles wouldn't leave me: that made a mixed sensation,
He was part of the house, and part of time, but alive.
I wanted to savour the room and the sounds softly
Blown through the shut thin glass, night noises striving
To enter the closed room of remembered youth.
I couldn't do that with Charles there, could but savour
Him in the setting; but he was part of the wind,
Part of the night, part of the soft blue paper
On the angled walls: he was like the scent of the matting.
He took my clothes off, gently beyond all reason,
Skilful with his long years of attending Grandfather.
He said, "You got no scars nor I can't see 'em."
I said, "No scars, it was just three ribs were broken,
The left-hand side, they mended in due season,
There's no pain now—discomfort, I'm stiff, a little,
It just takes time."
                              He said, "Just time and patience,

You're young, Mr. Tom, you'll heal, it will all be gone.
What makes you dizzy?"
                              I said, "I wish to gracious
I knew what, Charles, they say it is that concussion—
It'll pass in time, like the stiffness, the lack of strength:
Patience again." He laughed. "That's hard for young folks.
I can bathe you, I'm handy."
                              I said, "No, thanks,
I want to get back to doing the normal things
As soon as may be."
                              "I'll wait here to help your dressing."
"You needn't."
                              "Your grandmother taught me, 'Festina lente,'
Ain't it the truth?" I giggled. "Oh well, God bless you,
Wait then, Charles, you always tried to spoil me."
"You wasn't a boy to spoil. You kept me guessing.
Your brother was easy to handle, he did the same things,
Same sort of things. I hear that he's a major."
I went to the bathroom door but I paused to say,
"Yes, he's a major, he would be, he's amazing,
He knows his own mind, he follows a certain star,
He's never uncertain." I checked the words that rose
Up to my lips: I was going to say, He'd never
Crash in a plane, the damn thing out of control . . .
I felt the stick in my hands, and my toes curled
Against the rudder-bars, so, and the plane mounting,
The pulse and the quiver; the enemy earth receding:
Drawing away (not I), each second counted
Toward waiting, waiting—its mouth is wide with a hunger
Kind but insatiable . . . and the room whirls around,
Grasp the door post. The voice of Charles, soft, gentle:
"Want me to steady you?"
                              "No, it is past." I turned,
Entered the bathroom and closed the door behind me . . .
Into the tub, the water soothes and burns,
The skin is tender there where the corset held in
Arcs of your breathing . . . softly, so, relax now,
Here is the peace of the past, here is enfolding
Warmth and there is no questioning eye to tax you
With an accounting . . . softly, the water ripples,
Flings down the light rays in their soft, distorted
Rings on the lax limbs, lying in pallid liquid,
Softly, the light breaks into a thousand watery

Dimples of bright and dark, and the blood comes slowly
Into its own beat, slow, and gently retarded . . .
Charles is beyond the door . . . you have but to call him.

3

The duck was delicious; the burgundy did me good,
It rested me and relaxed me after my bath,
And there's nothing better than black duck properly cooked.
Grandfather talked for two, but spoke of himself,
Of the local matters.

He said, "You remember Jake?"
"The big, blond man?"

"The one that made you feel
So sick. Well, after you left, I gave him the sack,
He did odd jobs around. I gave him some—
I was sorry for him. Well, he tried to get into this war
But they wouldn't have him. Funny, a trained soldier,
He'd something the matter. I never could find out more
Than the fact he lost his temper, he just ran wild,
They shut him up in the jail for a week before
I got them to let him go free. He's not been seen
In Cottrellton since, I am told he's in Exeter, west,
But nothing to go on beyond a rumour. Curious.
A wonderful worker—just had a sort of a twist,
A scunner against the world, and against your father
For losing him the girl that he loved so faithfully.
It gave him the feeling the whole world was against him,
Pointing him out, and jeering, and crying 'Failure'—
He couldn't stand it. Poor chap, he dealt in extremes,
He'd rush for the good, he'd rush as hard for the bad,
He wanted to be the one who was doing it most
Whatever it was. He may have been slightly mad,
But however it was, I was sorry, the force was there,
Great force, all squandered wildly, crazily, sadly.
Nothing too much, they said. And, Know thyself.
They were wise old birds, the Greeks, they balanced wisely
Between the must and the may, the could and the did,
The tried-and-failed and the failed-for-lack-of-trying.
At least, they meant to, when trade wasn't too much threat-
ened,
When demagogues had sore throat and the Spartans were busy
Telling the youngsters the State was greater than they were

And the only thing that mattered. Poor old crazy
Jake, what a wonderful Spartan he'd have made:
He fell in Athens—but so did old Socrates."
He folded his napkin and called, "Hello there, Charles,
Bring in some port to the living room, if you please."
I said, "Are you drinking port?"

He said, "No, God damn it,
I've got to watch you. It's good for your disease
But poison to mine. Come along, push the chair in, boy,
And mind the furniture."

I got up slowly
And said, "It's the blind, now, pushing along the blind.
I'll do my best."

"I'm stupid," he said with a growl,
"Call Charles."

"Oh no, I'd rather like to try it,
If you don't mind."

"Go on. If you feel funny,
Lean on the chair and stop."

We made slow progress
Through the wide hall. "I'm not exactly running,
But maybe you like it better this slow way
Than scorching through the rooms." He laughed and said,
"You're doing finely. Keep it up. You put me
Right by that table, the lamp is back of my head,
You take the deep chair. First we'll have our coffee
And then we'll talk, though you ought to be in bed."
I giggled behind him and quoted, "Would you conserve
My strength by bedding me?"

"Did I say that?
By God, what a devilish memory you possess!"
"You use a phrase that sticks."

"Oh no, don't flatter,
I'll warrant there was a curse hung on the tag of it
That stuck in a boy's mind."

I placed him by his lamp,
And sat in the old, deep chair: I filled it now:
I thought of the days when I sat within its ample
Depths and imagined I was at sea in a boat
On piratical oceans and Grandfather's voice was the wind
Filling the canvas, the roar of the rope-checked guns,
The clatter of cutlass, the clank of heavenly, sinful
Pieces of eight that poured through our bloodied fingers

196

Onto the dead-strewn deck.
                              The memory dimmed;
I thought: it is now, this minute, the battle rages,
And I am absent, a failure. I heard Charles enter.
He gave us coffee and left us. We drank and smoked,
The thick blue smoke of our cigars curled gently
Into the lamp, as always, and came out grey
In a soft and light-pierced mist from the shade's narrow
And silhouetted circle.
                              He said, "You crashed.
Bad flying or bad luck? Chagrin or sorrow?
Tell me."
          "I don't know which. I was absent-minded.
You can't be that and fly."
                              "You mean, you were thinking
Of something else?"
                    "Exactly."
                              "Of what, my boy?"
"My binocular strap was loose, and one of the single
Ends with the buckle got jammed. The stick got jammed—
She started to rise."
                    "To rise. You hadn't been drinking?"
"No, no drink. She rose but then she stalled,
Fell off to a tail-spin and crashed. I remember the sound,
The tearing, ripping smash. That's all I remember.
I came to hours later, my ribs all bound
With sticking plaster, a blinding headache, a sense
Of failure that wouldn't go when the headache went
And the ribs healed up."
                    "Were you thinking of something wrong?"
"Not of itself, but all thought should be bending
To the one end of flight. I had got my leave,
I had got my brevet, my commission was on the way . . ."
I paused. He said, "Yes?"
                              "I'd had a letter, it ran
In my head."
          "They do, girls' letters."
                              "I didn't say . . ."
"You didn't have to."
                    "All right, it was from a girl.
I'd like to tell you about it, it's been preying
A long time on my mind."
                    He said, "Good, do so.

197

Help yourself to the port. That's right, take plenty,
But start at the very beginning—tell the whole story,
I see you need it."
                    "I do."
                              "And, by God, I'm empty
For all your story, and I need filling. Now talk, boy."

4

. . . ."That's how I met her."
                              "I see."
                                        "It seemed as though
I'd known her always, forever—the twenty-four hours
Were like long years."
                        "I know. They do seem endless."
"I hunted and danced with her, and I sent her flowers,
Wrote her letters . . . I didn't want to, really:
Half of me did—the other half protested.
Sometimes I worried. As though she were several people,
All of whom I had known. It was detestable,
Being forced to a state where you didn't know
Why you did or didn't love. The constant contest
Over the wherefore."
                      "You spoke of another woman,
The one she looked like. Tell me about her, too."
"I'd rather not, I'm sorry. It's so involved.
That was a fever. It ran a swift course, grew
Into a poison. It passed. I mustn't tell you,
It is mixed up with others." He nodded his head.
"Were you in love with Judith? Are you in love?"
I said, "Oh God! I don't know. I'm afraid.
I wish you'd tell me. Tell me what makes a man
Know a love from a passion, a passing passion."
He answered, "Let's hear the story. There is no touchstone
Gives you the answers. But one can imagine
The answer may tell itself in your own telling.
Give me the whole thing."
                            "I'll do it, after a fashion.
I tell it lamely."
                    "The lameness tells its story."
"Yes. I suppose it does . . .
                              . . . There was Cornell, then.
You know about the enlistment, and all the waiting.

198

I suppose Sam and I must have bothered you plenty,
Fretting around here. There we were separated:
That's like the army, you don't belong to yourself,
You belong to them, like a gun or a pair of boots,
They ticket and label and stick you up on the shelf
They choose for you. We had no say about it.
It left me lost for a while, and Sam was lost,
We wanted to stick together. He was my friend,
It was arbitrary as hell, all just because
They called him a week earlier than they called me—
His name begins with an A, that's true of course.
We'd meant to stick together. It made it tough.
I hardly ever saw him. He left before me.
We had one time in New York, I'll tell you later,
One in Texas . . . funny. Oh, nothing stormy,
Just a drifting process, my very best friend
Divorced for a week of work. At first it hurt us . . .
Hard on us both . . . then softened . . . and soon washed up.
I turned to Martin Fenton. Because his height
Was the same as mine, as Sam's. The army's stupid,
But you can't help that.
                              By God! they ran you ragged,
Between the lectures, drills, the constant testing,
The terrible competition, the mathematics,
Aerodynamics, wing curves, small time for resting,
Sit on a scaffold and spot the lights that flash
On a big relief map, telegraph the message,
Learn your radio, study till lights go out.
Sam was a week ahead and a world away;
Martin and I were together, we worried together,
We held our breath for the tests and were both afraid:
Iowa and New York, it was damned exciting,
But it wore us down while it drew us always closer.
Do you see how it happened?"
                                        "I see. It is always so.
But you didn't lose Sam, you weren't really a loser,
For you gained Martin."
                              "Yes. Oh yes . . . gained Martin.
Just for a little while, Martin."
                                        "Go on," he said,
"You've only begun, you're telling a story now."
I shifted about in my chair and I shook my head
To clear the vision. "Thanks. There's another problem

Bothered me then, and now. When I went to bed,
I should have gone straight to sleep. But it didn't happen.
I'd worried all day, wondering if I'd passed,
Wondering if I'd finish. And then the darkness
Suddenly came and covered the day at last,
And what do you think I thought about? Work or Judith?
No—I worried because the poor small hours
Over a week-end, had been unproductive,
I hadn't been writing, so please you! Such thinking sours
In the unsleeping times, in the queer darkness
Filled with the sound of a multitude of breathing
Men in the rhythm of sleep and you alone there,
Scraping the empty pot of your mind for leavings
That you may feed your devil, the devil that pricks you,
Jeers and stabs you and fills you with unbelievings,
Doubts and worries and cares. Had I gone crazy?"
Grandfather shook his head. "Oh no, that's normal,
Just an ambition stirred by the overtired
Nerves of the mind. It used to bother me formerly,
Before I grew so old—it bothers me still
When my unfitted philosophy wears too thin
And the seat of the mind needs patching." We laughed to-
        gether.
He said, "Go on, it's interesting. It has been,
Ever since man discovered he had a mind
And longed to use it. Don't tell your story alone,
I like to hear how you and Martin grew up:
Tarry at Jericho, until your beards be grown."
"Sounds like the Bible."
                        "It is."
                                "Our beards were growing.
We used to say, when the weekly tests were done,
'I've a long grey beard.' And Jericho makes me think
Of the Jericho Turnpike and flying over Long Island,
And seeing the chart-sea beat on the map-like beaches
In the October sun. Funny. The big and smiling
Country around Cornell, with Lake Cayuga—
There's almost no clear picture left—the lake,
The maples turning, the great, warm fields of buckwheat,
An image here and there . . ."
                        I paused; the picture
Flashed through my mind:

200

(We sit in a field, beneath a great tree spreading shadow,
The roofs of Ithaca now are blue through the yellow leaves:
        the blue haze of evening
Touches September hills, wraps them in colour
Softened to rest. He says, 'What are you thinking?'
'Nothing.'
            'Of Judith—no man thinks of nothing.'
'Mind your own business, Martin.'
                            A silence, peaceful, easy.
Then he laughs. 'You complicate things. Now in September
The big wide fields at home are stubble, the stubble is endless,
You see the sky to the next great wave of floating land
That lifts your head to the next, your eyes to the edges
Of endless horizons. The sky is big there. You see it all.
You touch the ground and it says, Be simple, Grow;
Hate or Love, but Grow.
                    You worry like little cut up fields, hedged
With mean stone walls; if the walls tumble,
Your neighbour will tumble into your field and Oh God!
What a calamity! Get wise! You're stupid. The East
Has wrapped you up in a waterproof, damp-proof fabric,
Preserving the roots for something—but they don't grow.'
I just keep silent. The edge of a poem flickers.
Through my mind: if I seize pencil and paper,
It will begin to leap to living in the black lines.
The sun droops in the haze of the west. The smoke
From Martin's pipe drifts over me, acrid. The effort
Is never made.)
                            I said:
"We went to Hazelhurst Field. We started flying.
But we got three days' leave first. Judith came down.
She stayed with an aunt in New York. I was still trying
To find the answer. I wanted too much, too quickly,
And didn't know why. I couldn't tell one damn thing
Of how she felt. It could have been love, or affection,
Or just excitement, a uniform, someone flying,
Just the war. I'd talk, or rather I'd lecture:
She'd listen. I'd watch her. I only saw her twice,
Once for lunch, once for a moving picture
And a ride on a bus . . ."
                        (The air is cold:
The thin, sharp lights on the Jersey cliffs are clear.
You huddle together.

201

'You'd rather go down inside?
It's warmer there.'
                    'No, let's just freeze, it's lovely, the water
Looks so black.'
                    The trees are unexpected: to see the belt of Orion
Through the dark leaves of a New York tree: to search
For the seventh star of the Pleiades when the buildings
Grant you the far sky eastward.
                    The boats sliding
On the invisible water of the North River, the green lights
Calling to your sea-eye: North; and red lights: South.
What could you do to seize time and so seize Judith strongly,
And seizing, what should you do? How long should you
        hold,
October passes, the winter snow will cover the open seats
And the other eyes of the warm interior of a light-filled bus
Must search you and find you.
                    Where is Maria Northrup?
Where is she, that all our swains commend her and one swain,
Where is he?
                    And you pay again, the two dimes in the clicking
Metal of time and the red lights on the water
Go your way and the stars are gathered together in the single
Multiplicity of the Milky Way, and Judith,
She is beside you, for a passing moment, under October night
In the pause between this and that.)
He said, "Fill your glass again."
                                "I may get slopped."
"That might not hurt you, it might be good to be tight,
In vino veritas."
                    "Yes. It may do me good.
I haven't seen her again, not since that night.
We wrote to each other—ordinary sort of letters,
Some of mine were silly, but when you're writing
Under the strain of flying, release of drinking,
You aren't always sensible. She's answered,
Sweetly—steadily—wonderful, simple letters,
Full of her steadiness, cheerful, her good sense cancels
The idiocy of mine and picks out the good parts,
Ignoring the rest. But I'll get ahead of my story.
After she left, I denied her. I said to myself:
If you don't know your mind and heart, what's more,
If you can't guess how she feels, even a little bit,

202

How in hell is it love? You'd marry? you'd dare?
Nonsense, it's just the trap of a pretty woman,
You felt that way about Clare . . ."

He said, "About Clare?"
"Damn! The name slipped out. It makes no difference."
I felt the blood run up to the roots of my hair.
He nodded his head in silence.

"I felt that way
When Martin and I found Sam and we all got plastered,
The last night of our leave; Sam was just taking
A night off in New York. The party lasted
Till early the following morning. We all went down
To the tip of the island, where Martin knew a sergeant
In the harbour police, whose trick began at four.
We went in his boat, we cruised around tugs and barges,
Up the East River. The dawn came on our way . . ."
(*The echo of day is flung from the long wires of the bridges,*
You see the light spread back of the black towering
Buildings each with a star or two of yellow
Hung in its captive night;
The oily water catches the red glow in its coiling
Serpent patterns, you hear the deadly whisper
Of the terrible tide telling and retelling
Secrets to dark and quivering, serried piles of the half-seen
        docks
That made the teeth in the mouth of the hungry shore.)
" . . . and the strong tide nearly stopped us by Blackwell's
        Island.
The bridges were wonderful, over the smooth water.
Some of the buildings had windows that glowed mildly
Yellow within their dark towers. One grew sober
Under the cool and the purer air, and the sliding
Motion of boat and water relaxed our tension
Strung to the night's high pitch. The slow talk turned
Under the sergeant's soft voice to the terrible
Tales of the corpses found, of a suicide burning
Just like a wick in the deep oil on the water
That covered Gowanus when the whole creek flamed,
A river of fire; of rats on Barren Island,
Where the dead horses rotted; patrol boats lamed
By floating water-soaked timbers; of opium smugglers,
Arrests on ships, with a hand-cuffed negro clinging
To a long rope ladder until he was beaten numb

And loosed the hold that drugs had lent to his fingers,
To fall to the boat below. The sergeant's voice
Dealt in horrors, but never lost its simple
Tone of a soft tale told for the fun of telling.
The light was beginning to grow. We heard a hail,
A cop on the end of a long dock was shouting:
We turned in to him. He said, 'They're raising hell
Up in the Ship Canal. A barge has bust loose,
She's loose with the tide, she smashed into another,
She's coming this way, git up there now and catch her.'
The sergeant rang the bell and said, 'Holy Mother,
What use will we be, it's a tug they're needing.'
We started again full speed. Up river a way
We found a fire-boat hitched to the runaway barge
And towing her slowly north. They yelled and said
That we'd best go on and see to the damaged one,
Pier Ninety or something, a man was off his head,
They'd sent for a doctor; the barge they towed was empty,
No one aboard, she'd just chawed through her hawser
And run with the tide. We left them soon behind.
We found the barge that was hit. Sinking, of course,
With her bow stove in half under a great strong dock,
Her deck-house razed. There were three cops and a doctor,
An ambulance at the pier's base. One cop was holding
Gently the arm of a tall, thin man . . ."
(*The look of a face in pain; but not his pain, but another's*
Transferred to the eyes that can see it, but not share it,
A face so white in the flush of a red east
The moment before sun is born.
                              The oily water curls
Red in the whisper of movement, the queer sucking
Noise of water drawn inward to the dark piles,
Into the sinking vessel, a bubbling noise in the clear peace
Of the flushed morning.)
                              . . . It was sort of shocking,
The look on the man's face: not dazed exactly,
But as if waiting and listening. I can't describe it.
You could hear the sound of the water filling the barge.
They told us not to bother after we'd tied
The little patrol boat up. But still we climbed
Onto the dock. Curiosity, maybe, guided.
Just as we came, the thin man made a sudden step
As if to release himself. The cop said, 'Easy.

You can't go there.' He turned to us and said,
'He wants to go back to the barge. We had to seize him
And drag him off it.' He spoke as if the man
Were somewhere else or deaf and so couldn't hear.
'His wife is there and his child. They both got killed.'
The man made another movement. 'Now, don't fear,
They've sent for the wrecker. You just stay here, it's safer,
You can't do nothing.' He turned to us again.
'He wants to get at the child. Well, I don't blame him,
It's better he don't, the way they look, a shame.
You can't get in to them, that is, to get them out,
The doctor seen 'em.'
                            The doctor slowly nodded.
The man stood still and moistened his lips with his tongue.
Then he said, 'Just get the wife out, gents, that's all,
Just get the wife.' Somebody said, 'She's dead.
There's no use to get her.' His whisper answered, grating:
'The child is dead. But not the wife. No, gents, no.'
They all stood awkwardly silent. Then he straightened.
'Gents,' he said, 'you can have the child. I give you
The child, my daughter, to keep, to have, she's eight,
It's a bargain, take her and give me the wife, she's mine,
A man can have plenty of children, but just one woman,
Just one woman, gents, now that's what I say,
Not two, just one. That's her. Ten years' lovin'.
What do you say?'
                        The doctor spoke: 'You bring him
Into the ambulance, and we'll talk it over,
That's the idea, discuss it.' The cop and the man
Walked slowly away to the ambulance. 'He'll recover.
I don't believe he's crazy and he's not hurt,
It's shock, that's all.' He pantomimed with his fingers
A hypodermic; said, 'That's the stuff will fix him,'
And followed after. A little while we lingered,
And then got back in the boat. We were sober now."

I paused for a drink of the port. The glowing, single
Ruby of gathered light at the glass's edge
Moved in the light of the lamp. Grandfather spoke:
"Interesting, very. You have some reason for telling
This particular yarn." He gave me a look
Faintly puzzled. I said, "It's not quite finished.
On the way back we didn't talk much, for a while,

Even the sergeant was quiet and the other cop
Running the engine. I saw Martin smile
And asked him what was funny. He said, 'New York.
It's a complicated, noisy sort of a spot.
It's so damn big and so damned impersonal
That when you find a *person,* you have forgotten
That human beings exist and breed and die.'
'And have their tragedies,' Sam said, 'though it's not
The deaths that hit me but the way that man
Spoke of his wife.'
              I said, 'He'll get over that.'
'No,' said Sam, 'not him.' I said he was silly,
The doctor had called it shock. Sam shook his head.
I said, 'You always romanticize. You fill
Every occasional happening up to suit
Your particular disposition. You think of love
As beyond recovery, always the broken heart,
You love to think of it so, put romance above
The cure of the day by day.'
              He shook his head.
'You do the opposite, then, and do it from fear.
Shock or no shock, that was the essential truth;
You might go around the world and never hear
A man so patently speak the truth.' He turned
To Martin and said, 'And you? Isn't that clear?
What do you think?'
              'With you. Tom doesn't know
The roots of life, he's scratching the surface rough,
But he's scared of the deep bits.' Suddenly Sam laughed.
'I worried at leaving him. It was sort of tough,
Wasn't it, Tom? But you'll do, boy, you'll do.
You watch him. He's just a child, he has no sense.
He loves his tragedies and he eats them up,
He needs to learn.' They laughed together and then
Martin said, 'Yes, I know. He likes to be harrowed,
He's scared of a fine sharp plough.'
              That made me mad.
It was curious, two to one, they were strangers, too,
I was the one they knew, the bond they had
For a moment's meeting. Oh, I got over it,
But I've never got over the thought of the thin man, sadly
Moving off to the ambulance, thinking still:
I can trade the child and so get back my wife."

I paused and I asked, "Does it happen often so?"
"Not often," he said, "though men are always striving
Toward that one consummation. You will write poems
For many, many years. Do you think that ever
You'll write one satisfactory one? You might, you may.
But for that one, how often will you endeavour
To patch the imperfect, see the faulty line,
Go through depression at the constant failure?
Will you give up because you do not do it
Save in the few rare instances? The grail
Was sought by a host, but look, how many found it?
There's truth in 'Say not the struggle nought availeth.'
It happened to me: I touched the consummation—
I have fed upon this since."
                                    His words were echoed
By something within my mind: that Sam had said?
After we dropped that girl? It hung for a second
On the edge of my mind and vanished.
                                    He said, "Go on.
Your beards are growing."
                                    "They grew at Mineola.
We flew, it was grand, always with an instructor,
Everything headed for one great moment: solo.
My teacher (and Martin's) was nice, a civilian, called Marsh;
We flew for an hour a day, if we flew at all,
For the weather was tricky. We practised landings and take-
    offs,
Beginnings of acrobatics, such things as a stall,
And tail spins: air attacking the plane at wrong angles
And there is no lift and you find you have started to fall
As fast as the devil.
                                    But then came the great excitement:
I beat out Martin to solo. You see, one day,
After about ten hours of dual flying,
I landed the plane and Marsh called out to me 'Wait!'
He climbed down then and made as if to examine
Some part of the rudder. He moved away, a few yards,
And yelled to me, 'Take her away.'
                                    I just looked at him.
He said it again and grinned. My heart beat, hard,
And went to my stomach. I taxied to the field's end,
As far as I dared to take her. Oh, gosh! I wish
I could describe it to you, the first time up,

207

Alone, so much alone, the funny, vicious
Pulse of the heart in the tummy . . ."
(And the ground leaves you, and the yellow trees, you are
past them,
They are a golden hedge now, and the market gardens become
Alice's chess-board;
Your feet on the rudder are Agag's, treading delicately,
Your fingers clutch the stick with an extra pressure, lifting
Your plane, your own, up into the safe blue sky and away
From the enemy earth, with its terrible golden hedges,
The shadows of bare poles: the shadows of disaster
On the far flats of ground.
You cruise: but cautiously, as a burglar moves
In an unfamiliar house. The corners are taken gently,
You feel your heart respond like a spirit level
To the least banking of the plane's grey wings
In the unavoidable turn, and your mind repeats
Over and over: You must come down, you must land,
You must come down, it is safe here, you must come down,
You cannot be safe forever.
And the plane glides little by little to the increasing earth,
To the widening field, to the leaping growth of the golden
hedges
Till they are trees again and the shadows are lost
In the shafts of the deadly poles and the rhythm of wires
Slung between pole and pole . . .
And so, to the breath held, to the Agag feet,
To the touch of sweating hands, the earth is assaulted,
The brown and dusty earth, it is here, the slight bump,
The motion slowly lost in the long dust
That winds behind you, a flag for singular glory.)
". . . but once you're up,
It's wonderful, like being drunk, the sky's delicious,
The sky is safe, it's the landing again that scares you.
It scared me badly. I didn't want to come down,
I was frightened to turn, of the plane banking too much,
You might just slip. But after you've been around
In one great circle, you have to take a grip
And set your teeth and descend and you hope to God
You'll judge the landing and not crash into the trees
Or the telegraph wires. And then the wheels touch sod,
And the dust springs up and you stop the plane, as proud
As a man can be. You've done it. You've flown alone."

208

"I'd like to do that," said Grandfather.
                                    "Yes, you would.
You'd have eaten it up."
                          "It sounds like a lot of fun.
What happened next?"
                      "Oh, we just stayed there then
Till about November tenth. We must have flown
Five or six hours solo. Marsh would watch us.
Sometimes he'd go up too, to correct a fault.
Then on to the harder flying, the tight spirals,
The figure eights, the deliberate slips. We thought
That this was heaven after the Cornell school.
They gave more freedom, stopped treating you like a child,
You got time off. Martin was close behind me,
He caught me up before we left Long Island,
He had wonderful steady nerves—his dead-stick landings
(The motor is cut, is dead—you glide to the earth)
Were miraculous. He could land on a given mark—
That was another stunt—and fetch his berth
Like a clever sailor coming in to his mooring.
But the weather was too uncertain and too perverse.
They sent us south.
              I tried then to see Judith
But the orders were sudden, we had one day to spare,
She couldn't make it. Martin waited with me,
He said he wanted to see her: foul or fair,
He wanted to see my future wife. I told him
I'd never marry. He'd laugh at me. But then,
He was the marrying kind."
                      Grandfather laughed.
"What are you laughing at?"
                          "Because you meant
To describe yourself as a permanent bachelor."
"Martin used to say, 'When you marry, Tom,
They'll prosecute you for a case of misogynation.'
He used to use great five-dollar words, and some
Sounded funny to me, in his Iowa accent."
I paused to drink.
              "I suppose the letter did come
I wrote in July of the life at Ellington Field?
It was all hard work, but we loved it, Martin and I.
We stuck together, we were damn lucky that way.
Our books were equal—the same amount of flying—

209

We came together and got in the same squadron.
Sam was at Kelly Field, he flew over and met me
Once at the Rice Hotel—where the Kiwis sit
And do their looping around the mezzanine."
"What is a Kiwi?"
                              "A bird that has no wings,
We called Ground Officers that. To hear them whoop it
Up to a dumb blonde, you'd think they were Guynemer.
Well, our group progressed. We did cross-country flying,
Did acrobatics, the Immelmans, the loops,
The Falling Leaf, whip-stalls and barrel-rolls,
Dual then solo. Then came Formations, suited
To three planes or to more. Then long cross-country,
Over to Beaumont, maybe, a hundred miles
Of great flat country, but something there to watch for,
A bridge in the building, or maybe once in a while
A cattle round-up, like ants from the high air,
Crawling about in the dust. And then one day
You find you are there, you've done it, your name is posted,
You've done your trick and you've got your R.M.A.
It wasn't official of course, but you knew it would be.
God! were we proud as hell! We went in to Houston
And found a guy who had flown a lot of whisky
Up from New Orleans in a crate for pigeons,
And we all got blotto. And then we got some girls,
And got them tight, etcetera. A way of bridging
The awful let-down of the too-strung nerves.
Don't blame us."
                    "No, I shan't."
                                        "I knew you wouldn't.
It didn't happen often. I wrote to Judith,
And said I loved her. Drunk. I knew that I shouldn't,
I carried the letter round for a couple of days
And then destroyed it. When I was sober again
I didn't know my mind. I didn't tell Martin,
He'd have called me a fool and said that I wasn't sane
On the subject of women. But then, he wasn't in love,
He just had his fine, Iowa thoughts about it:
Men and women as being made for each other,
And marriage the only way. He'd say, 'A spouse
Is the half of a husband, and marriage makes a whole,
That's the way God intended it, there's no doubt,
You muddy your life by doubting, you wish to see

Your fields grow rich but you're scared of the dull and daily
Cultivation that makes them grow and blossom
Under your calloused hand. You're scared of failure,
So scared you won't even try, but the fields are there,
They grow for someone, they even grow for nature.'
In some ways Martin was older than me. In some
He was so much younger—yet a practical creature
Who looked so steadily out from a narrow life—
And gaps of ignorance you could fly a plane through.
But he always set me thinking.
                                    I used to think
When we did the long cross-country and the plane flew
Over the flat fields and the unfenced miles,
With an observer along. I'd think the same few
Thoughts as we went our way: Do I love Judith?
Would she marry me? Do I want to get married?
Am I afraid, and is my fear a wisdom
Sprung from sound instinct? How does a man carry
The load of the years of marriage, after the fever
Of the first love is past? Such thinking ended
Eternally with the vision of that one woman
Under your hands, your touch, your heads bending
Ever together, and thought was destroyed and vanished.
There was nothing but feeling left, and a sweating palm
On the stick you clutched, the sense of the blood mounting
Into the head and behind the eyes, to drum
In the pit of the echoing ears."
                                    Grandfather stirred.
"Drink up," he said, "port does you good, not harm,
It loosens your tongue. I never have heard you talk
As well as this before."
                        "Look out," I said,
"You'll make me feel self-conscious."
                                    "Oh, no. I won't.
I'll give you courage for the next time, instead.
You can remember this."
                        "Perhaps. See here,
Are you too tired now, would you like to stop?"
"Tired? God damn it, boy, I can talk all night,
I haven't got anything else to do. Bilge and slop!
You talk like this to Judith?"
                            "No. I fumble my words,
I've always fumbled—everything. Well, to get on,

We did Formation, we shot with a camera-gun,
The observer shot, I piloted. Then we'd bomb
Over a house like a camera obscura,
The plane's clear image, it's tiny ghost, upon
The long white table in the dark of the room.
And then night flying. Wonderful! I loved that.
Scary at first, but afterwards you became
Sure of the night. You'd rise up over the flat
White-lit field and out to the dark sky
Where the stars were cold above you and warm below,
The constellations of Houston flung like golden
Stars, Andromeda thus and Perseus so,
Gold on the black beneath, and perhaps you'd see
The last grey skirts of light in the lifted west
In an edge of day forgotten an hour since.
And always then in the darkness, I could test
The memory of that girl, for then her image
Rose so clearly, but cool. Those were the best
Moments of my remembering. Then she seemed
Close and friendly and warm for the long days
Of a long life together. Under the sun
I thought of her as a lover. Under the rays
Of the Texas stars, to the roar of the plane at night,
To the sense of owning the whole great empty heaven
And the world beneath, and my destiny, and the span
Of life forever, I thought of her as the leaven
To life and living."
                              I rose and crossed the room,
Looked out of the window. I could see Chepaug Light
Flash in the blackness and I could hear the wind
Whisper and whistle in the dark cracks of night,
And the incessant wash of the unseen waves.
I was alive to hear it.
                              I said, "That rightly
Brings me around to Martin. We all flew down
To Galveston Bay and shot at the targets placed
On the long mud-flats. I can still smell them. Martin
Flew too low and he crashed at a frightful pace,
And the plane rolled over once and it caught on fire,
But he crawled out on the mud.
                              I went to see him
Up at the hospital. There wasn't much to see:
A mouth and bandages. He was just in a dream,

A fever world. He didn't even know me.
They let me stay five minutes. I said, 'It's Tom.'
He stirred a little. I said it again, and louder,
But the Nurse said, 'Let him be, don't be so dumb,
He don't know anyone.' So I sat down and waited,
A funny sense in the pit of my stomach, numb,
Not knowing what to do. He spoke, quite clearly:
'The silo's got to be mended. It's got to be mended.'
I said, 'We'll mend it.' Then he was still again.
The Nurse said, 'That's the twentieth time he's mentioned
The silo now.' I asked her to go away.
She said, 'It's against the rules. You've got three minutes.'
I asked if he'd pull through. She wrinkled her nose.
She said, 'Oh, he might, but there's really no hope in it,'
And shrugged her shoulders. She was a pretty girl,
Red-headed. I said to her, 'You're as pretty as hell.
I'd like to play games with you, pretty games at night,
I'd step you out for a nickel. You might be swell.'
She giggled and smirked and said that fliers were fresh.
I told her, 'Yes, we're fresh, but hot as well.
Would you go tonight?' She looked at me and nodded.
'You look O.K.,' she said. So we made a date.
I rose and took her behind the screen and kissed her,
Though I'd just as soon have kicked her. I said, 'That's great.
Now listen, sweetie, just leave me alone a minute,
Just for two minutes, nobody else will know.'
She said, 'You sure can kiss. O.K. I'll leave you,
But for God's sake make no noise.' She turned to go
And said, 'I'll wait for you, handsome.' And then she left.
I went to his bedside and I whispered, 'Martin,
It's Tom, just Tom, do you know me?' He said nothing
For a little while and then he said, 'For certain.
Stone-wall Tom, cut up into little fields,
Afraid of his woman. They've pulled the God-damned curtains
Over the parlour windows, why should it be dark?
But Tom was a long time back.' I held his hand.
He said, 'I'm glad they're mending that bitch of a silo.
Now I'll go fishing.'
                              I sat quite still then . . . and . . .
She came without my hearing and rumpled my hair.
She said, 'You shouldn't have touched him, it's time you
     started—
A big grown man and holding a man's hand, too.'

I said, 'You've a lot to learn,' and I rose and departed.
But she just stared after me. Maybe it was a cheat.
I didn't care just then. He died in the night,
In the little mean hours, in the lonely hours,
But they wouldn't let me go near. Perhaps they were right.
I didn't care much by then. When I thought of Martin,
It made me think of Judith. I tried to fight
The double image, but even the drinking failed me,
It made me feel more lonely, I'd think of both.
That was the way he died."
                              "That happened when?"
His voice was gentle and seemed to be remote.
I said, "In the end of August. About three weeks
Before I crashed."
                      He said, "It's a tragic tale."
"I shouldn't have told you about the nurse, bad taste."
He answered: "Heave taste to leeward and so sail
Close to the wind of living. That shook you up?"
"It made me sad, depressed me. I needed and missed
The lift he gave me. He took me beyond myself.
You know what I mean?"
                          "Yes, surely, a catalyst."
"It left me low as the belly of any snake,
I'd felt so high and went so down with this."
"Each hill that we manufacture makes a valley,"
He said; "It is always so. Tell the rest of the yarn."
I thought for a moment. "There isn't much more to tell,
Except what went on inside. We went right on.
We flew and shot, and we did some more night flying,
Tricky formations.
                      I wrote to Judith again,
I felt as if Martin made me begin that letter,
Though I wanted to write it. The hand didn't guide the pen,
The pen ran away with the hand. A silly letter,
Proposing marriage, or more truly, demanding,
To save my life from the loneliness that his death
Left inside me. Now I don't understand it,
Don't see how I did it or why. I got no answer.
I waited awhile and then I began to be angry
And wrote again. It was worse than the first, it said
All sorts of foolish things, it brought in death,
It talked about going abroad—Sam had his orders,
He was in heaven—that was our daily breath:

214

Getting to France—oh hell, it was just a rotten
Sort of a wail for comfort. And then I waited,
Waited and waited, and cooled off a little.
The days slipped by, I began to think I hated
Myself for writing but couldn't recall the words
Of what I'd written.
                    You see what a poop I'd been?
From doubtful loving to sudden command to marry;
From hesitation, from deep distrust, from keen
Desire to work alone, to a sudden rushing
To a woman's arms, for life—no space between
The extremes of living.
                       And then I got my answer.
It came one morning. I read it. Amazing letter.
I guess she's got a temper—I'll give you the gist.
She wrote, You are sick. Get well. When you are better,
After a time has passed, write me again;
Write to me as a woman you love, and not
As a hot-water-bottle to warm your present illness;
Write when the war is over and you've forgotten
The war's dramatics. I'll have no fatherless children,
Marriage is fine but not with an absentee lover,
Stranger returning to his stranger wife.
She wrote one phrase: 'I know you are torn and suffer
Because of Martin, but friends go on for ever,
We must be friends before we try the other
Love that I wish for too.' "
                           Grandfather cried,
"By God, you've got a jewel—if you can get her.
Where did she learn such things?"
                                  "She's wise," I said.
"She is! she is! Was there any more in the letter?"
"No, that's all."
                 "Go on then, tell me the rest.
What happened then?"
                    "I crashed."
                                 "Oh—yes, I see.
That was the letter you spoke about at first."
"Yes, that's the one. It did something odd to me,
Something that hadn't happened before. It took
My mind off the job of flying. I thought at first
Nothing could do that to me.
                            Well, then the pain,

215

The hospital after. The first three days were the worst
Before I got my corset. To move at all
Was pretty fearful. I just lay there and cursed
Whenever they touched me. The headache was awful too,
And the breathing hurt, except when codein began
Just little by little to sweep the pain away,
Till presently it was gone and then there ran
A sense of well-being, better than ever before,
All through the body, and then the drowsiness came
And you edged your way into the down of sleep."
"I know it well," he said, "I have felt the same
Sense of relief, retreat to sleep."
                                        "Oh well,
It wasn't serious. There was fluid the fourth day,
Down in my chest, it came when the pain first eased.
They let me sit up then, and after my stay
In bed, it was wonderful. Bed for concussion, of course,
But after that danger was over, it was O.K.
To sit. You couldn't be comfortable lying down.
Oh, they were thorough, but hurried. They tested eyes,
They looked at the ear drums, they watched me for stiff neck,
They never left me alone, had a new surprise
For every hour: something more they could do
To make you jumpy. Well, hospitals can be dull,
You're glad of the fussing, you're glad when they gaily say
That you've broken only ribs not the base of your skull,
It makes it sound so little. And yet there are times
When you wish to God they'd only leave you alone,
Just let you be. The nurse was plain and kind,
Not like the red-haired wench. She was rather prone
To spread her duties out, fifteen minutes between,
Instead of getting it over and getting it done.
It wasn't that she was unkind, but that she fussed.
I'd try to think, or I'd try to plan in my head
Or focus my mind on Judith, and there she'd be
With her damn thermometer, sponge for a bath in bed,
Something to eat or something to ease the cough
That hurt so like the devil. That cough was fierce,
It stabbed in the side, I have it still, a little,
A light, dry cough, no pain. It used to pierce
Into the ribs like a knife.
                              But this is dull.
You know pain better than I. It healed in time.

216

There's nothing left but the cough and the dizzy spells
That come from exertion.
                        Nothing is left—save the line
Of images on an endless belt that pass
Before my eyes in the dark, and the half-sublime
And wholly terrible dreams that fill the night
Between the short spells of my uncertain sleep.
What can I do? Shall I ever get back to war?
Would I keep my nerve to fly? Have I nerve to keep?
It makes me flinch to think of a mounting plane,
I feel so frightened now, by night and day,
Scared of myself, you see.
                        And I never wrote
Again to Judith. What could I find to say?
I used to be sure about this: now I am not sure.
What shall I do? Marriages turn to stone,
The man can grow to hate and the woman to hate,
And I am an artist. Shouldn't I be alone,
Travel untrammelled without the awful chains
Whose links are the trifles that clutter the prison of home?
I want to be happy, to do. And I love Judith.
Maybe she meant what she said and would love me, too—
How do I know? It might be the deep dark pit
Of misery for us both."
                        He said, "Why, you . . ."
But checked himself, and we sat in silence then
For a second or so. I could hear the night waves ride,
Charging the shore.
                        He said, "Blast! my cigar's gone out!
Get me a match, boy."
                        I struck a match by my side
And carried it over: it made me feel so young,
The echo made happy the child that his great, strong voice
Would rise so soon to comfort.
                        He puffed his cigar.
He said, "There is no answer. It's a free choice.
You make it yourself, no man can make it for you.
Marriage can be completion or be the void,
The emptiest desert of all; sometimes it turns
Into the quicksilver that eludes the touch
And breaks to many running, separate drops,
The epitome of futility and flux,
Ungoverned, ungovernable. Yet marriage can

'Fasten him as a nail in a sure place'
To borrow Isaiah's phrase.
                              But let that go.
It's not important, yet. You are just a case
Of a boy whose nerves are rocky because the body
Is still unwell. Take time. It all takes time.
Let the poor body heal and the mind will heal.
You cannot foresee the future. There is no crime
In being afraid, but to conquer fear will need
The body forgotten, subdued. Let the spirit climb
Onto the sure rock of its health. This war
Has been a long time: now it is almost spent,
You may not need to justify nerve that flew
Once without hesitation. I know. I went
Through the dark days of wondering and of fear,
I had to wait on the spirit's slow increase
Into the power of all its yesterdays,
Cut suddenly apart.
                        In the search for peace
You must choose and mould the choice to the way you go
When the way seems right again—while it still seems right.
You look for happiness. Don't. The world is dark,
We stumble through it, my boy, it is mostly night
On an unknown road. The only road you see
Is the road behind, visible in the bright
And phosphorescent glow of decaying days
Heaped up and weighty. There is no happiness
Sure to the grasp, but sorrow and grief are sure.
Yet we persist, and persisting, manifest
That joy is in the struggle, that we can build
Tall towers of sharp, small stones that cut our feet:
From towers such as these the world looks large,
And strangely beautiful, yes, and strangely sweet
And still to be desired.
                            The single man
Governs his destiny: he goes his road
Untrammelled, free—or so he thinks and hopes—
Forswearing ties, forswearing all the load
Of petty domestic trifles heaped and piled
On the path he has forsworn. There is no cloud
Over his sun? His pain shall first begin
With the brief sight of someone's sleeping child
Bearing a name and future, but not his,

Into indefinite futures. There's a wild
Loneliness in the morning light that shines
On solitude, and night can trap the single
Heart to its own despair. Content wears thin
In any woman's arms when daylight brings
Only the body's satisfactory surfeit
And day's continuing, solitary, lonely
Passage through its long hours.

                    Now I have learned
The spirit feeds on a plant that first was sown
In the young years, and of its delicate fruit
Only that ripens that has a long time grown:
But the best was tended by someone else's hand.
Here at the fringe and end of life, I eat
Always the old fruit, and its taste is ever
Nourishing—though the bitter outweighs the sweet."
He paused for a moment.

                "Choose. There are many ways.
Choose from the consonance of the mind and heart.
To hell with happiness! This is life, it's life,
There is no easy way, nor a road apart
That dodges the hills and valleys.

                 No man that lived
Has yet succeeded in covering up his heart,
Locking it safe away. He gives it, always.
Maybe he gives it to his horse. He parts
With his immunity. Even a dog can cut
Deep to the seat of feeling. Love is barter,
A quid pro quo, and places, houses, work,
Mistresses, anything, give back to you
Only the feeling you have given. Or worse,
Receive, and do not give, till love is through
One-sided giving and turns to the knife of hate
Clipping the flesh.

              And yet there's little strength
In singleness to resist. But two can breed
A courage greater than both could rear at length
In solitary search.

             Oh, life is grand,
It's all mixed up together, the good and the bad.
You sort it out, it's a game: you lose: you win—
But never by cowardice, never by saying sadly,
'This is the way to unhappiness.' Let it come,

For in spite of you, it comes.

                                    I married. I had
A wife that became me and I merged in her.
Am I the loser? Was she? It tied me down,
My thoughts were given colour because her love
Was the pressing need, and the pressure always bound,
But binding, gave a strength, like a barrel's hoop
And the staves contained their matter, and stood up firm,
And the damned old keg still holds, though it leaks a bit,
For the hoops were borrowed and soon must be returned.
Dixi! Enough! It is time we went to bed.
Think, think, my boy!"

                                He rang the bell by his side.
"Charles will be tired of waiting." He smiled and said,
"Get after Judith—and let me see her, too,
For I may lose my heart—or you, your head
And a good thing too."

                          "I'm grateful."

                                  He smiled again.
He said, quite softly, "No matter how you may choose,
I am your grandfather, you have had my love.
You have it now. It is something you cannot lose."
Then he called, "God damn it, Charles, have you gone to
    sleep?
It is past my time," and he laughed, and said, "By George,
It is past it more ways than one."

YOUR madness is my sanity. Do shells
Proclaim the wind in echoing the sea,
Or are these ghosts of a dead tide whose swells
Make prisoned music through eternity?
My hatred is your love. Are these wild gales
That press September to the golden fall,
Children of Equinox, or the sun that fails
To halt the turbulence of its cloudy pall?
Your God is not for me. Shall you and I
See more because the leaves have fallen, or less

Now there are but bare branches on the sky
Where once the foliage tempted us to guess?
My madness is your sanity; let it be:
You'd wear my madness with poor dignity.

✦   ✦

I WALKED the woods with Judith on the day
That the war stopped: I took my gun along,
Hoping for partridges, or perhaps a duck
In the long coiling where Deer River ran
Through wavering reeds. The hollows of the ground
Gave forth a chill and moisty scented air
Of earth thin upon sand, and here and there
Our feet were carpeted on bronze pile of leaves
Where bear-berry grew in topiary islands
That only time had clipped with slow intent.
The full red harvest of the maples lay
Reaped by the sickle of November's wind.
We hardly spoke. We watched my pointer bitch,
Let her run out, while we admired the white
Of her swift, graceful body through the brown
Of stubborn oak leaves. She would disappear,
Make her long circuit and come back to me.
I'd pat her then, with love run down my fingers
Into her shining coat; she'd push her nose
Against my knee.   "She loves you," Judith said;
"And now where next? I'd like to see you shoot.
I never have. We've hunted—oh, next week
There is a drag at Penny Hill on Friday,
Could you come out?"
                          I patted Speckles' head
And said, "I'd love to, if they'll let me go,"
And added foolishly, before I'd thought,
"There's lots you haven't seen me do, like shooting.
You've seen me dance, but never seen me fly.
You've never seen me crash a plane."
                          She cried:
"Leave it alone, Tom! I thought we had agreed
We'd let that ride? The war is over now."
I said, "It's over. It seems a funny thing
On this day of all days to seize a gun

And rush out to the wilderness to kill
When all the million guns have stopped. It's done:
Now what's a uniform?"
                              "I like you better
In these old clothes."
                              "But how shall I retrieve
My failure in these clothes?"
                              "You worry so!
Be patient, Tom. You're tired. Shall we go home?"
"Not yet—a little longer. Just a little.
In spite of all my woes, I find it heaven
To tramp the woods with you. I'll bottle it.
It just pops out. Come on, we'll walk a way.
There is one place below where the duck use—
They may be there."
                              We walked on through the pines.
There was a thin path. On its springy moss
Our feet were noiseless. I could hear the wind
Rich in the tree tops. Now and then it came
Down in a whirl, we'd feel the force of it:
Its chill and evening power numbed my fingers
On the cold steel I held. We did not talk,
But walked in silence, Speckles called to heel,
Judith behind me.
                              So for half a mile,
Till the green pines gave way to sandy flats
Patterned with tracks of deer: across a wide
Ridge of the low and leafless huckleberry
Hedging the wilder undergrowth and oaks,
And down a steep slope to bog meadow grown
To great tough grasses and the scratching twigs
Of giant blueberries. There was a path,
The remnant of a road: we followed it,
Slowly and carefully; then all at once,
Rounding a clump of cedar to the still
Deeps of a river pool. Its silver ran
Empty of life, flawed by descending wind.
I peered in disappointment up and down:
The river stretched away to east and west:
There were no ducks.
                              I said, "Well, nothing here.
Too bad."
                              "Oh dear," she said, "But what a shame!

I'd hoped we'd find 'em."

                  "So had I. My luck
Is badly out. It seems to run in waves."
She flushed and said, "And yet—you telephoned
Only this morning to see if I was free
To come and shoot with you. On this one day
When all the world is crazy and the streets
Are just an orgy. After a whole year,
Is that such awful luck?"

                 I felt the blood
Run to my face. "But you're not luck," I said,
"You're something different."

                  "What?"

                        "I do not know."
I heard my own words and I turned to her
And said, "That's been my war-cry: Do not know."
She looked at me and smiled and slowly said,
"Let's try again, Tom."

               I could not answer her
Because I did not dare: she put a meaning
Into her words that stirred and frightened me
In my long indecision.

             We left the bog.
I let the bitch run out, to look for partridge;
We should not come back to the water soon,
For we were crossing a wide neck of land
Where the long curve of river made a bend
Around a high peninsula. Our way
Followed the path to join a sandy road.
Here oak grew small and birches tall and white,
And pine was mixed with both. The land was grey,
Over its poverty, with the reindeer moss.
We walked now side by side, but did not talk:
The only sounds the crunch the gravel made
Beneath my heavy boots, the occasional
Rustle and snap as the white pointer pushed
Through the brown thickness of the scrub-oak leaves.
But then we heard another sound: it grew
From a soft metal tinkle to a clanging
Loud, rhythmical and strange.

                 We turned a bend
Around a group of arbor-vitae clumped
In an old burying-ground, and there we saw

Against the greening blue of evening sky,
A large man's figure on the rutted road,
Approaching us. In two great fists he held
The handles of a rattling iron barrow
Whose steel-shod wheel made sparks against the gravel
And banged and clattered as it rolled around
Upon its twisted axle.
                  We stopped and stared.
He stopped as well. The sudden silence lent
A carrying power to the sound of wind
Caught in the taller pines.
                  I looked at him:
A powerful figure in a cotton shirt,
Blue denim trousers; a familiar face
Made strange, unplaceable, by a great blond beard
That covered up his neck. He stared at us,
Looking awhile at Judith, then at me,
A careful look, with something tense and taut
About his waiting pose. Then suddenly
He burst out laughing, dropped the barrow's handles,
Rubbed his huge hands together and cried out:
"Well, well. Growed up! Walkin' out evenings now,
But spring's the season, fall's a poor, mean time.
No leaf to hide you. No. No place to hide."
He laughed again: then stopped, at once. He said,
Running his left hand through his golden beard,
Then up his face until his fingers lay
Hidden in the long hair upon his head,
"The leaves is fallen, mostly. Ain't no use
In trying to hide when all the trees is bare."
Then, with another change, he straightened up
And spoke in a flat, ordinary sort of voice,
Saying, "How-do. Your name is Tom, or was."
Judith had drawn close to me: I could feel
Her hand upon my arm. But all at once
That flat voice stirred my memory, and I said:
"Why hello, Jake. Jake Caswell. That's the name.
What are you doing here?"
                  He cried, "By guy!
He knew me, beard and all!" He looked around,
Nervous and apprehensive, and he whispered,
"I hide, I do. Ain't no one knows but you.
I hide and push my barrow, back and forth,

So folks won't find our house. Each night, each evening,
I give the wheel a spin. I ain't done nothing:
Folks haven't got no use for me. Well then,
I got no use for folks. Except for two.
And—" here he glanced again, a circling look—
"Ain't no one sees them, no, nor knows them, neither,
And when they walk, they go as silently
As deer does, while I push the barrow where
She makes her cletterin'. You can't keep a child
Housed up forever, can you? You might have children?"
I shook my head. "I wouldn't say you was married,
Nor wouldn't say you wasn't."

                            I answered, "No."
He sighed and said, "Well, you got time." Again
His manner changed. He looked at me and said,
"Your father fired her. I couldn't find her.
I looked an' looked. You see? I ain't forgot.
You told your grandpa and he fired me.
I ain't forgot that neither. But you was little,
You didn't know much. But your grandpa is good,
He helped me, yessir, and he stood by me
When folks got angry at me. I don't forget.
You're a grown man. You got a girl along.
You'll tell no stories now. You used to come
And shoot my bow. You see? I don't forget.
They want to find me. But you wouldn't tell:
You wouldn't dast to." Then he bent his body
And seized the barrow and banged it on the road
With fearful strength. "I got to make a cletter
Just now and then."

                    I heard a rustling grow
In the thick bushes near us.

                          He cried, "What's that?"
I said, "It's just my dog." I whistled then
And Speckles came out from the neighbouring clump
And stood and wagged her tail and looked at me,
Her mouth wide open and her tongue a-flap
In joy and eagerness.

                  Jake said, "Ah! gunning!
Had any luck at all?" It was so normal,
His old flat voice, I almost jumped. I said,
"No, not a thing. I'd hoped to find some duck."
He dropped the barrow again and said, "Ah, guns!

You'd ought to use a bow an' arrer. Them—"
He pointed to my gun—"makes too much noise.
An arrer's quiet."

        I asked, "Still got your bow?"
He looked around him and he answered, "Sure,
Got that one and two others. Make my own.
It's so we feed. Don't no one know. Come on.
I'll get you duck. You foller me." He started
Down a steep slope I knew led riverward.
As he moved off, Judith came nearer me
And whispered, "Tom, I'm frightened by that man.
He's mad."

        I said, "Don't worry. He means no harm,
Just touched."

        Jake stopped and called again, "Come on!"
But Judith would not move. He climbed again
Till he was near us. He looked at us and said,
"You wouldn't be scared now—would ye? I'm a man
Is kind and homely. Foller me, go easy,
Keep your dog in." He grinned and turned again
Down the steep slope, and went on fifty yards,
Then stopped and waited. Judith clutched my arm,
And asked in a low voice, "Must we go, Tom?"
I said, "We'd better. It's quite safe." I laughed,
Saying, "You're silly." I had no time for more;
Nor wish to tell her how he frightened me,
How madness terrified. "Take hold of me."
She took my left arm firmly in her grasp
And we moved then and followed him. I thought,
You must not anger crazy men: pretend,
Follow a little, and then give him the slip.
If we leave now, he'll follow: that's not wise,
Work to his present humour.

        He moved ahead
In the grey light of the late afternoon,
Enormous, silent, with his beefy hands
Hung open, swinging with his clumsy stride
So nearly noiseless. He did not take us far:
We passed great oaks that sheltered groves of birch,
We skirted clumps of laurel huge and thick,
We dropped into the hollows where small growth
Made progress dusty. Poor Speckles, held at heel,
Reared back her head to avoid the whipping twigs

226

Our double progress cocked to quick release.
Jake stopped and beckoned us. We approached to him.
"See there," he said in a low voice, and pointed.
"There is the river. Just go down the bank
And set along her edge. Don't make no noise,
Sound carries hereabouts, they got sharp hearin',
You jest set quiet. The ducks is up above,
Only a little way. I'll walk up river,
Get me above them and I'll scare 'em up,
They'll fly right over ye. They foller water.
Shoot high, I ain't so very far away,
You listen for the quackin', that's the soign,
I don't go hollerin' evenings hereabouts:
Who knows what ears there be?" He turned away
Swiftly and heavily, and he disappeared
Behind a clump of laurel. So we stood
Unmoving till the little sounds he made
Had ceased entirely.
                    Then I felt Judith tremble,
And our eyes met. I smiled. She said, "Let's run.
Can't we get out of this?" I thought about it.
"He'd hear us, surely, and he'd follow us.
We'd meet him at the car, perhaps before.
It isn't wise to anger men like him,
He's harmless now. Look, Judith, further on,
Where the small oaks are growing. We can hide,
It is beyond the place he pointed out
And screened by trees, even from where we stand.
He'll come and miss us. Then he'll go away,
And think we are the crazy ones." I smiled
As best I could, though smiling seemed to take
Tremendous effort then.
                    But still she stood
Clutching my arm, and did not move. I said,
"Come, Judith, come. Do as I tell you to."
She said, "And Speckles? She is white. He'll see her."
I answered, "We can hide her. Wait and see."
She looked at me and sighed. She said, "It makes
A horrid, sneaky ending to a day
That once began so well. I'm frightened now,
I hate this hiding."
                    "But I have my gun."
"You wouldn't use it? Tom, you wouldn't shoot?"

"Not if I could avoid it."

                  "Oh, not at all!
Please tell me, not at all?"

               I said, "Be still.
We cross those bridges when we come to them.
Come on, the time grows short."

                   But still she held
Hard to my arm and did not move. I jerked
My arm from out her grasp and seized her wrist
And shook her, slightly, and I said, "Look here,
You're acting like a fool. There's nothing wrong.
The man is touched, that's all. It's easier
To let him miss us than to get away
By ordinary means. He wants no harm.
You'll come now, or I'll carry you." She cried,
"I may be scared, but who gave you the right
To order me?" I said, "The time and place.
You'll walk or you'll be carried. Which?"

                         She frowned,
Looked at me hard, I felt her temper rise,
And wondered if she'd lose it. But she said,
"Go on. I'll follow you."

                 I led her then
To a thick growth of little oaks that lay
Like a small point in front of the dense laurel.
I placed her in them, and I placed myself
And called my Speckles and put her by my side
And covered her with leaves and with the scarf
I'd worn around my throat. I said, "Remember,
When he returns, stay still and don't look up.
Look down upon the ground. One sees the white
Of faces quickly."

            So we sat and waited,
And time crept past. One heard the little sounds:
The shrilling of a chipmunk, river-music,
The rustle of a wing, the dusty noise
Of Speckles' tail a-wag in the dead leaves
At the least motion of my body near her.
I looked at Judith, and she looked at me.
Her eyes were large and round. She did not smile
But eyed me strangely, with her lips compressed
In a firm line. I thought: she hates me now
Because I ordered her about. I manage

228

To wreck all matters. Then I thought of Jake,
His bulk and the queer eyes, and felt my stomach
Contract in fear. I thought: make up your mind;
If there is trouble, shoot, and shoot at once.
So I decided.
                    We sat in silence thus
Eternal minutes.
                    Then I heard a sound,
A distant roar and placed it, and my mind
Leaped to the river, saw the invisible scene,
Watched the black duck that vaulted from the shattered
Mirror of their content with flailing wings.
And then I heard their quacking, and I heard
The sharper whistle of their wings in flight
And saw them stream down river, black and swift,
And squarely over the small bay where Jake
Had wished to place us. But we did not move.
I held my hand on Speckles, pressing hard
To still her excited movement. Judith sat
With eyes cast down, and motionless. I felt
A sense of foolishness sweep over me
And knew I blushed with it.
                    But still we sat
Wordless and still. I listened to the wind.
I peered up river and saw the day was gone
And evening coming. The bare bushes lay
Blue and remote; the river held the light
In an increasing radiance against
The darker banks.
                    I raised my eyes and saw
Jake Caswell standing in a clearing, sharp
Against the green of laurel leaves. He'd come
Without my hearing.
                    There he stood and looked,
Peering below him. Then he moved again,
A pace or two and looked and looked again.
He did not speak or call. For a long time
He waited motionless, save for his head
That turned first this way and then that. At last
He shook his head. He raised his hands up then
And put his fingers in his mouth and gave
A strange and piercing, bubbling sort of whistle
Like a deer calling. Then he dropped his hands

229

And waited motionless. The minutes passed:
I dared not look at Judith. At length I heard
A little rustling, the crackle of dry twigs:
And saw Jake turn: and saw a woman step
Out of the bushes.
                    She was small and dark,
She wore a black shawl and a bright green skirt
Acid in colour like a copper flame.
She carried a baby cradled in her arms,
Wrapped in a blanket.
                    I thought: she is a negress—
No—perhaps Indian, I cannot tell.
She went to Jake. He smiled at her. He laid
His great hand gently on her head and stroked
Her black and shining hair. She smiled at him.
He touched the child. And said, "All right?"
                                      "All right,"
The woman answered. Jake looked round him then,
The nervous hunted look. He said, "They've gone.
Tom Cottrell and his woman. They were here,
I sent them duck but they were scared and left,
Scared of old Jake." She raised her head and laughed.
He laughed and patted her and said again,
"Scared of old Jake. Of me—and you—and her—"
He touched the child. "Why, ain't that silly?" Then
His whole expression changed. "Get back," he said,
"We got no business standing here. You go,
You stick to cover. I'll get to the barrow,
I'll . . . " here he looked around him. Then he raised
One hand again and ran it through his beard
And up his face to hide it in his hair
And stood so, awkwardly and lost. But then
He kissed her suddenly and smiled and said,
"Jake won't let nothing harm you." Then he turned
And left her quickly, noisily. I could trace
His furious progress. Still the woman stood
Smiling and looking after him. She sighed,
Shifted the baby, turned and disappeared
Softly and swiftly.
                    A short space of time
The silence lasted. But from far away
We heard a clang and then another clang
And then the metal clatter of the barrow

230

Grew soft and softer till at last it came
As distant music on the pebbled road
Off in the twilight.
                    For a little while
We sat in silence. I looked at Judith then:
She too was smiling and her eyes were bent
On the now empty clearing where they'd stood
To play their scene. I did not want to speak:
There were no proper words for this. I felt
My whole heart rise to Judith in a wave
Of terrible longing: my whole life lay hemmed
For that one instant in the small, contained
Circle of her warm smile; and yet I knew
We could not stay in this protracted pause
Between two ways of being. Through my mind
I heard the words that I should say. I stirred.
The leaves about me rustled: Speckles rose,
And shook herself. I said, "I've been a fool.
For a long time. But now I know, at last.
I love you more than anything on earth
And earth is all I know."
                        She turned her head,
Unsmiling now and looked at me. "And I.
I'll walk your woods with you." I took her hand
And kissed it, gently, and I said, "I'll push
The barrow down the road of every day
Until its noise is music in our ears,
A wall of music to protect us."
                                So
We sat unmoving till presently we felt
The petty particles of disjointed life
Cleave to large unity, and we bent our heads
Each to the other, till our lips were joined
In consonance with the echo of the metal
Music that turned our dissonance into love
No longer sundered.

2

The dusk was a pall: so hidden
We drove in the dusk, in the darkness soft
There were no looks and no words forbidden:
The ties and the bonds were doffed,

And the tongue was entranced with freedom and spoke of
    the heart
Till the road was the way of life: the road that by day we
    had ridden
In silence; our souls were borne up in the dark, not apart:
From the world of our earth-days reft, we flew through the
    sky aloft.

This shall come and shall go in a flash:
The touch of her hand on my own could bring
The sound of music, the cymbal's crash,
The pain of the strings that sing,
Till the world was no longer: was turned to an essence, an
    urge;
It was turned to the fury of music, notes that can strike and
    can lash:
It was turned to the fusion of being, two spirits that merge
From our bodies forgotten a space—yet the flight from our
    flesh took wing.

We drove through the dusk, two lovers,
The path of our light like a path of flame
That ever more winding road uncovers—
Oh, never again the same!
Ahead in the darkness awaits unbelievable end:
It is here: it is now. Time begins. And yet the fused spirit
    hovers
In the air of its passion; is severed; the wings descend—
Let us kiss to be joined! But the spirit was trapped in the
    fleshly frame.

We speak, little words: My hand,
We are here, let us go within, let us tell,
Will he like me, be kind? He will understand
He will love you: I love you so well.
So the spirits are cloistered again in the wall of our speech:
Yet they beat—the breath in our mouth is a pulse of the heart
    that was fanned
By the flutter of wings we have seen, that were once within
    reach,
And we move to the rhythm we felt before the wings
    trembled and fell.

There lay a great space of time between me and the door:
It was palpable, like a mist. I looked and I said,
"See, this is Grandfather's house." I would have said more
But Judith pulled back and whispered, "I'm shy. Let's go.
I don't want to see him, anyone. Take me home."
I looked at her and I smiled and I said, "You're afraid?
Afraid of an old man, sitting at home alone?
He will love you, just as I do. Be kind and come,
He has been a part of me and he is a part,
You must share him, too."

                She drew a deep, long breath,
Said, "If he is yours, he's mine. With all my heart.
Kiss me—to give me courage." We kissed. The fire
Ran in my blood; in my temples: my breath came hard.
We ceased and we swayed. The world became all black,
I reached for the door, it was gone; but I felt her hand
Suddenly strong on my arm and I heard her voice
Cry from a distance, "Tom, are you ill, can you stand?"
Then the blood retreated and left me trembling now,
And I saw her shape in the dark and an oval face
Peering up into mine. I said, "It is gone,
It was just that it made me dizzy, it's too much haste,
We have been so far."

             I reached and I rang the bell
And I heard its answering tinkle away and away
In the distant rooms of the house. We stood quite still
In silence now, and I thought, If I even sway
It will frighten Judith; be strong, be steady and strong.
And I suddenly thought of Martin. How could I pay
A debt that was owed to the dead? and I saw the fields
Of the buckwheat ripen, my mind recalled stone walls,
And a nurse in a white cap with her bright red hair,
And the image of Clare, and the Persian curtain falls
With a small quiver, and Father's voice in the dark,
And the doors of music, the slap of the silly cards:
But this was Judith. And the door opened wide
And a voice said, "Evening. Gracious, you're white as lard,
Come into the warm, good evening, miss," and an arm
Went round me then and the blackness came again
And the world and my happiness and the images

Vanished within it . . .

                     . . . I heard their voices then
Distant and soft, but I did not open my eyes,
I had not the energy and I lay content
To listen in silence, to see the light be warm
Against my eyelids. The voices grew more clear:
I heard my Judith speaking, she said, "That's right.
It was my fault, really, I've tired him out, poor dear,
I didn't realize, he hadn't told me of this."
"Of course not," Grandfather said. "He's a fool and young.
I was both but am only one of them now." He laughed.
"A curious welcome: but welcome it is. My tongue
Was never apt to the mannerly phrase." Then a pause.
"How did you know?" said Judith. "How did you know?"
"It was written upon your face. When you grow old
You'll have seen it often: as plain as a flower growing
Against green leaves."

              "Oh!"

                  "But he told me, too,
About his feelings." His voice took a pride that showed
In the sudden increase of strength. "He told it, all;
He posed his new problem and got back old advice."
I heard a movement then, and I felt, quite sharply,
Judith come near me. I thought, I must open my eyes:
This is not fair. I stirred and I raised my lids
Though the effort was great. Judith was by my side,
Her face bent down. I smiled and said, "I'm fine.
I'm sorry I fainted," and sat up then and I tried
To look as though nothing had happened. But Judith said,
"You were wrong to have made a secret of this to me.
Suppose it had happened before?"

                       "It passes away.
It only lasts a minute, as you can see."
I rose to my feet. Grandfather sat in his chair,
His hands on the wheels. "You listen to her," said he,
"She makes more sense in a minute than you in an hour,
You're just a damn young fool—but a lucky young fool.
I like your Judith. For God's sake, boy, sit down,
Have you got no sense?"

                 We laughed. He said, "It's cruel
To know as much as I do and not be able
To be an example but only a horrible warning."
I sat, and Judith sat down beside me then.

234

"I'll go home now, Tom. I'll call you up in the morning,
And see how you are."
                              I said, "But I'll drive you home.
I'm all right now."
                              "You're pale as a piece of cheese,
You'd take that girl in a car, on the road at night,
And faint and bend the car round the nearest tree
And smash yourself and the girl to a bit of jelly—
To go with the cheese. Sit still, boy, take your ease,
John Ward will take her." He rang his bell. "We'll drink.
You don't get better chances than this to drink."
As though he were waiting, Charles came into the room
Bearing a tray, decanters and glasses clinking,
And he put it down on a table and started to serve.
"Tell John to get the car, and be ready to drive
Miss Carpenter up to Providence."
                              Charles said, "Yessir,
He's outside now in the car all set for the ride.
Perhaps you'd rather have sherry than whisky, miss?"
She nodded her head. He poured and he gave her the glass.
He gave me whisky, strong. "Mr. Cottrell, sir,
I'm giving you whisky and milk." Grandfather said, "Blast!
Oh well, all right." He took it. "We're drinking, Charles,
To the Mrs. Cottrells future as well as past."
"Amen," said Charles, and he turned to Judith then,
And he said, "My wishes, miss, and I welcome you,
For it makes me happy." And then he bent his head
In the shade of a bow and he swiftly left the room.
I said, "You have gone a long way since I fainted.
I feel left out—I had wanted to tell this news.
But now it is told."
                              Grandfather raised his glass.
He said, "It was told in her eyes. Drink up, you two,
Long life if length be happiness, but at best,
Life to you both together, as one and one
And a common third to the world of the two you make."
We drank and I took her hand and I thought: it's done,
The guessing is over, the doing lies all ahead.
So we sat for a second's silence. His voice said, "Son,
Send the girl home now, the time grows late, too late,
You ought to be in your bed." And Judith rose,
And went to him and she said, "It all seems queer,
It's happened so quickly, so strangely—oh, I suppose

235

These things are all unplanned. I'd have liked to come
Quietly to you, to meet you, to let you find
What sort of a girl Tom picked."

                                "I have," he said.
"I knew your grandmother. Child, I am not blind,
I see with the eyes of age, that are but the eyes
My own youth lends me; my eyes are a memory
Of the fine brave eagerness of the good old days
When I raised hell in the pasture. Oh dearie me,
What a devilish good time for a gay young man,
But it left me able to see you with sympathy
And watch Tom's face like a mirror reflecting mine
In imperfect image. Good night. The car is waiting.
We'll all meet soon, and we'll wear our spats and hats
And bow like blazes and say 'Felicitations!
My dear young lady!' I'll let Tom go to the door,
But mind he goes no further! The entrance light
Is switched by the jamb, Tom knows, John Ward won't see,
And don't take cold because you are wrapped in night."
She said, "Good-bye, I am glad that it all began
The way it did." So she left the room. I followed.
I heard his voice in what he thought was a whisper
Say, "How the devil does Charles think a man can swallow
Whisky and pap?"

4

I went to his room to say good night. He lay
In his great, wide double bed, alone and small
And bolstered up with pillows as was his way.
He said, "Good night, Tom. That was exciting stuff,
She's all that you said. She'll win her race in a walk.
I'm glad it's happened. Now go to your bed and sleep."
I answered, "How can I sleep? I want to talk."
He said, "You can talk tomorrow but not tonight,
You'd say too much—why, the first thing that you knew,
You'd be telling me how it happened. Now listen to me.
There are some moments in life, they are just a few,
That had better be kept to yourself, and this is one.
I don't want to hear any more—I lie like a Cretian,
I'm stuffed with curiosity, but, by God,
I will not listen. Be off!"

                              I thought of Jake:

Grandfather'd have loved that; yet, perhaps he was right:
One should keep silence. He said, "You have got your cake,
Now go to bed and dream of it. Good night, Tom."
I said, "Good night," and I turned to leave the room;
He called to me as I reached the door: "Don't think
I'm hard—it is not hardness. But there are some
Moments for talking and some for keeping peace.
This makes me feel too old—old and alone.
I fed on a memory: this is too actual,
It dims the recollection. But I have known
The choice of the great things. Such is the use of love,
It is the difficult and the rewarding one
If you follow it out to its proper end. But now
I am an old man: the sight of your young love
Tears at my vitals. It makes me aware of fear,
Of the end in sight. It wouldn't take much to shove
A battered old hulk like me to the bottom now.
I'm near my end."
                    I said, "You are fine and strong,
You've a damn long time ahead yet, I'm glad to say."
He looked at me and he said, "You're a fool and wrong:
You're a fool to stop an old man when he speaks
Of the death he sees; you're wrong to believe the end
Can be postponed by heartiness. We may live
Till the spirit flags—no longer. My way is spent:
To whom can I speak of my death if not to you?
I am old and full of fear. Will you then prevent
My ease by silence?" He paused and he grinned at me
And he said, "I'm had for a mug. Go on to bed,
I'll live till morning and find me a curse or two
To dash against the innocence of your head
For a little longer. Be off, and dream of love.
By a great mercy on the Almighty's part,
I still can dream of it. And I shall. Good night!"

5

You may not sleep:
This is the very fringe and edge of waking,
Here is the darkness, it shall enwrap you warmly:
But the edge dissolves into the grey of waking,
The great flats of no sleep, a land without horizon.
You may not sleep: you may dream, awake,

237

Closing the day's-eye to the darts of time,
Turning reality to a vision moulded, unedged, to comfort—
And yet you desire sleep and you may not sleep, and happi-
　　ness
Surges up till the sinews are taut, become
The wires of your happiness, telling it to the tired flesh
From the rushing wheel of the mind.
These are the near sounds of November night,
These are the dear sounds of the nights well known;
These are echoed from the tempered board
Of your new being: the waves, the wakeful rocks,
The wind that whispers, the tiny rattle of blinds in the airs
　　of night:
These cry 'Happiness, happiness!'
So it sweeps up over
The barriers of the years in a huge blooming
Till the great flats of wakefulness are the strewn plains
Of incredible joy.
Do not open the eyes: though you may not sleep, keep close
The lids of day against the permuted night:
Back of your lids lies Judith.
The room is await: it shall take you, in the lighting
Of the next dawn, it shall recapture you.
Now it is hid by the lids of the sleepless eyes
That harbour Judith.
These are the sounds of water, the tread of the tide
In the eternal steps of the ebb and flow of the waters,
These are the sounds and notions
Of young sleep.
What did he say? Con it over, the words
Are separate entities, each word a thing to itself:
Sleep well, dream well, sleep,
This is the choice of the great things: this is the hard
This is the difficult, this the rewarding way, this is the use of
　　love—
But not these words, words like them,
These are your own words, but over all these syllables lies
The veil of the hope of sleep that breeds the dream
That says eternally: Judith: a kiss: the fire
Of kisses given and given. You may not sleep.
Here is the flash of returning little light:
That is a lighthouse, it bears a familiar name,
But now is the light only: Judith; one must not stray

From the passion of greatness to the little, old
Sleep-bearing things that cover the closed eyes
To an ignorant darkness.
What did she say? What did she say? What are the words?
Gone: to the touch remembered? fused in the memory
Of a rustle of dry leaves, the sound of metal struck
By the flints of love to music?
The waves re-echo the familiar, the child-forged sound:
Think of the love you bore, you bear, she gives,
Or to the touch of . . . sleep? . . . or lips?
Happiness wells up like the autumnal tide
Into the bays of the recipient heart
In the sounds of night, into the steps of the waters:
These are no longer the sounds of singular sorrow:
These are the flutes of joy in the long bones
Of doubted happiness, something to come, to seize,
The consonance of the night, of the spoken love,
Of the weary body, of water and wind that wells
Out of the long years, into the flittering thoughts,
Into the whisper of memory,
Something sweet
Into sleep . . .

PART FIVE

SLEEP IS outdistanced by the heels of mind
Whose swifter pace leaps over the poor sense
Of daylight hours, and in new fields can find
Shame and contrition without new defence.
Sleep is the bearer of the cup of rest
That all the fretful wakefulness shall spill
In useless anger savaging the breast:
An anger without purpose, against will.
Sleep is the ultimate and timely death
To all the petty, flourished wrong of day
That having fearful life yet draws its breath
Through the dark hours to keep its end away.
Sleep is the hunger that our mind denies
With bitter nourishment of remembered lies.

THIS WAS the melting of the snows of use
From frozen ground: our earth in its hard state
Was bound to impotence, but its covering ran
In silly rivulets, impenetrant,
Into a sea of waste.
                          I know my nights
Are troubled yet, when the reluctant sleep
Is still ungrasped, to think upon the folly
That neither ignorance nor blindness might
Surely excuse; the folly of the mind
That shook itself frenetically free
From war's hypnoses, and so plunged again
Into the compensation of such mad
And pointless humours. So I tripped myself
Into the errors I already knew,
From impetus of living just beyond
All normal pace. Perhaps such things must be
To free a generation: but the cost

243

Is dear in latter years when the blood runs
Less thumpingly about the corridors
Of the long veins. The memory of these
Fond, curious weaknesses is like pain. It seems
So incommunicable: mine must be.
I put this from me in the day by day,
It was some other person, never I,
It is so distant and so drowned in time.
Yet in the reaches of the darkening hours,
The primitive, veracious fields of night,
It is myself, as though my very skin
Had borrowed tongues to be a pentecost
Of witnesses against me.
                              I returned
To Harvard for the winter: the whole place
Was topsy-turvy with the drunken heroes
Who had or had not gone to fight their war.
God! how we drank! And how we laughed and played
Till the dawn hours, striving to retrieve
Time that had slipped and gone. We did not know
That time was irrecoverable: we lived
Always in hot and sometimes gay pursuit.

I lived alone then in a double room
Waiting for Sam's return: it was postponed
Till late in April. When February came,
I was left desolate: I had said good-bye
To Judith in New York whence she had sailed
To see her aunt in England. Till that time
I had been back and forth to Providence,
Staying with Mother, spending every hour
That I could snatch, with Judith, till our love
Grew heavy with its passion. But such days
Were curious and troublesome: they built
A powerful discontent; each parting seemed
Each time more hard; and I was loath to go
Back to my mother, who was sad and hid
Her sadness poorly, turning more and more
To Ethel Darnley, and cut off from me
By hatred of the marriage we had planned
So imminently in June. So Judith's going
Made me more anxious for Sam Allen's coming,
That I might have a friend to talk of this,

To talk of everything.
                        There came an evening
When the first passionate promptings of the spring
Charged the soft air of a late day in March,
And made the curtains at the windows sway
Across the moonstone pallor of the sky.
I sat removed and lonely, with a longing
For something undefined and unpossessed,
Roused by the season. I tried to write of spring:
But spring was too immediate, unremembered
In those distilled, compacted images
That fill the lens of time. I paced the floor
Uneasy, languid, wishful, out of sorts,
Wanting and yet not wanting things unphrased,
A victim to my years and to the season
Now joined again. And suddenly there ran
A sharp, clear image through my mind; it fled
Before I'd grasped it; yet it came again:
A girl beside me in a rocking Ford
In winter's evening. Then I stood quite still
And searched my memory for her name; and so
Whispered it: Rosemary—and Frank Whittaker—
Name in the phone book—and I saw the house
So dark and so forbidding in the night
Of the dim-lighted snow. I picked the book
Up from the desk; but then I put it down
Hastily and unopened and I thought,
But this is silly . . . and perhaps it's wrong . . .
And other girls. Yes, other, pretty girls
In Boston houses—but that world belonged
To Judith now and there was in my mood
Something at conflict between her world and this
That flashed its image. But so long ago . . .
Not there, forgotten . . . and I would not play
Her game at her time—why should she play mine
When now it suited? But should I be suited
With such a game? who once denied, believing
Its singular unworth?
                        The air was soft,
The lamps on wide Mt. Auburn Street came on
In flickering moons against a dying sky
And its persistent death. There were the sounds
Of music played, the distant clanging bells

Of the impatient trolleys; the quick whisper
Of young feet shuffling happily on the street . . .
To what appointment? Again the picture ran
Bright through my mind, Rosemary, pretty, quick,
Alien to my world: but different, new,
Kin to the moment and the strong unrest
That the wind brought.
                              I took the book again
And bore it to the window, being loath
To light the lamp and so shut out the light
Of moderate evening. There I found the name:
Frank Whittaker, the number—wrote it down
On a small slip of paper, closed the book
And sat again in attentive idleness
Waiting for something. But one waits in vain
For answers to such problems. At last I moved,
Crossed to the telephone and called the number,
And waited breathlessly. I heard the dull
And whirring ring repeating time on time,
Interminable, and I thought, They're out,
It is all over: disappointment now
Made eagerness of what had been a whim
Hardly desired.
                              Then suddenly a voice,
Thick, masculine and annoyed, called out, "Hello!"
I said, "Hello, Miss Whittaker at home?"
"Who, Rosy? Yeah, she's here, just hold the line,
I wish to gosh she'd answer her own calls.
Hang on." A further silence, a long space.
Then a girl's voice said, "God, I told you twice
Not to call up till seven."
                              I said, "I'm sorry,
Shall I call back then?" But there came no answer.
I said, "Hello, Miss Whittaker, have you gone?"
She answered then and said, "Oh. Who are you?"
"You won't remember, it's a long time back,
My name's Tom Cottrell."
                              "Who?" I spelled it out.
"I don't remember you. Where did we meet?"
"In 1917," I said. "We drove
From Dedham back to Somerville, a Ford,
One snowy day. I'm back in Cambridge now,

246

Out of the army."
                    She answered, rather slowly,
"Oh yes. I know. Which is it? The boy that drove?"
"The other one."
                    "Oh, the stuck-up one."
                                        I said,
"No, not exactly. But the other one
That didn't drive."
                    "What do you want?" she said.
It wasn't promising: her voice was hard.
"To see you." But no answer came; I went on,
"Two years is a long time. I've changed since then.
And see, I did remember, all that time."
Still silence; so I cried, "And so did you."
She laughed at that. She said, "Oh yes, indeed.
I haven't often seen two men so big
Jammed in together in a Ford's front seat
With a girl between them."
                        "Do you like to dance?"
She said, "I like to dance with those I like."
"Try me," I said. She answered only, "Why?"
"Because."
          "It's not a reason."
                             "Try it once."
"Try what?"
          "Me, and my dancing."
                                "No," she said,
"I've got my troubles now."
                          "But none like me."
"That's right," she answered, "I've been lucky, see?"
I drew a quick breath and said, "Change your luck:
It might wear out." There was an instant's pause,
And then she laughed. "Behave yourself! You're right,
You've changed—or else you're tight."
                                    I said, "I'm drunk
With the fresh air of spring, that's all."
                                        "Oh my!
You say the damndest things!"
                            I said, "Well then,
If you were free tonight we could step out
And give our dogs a work-out, and have dinner,
And hoist a few—I have got gin and whisky—

Go out Jamaica way, there is a place
Quite near the reservoir, the music's good,
The food's not bad. You'll come?"

She said, "I can't.

I've got a date."

"Well then, tomorrow night?"

"No, not tomorrow, nor Friday, Saturday,
Nor even Sunday."

I got angry then,

And said, "O.K. Be good and you'll be happy,"
And rang off quickly. Then I sat and thought,
You silly fool, of course: you asked for that.
What made you think that she'd remember you
Save as the boy who wouldn't, once, respond,
Until you'd angered her . . . a woman scorned . . .
Oh hell . . . and yet it's just as well, at that,
It would have been so silly . . . and such fun.
The day was gone now, and I sat in darkness,
Knowing the lamp would light another phase
And wanting without reason to maintain
This phase in spite of failure: unadmitted,
Until the light should cut the tenuous cord
That bound the mood to me and to the dark
And the soft, chilly air of night

I heard

A gramophone across Mt. Auburn Street
Play the St. Louis Blues: it touched my mood
With perfect harmony. Then the telephone
Rang at my elbow and I jumped: the sound
Startled. I did not touch it till it rang
A third time and a fourth. And then I answered,
My heart quite in my mouth.

"That Mr. Cottrell?"

"Yes."

"It's the tailor. You have burnt a hole

Right in the front of your blue pants. Three bucks
To fix it up like new. O.K.?"

"All right,

Do a good job."

"You'll never know the place,

I'll get them back by Tuesday. Thanks, good night."
I said, "Good night," hung the receiver up.
Then I switched on the light, saying aloud,

"She doesn't know your number—nor your name—
Why in the hell should she call you?" I lit
The lamp beneath the kettle to make tea,
And fetched the cup and biscuits and a spoon,
So to divert my mind. The spell was broken:
This would be just another night. I'd go
Back to the club for dinner and some bridge,
Perhaps a movie later. Well. Oh well.
It was as well. I filled the kettle up
And placed it on the stand above blue fire.
I closed the window to shut out the air
That made the pale flame flicker: so the night
Withdrew yet further. Yet I could not sit,
Waiting in patience but must pace the room
Urged by a sense of time slipping so fast
That only in motion might I capture it.
The telephone bell rang. Good! something doing:
A poker game, perhaps. I looked to see
How near the boil the kettle was: it sang
In its first quiet tune. The telephone
Again rang loudly in that quiet room.
I answered it, still standing, said, "Hello."
No voice responded. I said hello again,
And louder. A rather weak girl's voice replied,
"Is that Tom Cottrell?"

      "Yes," I said, "that's me."
"I shifted it—my date."

      "You shifted what?"
"The date I spoke of. Don't you understand?"
I said, "Oh. Yes. I see." There was a pause:
I thought I'd punish her. "And for which night?
Friday or Saturday or Sunday, even?"
She said, "I tried to call before. Your line
Was busy."

   "Yes, it must have been."

       "I made
Arrangements to be free tonight."

       I thought:
Just one more flick. "I'm stupid—who is this?"
She answered quickly, "Rosy Whittaker,"
And then, "Oh, you are horrid!"

      "No," I said,
"Not really horrid, but too happy now

249

To swallow happiness in one big gulp
Without the taste of it."
                              "Do you always talk
In such a fashion?"
                              "Yes. What time and where?"
"You have a car?"
                    "That Ford."
                                        "Can you remember
How to get to my house?"
                              "I have remembered
Vividly for two years. And how you shut
The door so quickly—and the snowy streets—
And my own foolishness, just standing there
To see you go."
                    "Go on."
                              "I shall go on
After I see you."
                    "Don't go on too much.
Come round at eight. Just wait outside the house.
Don't blow your horn or ring. My father's home.
I'll come out quickly—you won't have to wait."
"How do you like your drink?"
                                   She said, "With you.
What, doesn't matter. Good-bye. I'll see you soon."
Then she hung up. I stood a moment more
Holding the black receiver in my hand,
Astonished at its silence, as though it should
Have spoken of itself and said, 'Well done!
We did it, didn't we!'

2

                    We dined that night
Out at the inn Jamaica way. I'd found
Her house so easily; but there was no snow—
The air was chilly and was soft with spring
Waiting a little distance off. The house
Looked still forbidding, but less forbidding now
With an odd light or two. The porch in shadow
Still seemed a guardian, but guarding what:
Some secret of its own perhaps, or keeping
Night at a distance with its own maintained
And special night? I did not wait there long.

Soon she came out, swiftly and quietly,
Got in the car and said, "Go on, go on,
Don't hang around here." She sat stiffly then,
Apart on the front seat looking ahead
Till we had gone a block or two away.
Her silence and her stiffness seemed so odd:
I said, "Good evening, fancy meeting here!
This is Miss Whittaker, I presume?" She laughed,
And sank back in the seat and smiled at me
And said, "Good evening, lover."
                              "Oh," I said.
She moved then close to me. "You knew?" she asked.
"Knew what?"
              "What I just said?"
                                "You go so fast.
You leave dull wits like mine so far behind you."
"Oh, are you dull? I should have called it shy—
A little poky and conventional,
A little frightened and inexperienced,
A little limited in your point of view—
Like all good church-school boys. I'd hoped the army
Might have—well—made you quicker."
                                "Quicker? How?"
She didn't answer, but she looked at me
A long time without speaking, smiling still,
Letting her eyes rove over me. She said,
"As I remembered. He is big and blond,
Not quite an open face, some things are hidden,
A beautiful dark woman crossed his path,
The war has aged him. He is stronger now.
I'll like him better."
                    "You've remembered me?
Or is this just your line?"
                          She sighed and shook
Her head, and her red hair shook to the motion,
Hair short and curling from her close green hat.
She said, "Not stupid, exactly. We must start
Right over from the beginning." Then she laid
Her hand upon my arm and said again,
"Good evening, lover." Then as I still drove
In silence, she said quickly, "Three, three times.
How many times must I begin?"
                            I said,

"I rang you up. That's one for me."

                                            "For what?"

"To see you."

                 "Why?"

                          "Because you are so pretty,
And possibly . . . " I hesitated there.

"Yes? do go on!"

                       "Because I can imagine
You know more than I do."

                           She laughed again,
And shifted in her seat. "It's a tough job.
You only want to learn from me?"

                                 "Oh no,
You twist my words. I paid a compliment."

"I don't want compliments."

                       "What do you want?"
She said, "You don't have red hair, you don't live
In Somerville for nothing. I had hoped
You'd jump right at it. Do girls call you back
Often when you've been rude?"

                              I didn't answer.

"Do they?"

                 I said, "They don't."

                          She cried, "Well then!
Is it all clear now?" We were on a dark
And winding bit of road. I stopped the car.
I said, "I'm lost, now, Rosemary."

                           "Yes, you are.
More ways than one."

                   "That's what I mean."

                            "Then kiss me."

"With pleasure." I turned to kiss her, but she held
My face away from hers with both her hands
And said, "Oh, no, not pleasure. Because you must."
I said, "I must."

                 "You lie, you lie," she cried,
"But it's no matter. Can't you see, you fool?"
"See what?" I asked, half angrily. She sighed
Again and heavily and said patiently,
"I'll try to tell you. I'll begin again.
Listen, young, big, blond, inexperienced dope!"
Then she leaned forward and she said so low
That it was but the shadow of a whisper,

"Good evening—lover." Then she pulled my face
Down to her own and so we kissed.
                                        I felt
A curious fear go through me with the pleasure
That dwelt in this: and many pictures ran
Uncalled for in my mind; and in my ears
I heard the rustle of dead leaves that stirred
In autumn twilight; and I felt a pulse
Beat that I had not known since long ago
I felt its power when the rain was soft
Against great windows on a darkened stair.
So she broke free at last, but held my face
Between her hands and stared at me, and said,
"You kiss two women while you're kissing me.
But that's the way of it and I don't care—
My life was made to fall in love with men
Who took and left and never loved me back,
And you are one. I wonder why I do it?
And why I must."
                        I said, "What pain is this
That hurts you so?"
                            "It's you. But you are just
Another man, one of a series. Yet,
You are more—gentle than the rest. Now, lie,
And say, 'I love you.'"
                            "No, you go so fast.
Too fast, my Rosemary."
                            "Call me Rosy."
                                                "No,
For I like Rosemary."
                        She echoed me:
"For I like Rosemary. But does not love.
And I won't love you, no, and I don't know
The first god-damned thing about love, at all,
Not yet, oh Jesus! but I'll find it out."
And then she laughed, and settled in her seat
And said with an incredible change of mood,
"Drive on, big Thomas. I want food and drink.
You've had a fright. But it won't last. Go on!
I want some food, and then some drink. I want
To dance and dance and then you'll take me home
And let's be late as hell. I like it late."
I started up the car again. We drove

For a long time in silence, while my thoughts
Were puzzles that I could not then unravel,
And a queer sense of fright that I had lost
My way most dangerously.
                                    We dined and danced.
Dancing with her was but a single action;
She was my thought as I projected it
To the excitement of the music's beat
In its clipped rhythm. I had danced with none
Save only Judith who could move like this
In effortless unity. Between, we talked:
Her talk grew more amusing as we drank
My flask to nothing—yet we did not speak
One word of love, but told about ourselves,
Our lives and happenings: there was much to tell.
I marvelled at her knowledge of my world,
But when I questioned it, she evaded me,
Leaving me to deduce that she had known
Full many of my kind.
                                    But as we danced,
She held me close; or would smile up at me
A smile that should have spoken as clear words,
Yet left me wondering, puzzled, and on air
From its strong power. Dancing, she was one:
Seated again, another, with a veil
Strong as a barrier between us then.
And always in my mind I carried the queer
And frightening sensation she had roused
By word and action on the lonely road
When I had stopped the car: I could not shake
That puzzling memory, so disturbing me,
So difficult to assess. What did she want?
Or (strange admission!) what did she intend
Whose force gave her intention such a power
As though to will were but to have or be
Through simple willing?
                                    Then the music stopped;
But still we talked. And then they heaped the tables,
And dimmed the lights till all that room took on
An attic semblance, full of all the ghosts
Of dancing couples. Yet we stayed, and talked,
And talk was eager, being more promoted
By dusky isolation in the mists

254

Of human-tainted air. The waiter then
Must ask us to get out: we went, reluctant,
Into the darkness and sweet-fresh air of night
And its abnormal silence, till we, too,
Fell silent, letting the car's motion speak
For our night-halted tongues.

                              She held my arm,
Rested her head against me: that was all.
We did not stop, we did not speak, save when
She sighed once, murmuring after, "It is cold,
But I am warm." She did not look at me
Although I often glanced at her: her eyes
Were fixed ahead on the illumined road
That swept beneath us and so moved with speed
Back to its normal dark. And still the air
Was filled with the expectancy of spring
Not here, but near us, waiting on our wish.
We drove through the long streets of shuttered houses,
Past the head-hanging of the milkman's horse,
Past cars that made one wonder what possessed
Their occupants to be abroad at such
Unearthly hours. And so at last we drew
To a slow halt before her curious house
And its dark, guardian porch. She sat a moment
Utterly still, and then she stirred and rose,
Opened the door and climbed down to the street
With her quick motions. Then she said, "Good night,
Thanks for the dinner," and turned away and walked
Up toward her house. I did not dare to call;
I climbed down rapidly and caught her up
Under the shadow of the porch; I seized her
Roughly and said, "Hold on!"

                              She said, "For what?"
I answered, whispering, "You can't go like that—
Do all your words mean nothing?"

                              "Everything.
I am too truthful. Let me go. I want—
To go to bed, please." Still I held her arm.
I thought, You go about it cleverly:
This is the way to make a man desire,
By this withholding—and suddenly I thought,
I'll say it, and I said, "That is the stuff
To fetch a man—you're clever." Then she turned

And gently freed her arm, and raised her hands
And held my face and stared at me and said
In a low voice, "Don't be so horrible.
I fell in love with you when I first saw you.
I fell in love again, just at your voice
Over the telephone. I told you this.
You say, 'Don't go so fast.' If you had loved me,
You could have had me, every way, at once,
Now, in my bed. Not now, though, it is gone.
What do you want? You want a girl, tonight,
One quick excitement, and good-bye, my hat,
So long. I have been hurt too many times.
Is this the truth?" I could not answer her:
There was an earnestness that made her words
A barrier to lies. I said, "Good night.
I liked our evening. Shall I come again
On these new terms?"
                          She slowly dropped her hands
And said, "Come often," and so turned and ran
Up the dark, hollow steps. I stood again
To hear the unlocked door open and close
To her swift passage.

3

                          And for three weeks more,
Each possible occasion: like a drug,
I could not stop it, always wanting more,
Always a little shamed, a little angry,
But not with Rosemary—with myself. I knew
Clearly what kept me going: the desire
To break resistance down, to sleep with her,
And on my terms. And every single time
She held me to the distance she desired,
With skilful words that nevermore repeated
Their first strong promise. Yet, when I had gone,
When I had left her presence, I would know
Each time that had I passionately wooed
I could have won: but yet I did not woo,
Hating the lie too much, unwilling then
To say or do more fully what my first
And cautious answers had made manifest

As the whole truth of this.
                                                        But yet I'd fill
My mind with images of Clare, and see
Her reckless taking at her mind's behest
Without the heart's involvement; and I'd see
My father, separate, cold, seizing on this,
Yet more detached than Clare who could not part
Herself from his detached desire. And yet,
These would not justify: Rosemary remained
Common, uncommon, and ununderstood,
Passionate, vulgar, and controlled; so full
Of her intention that I could not see
What the intention was, but still went on
Hoping that soon her barrier, self-raised,
Would drop and let me past—to end a time
Feverish, unreal.
                            Sometimes we dined and danced;
Sometimes, when spring was strong in the night air,
We drove long distances, and found new inns
Out in the country, and drove home again
In the grey hours of morning. At all times
We talked and talked. I can remember once
She asked me what I'd be. I said, "A poet,
Perhaps a writer of prose too."
                                                        She said,
"And live on that?"
                                "I shall have cash enough,
At least for simple living."
                                        She exclaimed,
"Simple! You don't know what that means: to live
With nothing more than the bare needs for life,
No single extra thing."
                                "But you," I said,
"You dress so prettily—I rarely see you
Twice dressed the same. Is that simplicity?"
She paused a moment. "It is good for trade,"
But added quickly, "Do you really know
Enough of life to be a proper writer?
You're young—it's all just promise."
                                                    "Not performance?"
"Yes."
            Then I said, "I am what I may be,
And when the time comes that I say, 'I am,'

The growing's over, the promise, and all life
Is but to polish, not again create."
She shook her head and said, "Too highfalutin'.
I don't know what you mean. I only see
The traps ahead and wonder where you'll be
When you've got into one or two."
                                        I answered,
"I have just fallen into yours."
                                        "I know:
And that'll learn you, maybe."
                                        We fell silent.
Another time we spoke of this. She said,
"My father played the organ in a church
But wasn't good enough, and lost his job,
And played piano at small theatres next,
But wasn't good enough, and sold pianos
And couldn't make it go. So now he sells
Records and gramophones at old Filene's.
My brother joined the navy, stuck with it
Till he'd become proficient, a machinist,
And left it, just before the war. He tried
To find employment and had just begun
When this war caught him up again. And now
He drives a coal-truck—it's a big machine—
He'd like to make them. There's no opening,
Everything's shutting down. For all I know
He'll go on driving to the end of time.
And you—" she paused to look at me—"and you,
You can support yourself, you have the money,
Even if you write lousy poetry
And phoney stories and don't sell a damn
Thing that you write, you can go on and write
Because you've money."
                                        "But perhaps I'd stop
After I found out I was bad at it."
"Who says so? People kid themselves for life,
And never do wake up."
                                        "What can I do?"
"Do? Oh, do nothing. On your feet and dance,
There's always dancing—here I am, I'm hot,
My God, I love to dance!"
                                        "With me?"
                                                "Don't ask,

258

Just dance. I wish you could write tunes for me
Instead of poems that only dopes will read
And no one understand."
                              We danced again,
And as we'd dance she'd smile at me, hang close.
And this I lived for then.

4

                    There came a day,
Cold, with the feel of snow, in latter March,
When this was ended: shame caught up with me
And tapped my shoulder, all too obviously,
Under the grey sky and the blowing clouds
And the cold truth. Perhaps fatigue had added
Its weight to decency and common sense:
I am not sure now; so simple to assign
Plausible reasoning after the event,
When the complexities of instinct seem
Reduced to reasonable will. I saw
Suddenly, clearly, the whole picture; knew
That I was wrong according to my lights
And that it mattered nothing that those lights
Might later dim or change: prove wrong or foolish.
So I decided, on the instant: stop,
Cut clean and go; be kind and yet be firm,
And finish with a courage you have lacked
In all this drift.
                    It was no sooner made,
This fine decision than assaulting thoughts
Arose to trouble: here was June, so close,
With marriage and an ending, freedom put
In pawn for happiness. Yet could one pawn
For any value what one had not had?
Or giving up all these tempestuous things
Almost untasted, would the appetite
Grow into greed that's fostered by the mind's
Enlarging eye?
                    And still I put these back,
Dismissing them, for once contolling thought,
And covering doubt up with the sure device
Of one conviction stronger than all else:
Out of this matter, unhappiness was bred

Greater than all enjoyment.
                              That last night
We went again to Jamaica: it seemed fitting,
Closing a cycle. We had dinner there,
We drank and danced. I had said nothing yet:
I lacked the courage. Rosemary was less gay
And looked more tired than usual. At last
When it was nearly time to go, I said
"Come on, let's dance. This is the very last
Time I shall ever dance with you." She rose
Without a word or glance, and then she stood
A long time by her chair; but finally
She moved out past the table to the floor,
And raised her arms. We danced. We did not speak.
It was a good tune, Dardanella. Now
I rarely hear it: then it recreates
The scene so sharply: I even smell her hair
And the sweet, over-burdened scent she wore;
And even now on certain city nights
I pass some shop-girl from whose dress there rises
The same sweet, cheap, and most recalling scent,
And in my ears is born the tune and all
The brassy sound of it, and through my arms
Runs the concise conclusion that they touch
Again this odd and dancing girl, whose power
Was still too great for nothing, and too little
For something great.
                         And then the dance was done,
And we sat down again. She took her bag,
Powdered her fine and faintly curving nose,
Painted her lips again with a sure touch,
Snapped the bag shut and looked at me at last.
"And so," she said.
                       "And so," I answered her.
She said, "You are not tactful, just courageous,
Most of them find it best to disappear.
You know, saves scenes."
                            "I'd like to tell you why."
"Why should you tell me? Think that I don't know?
I'm clever, boy, I know about these things—
I'm an old hand."
                     "You're an old hand at what?"
She looked at me and laughed. She said, "You're cute,

You are so innocent. So God-damned simple.
I am a high-class prostitute. Twenty bucks.
Appointments made by telephone. My father
Is not my father, but the Madam's husband—
Didn't you ever wonder why the house
Was closed to you? Why I was closed to you?"
I said, "You're lying."
                        She said, "Yes, I'm lying,
I work at Siegel's down on Central Street,
The women's wear. Come down some time, it's cheap.
I'll show you all the stuff that's fit to buy.
The bargain basement's swell." She laughed again.
"We've had a good time. Let's pay up and go."
I called the waiter and I paid the bill,
But still she didn't move. She looked around
With a bright look, watching the couples dance.
She said, "You see the two girls dancing there?
Ain't that pathetic?" Then she rose and walked
Straight to the door and out without a pause.
I followed her.
                We drove toward Somerville.
It might have been as always. She sat close,
And leaned her head against me. The night was cold:
I wrapped her in the rug, for the sharp wind
Came through the broken curtains.
                                  I searched for words
But could find none that answered; so we drove
In silence to her house. When the car stopped
She turned to me and spoke: "You can come in."
I answered nothing. She went on. "It's safe.
I live on the ground floor. No one will hear you,
Coming or going." Silence. "A short while.
What are you scared of?"
                        "I'm not scared," I said,
"I made my mind up: it was difficult.
I don't propose to change it."
                              "There's no need.
I wouldn't see you, never, ever again
For love or money."
                    "Wouldn't you?"
                                      "Not ever."
She took my hand and held it. "It's what you wanted.
Nearly a month now you have stepped me out,

And wined and dined me. You have had one kiss,
And I have cuddled cutely up against you
Each night, all the way home. Oh, let it end
The way you wished it to. Now kiss me, Tom."
I stirred uncomfortably. "It is too late."
"Never too late. Come in."
                    I did not move,
I could not see my way. She said, at length,
Sighing, and softly, "For me, to remember.
You have forgotten that I am in love."
I had forgotten: it was true. I said,
"I have grown fond of you. Too fond, entirely.
I have been silly. Let me go, right now,
This is just fixed to make it harder, isn't it?
Harder for me, and you."
                 She said, "You fool!
You big, blond, lovely fool!. For all your life
You'd wonder and regret. What was she like?
Why didn't I? Don't you know anything?
Can't you see, even, that for just my sake
It is the only kind thing you can do—
If you still want to?"
             I sat and thought, and stared
Hard at her face; it was so difficult
To get at truth. I chanced it, and I said,
"You're lying again, Rosemary."
                   She looked
Out through the windshield at the long, dark street;
I felt her grasp tighten upon my hand.
"Oh yes," she said, "it is an awful lie.
I've lied and lied, and tried to tell the truth,
But they get mixed. You're nice. Remember me,
I shan't forget you. It was fun. We've shot
Craps with a pair of bones that had no spots.
O.K. Good-bye." She turned her head again;
Half-rising, kissed me lightly several times
Full on the mouth. Then she got out, her movement
As sure and quick as ever. Once outside,
She turned again and said, "Don't come to look
For anyone like me at Siegel's store,"
Then fled, for the last time, to the dark house,
And left me to the puzzle of her words,
The wrong and right so powerfully mixed,

To breed forever a shame and a regret
And both illogical.

NOW IS THE lax heart in the warm April sun-bound
To the brown run of water; now will the wild song
Faltering in the bronze trees loose the nerves, unwound
From tense coil and rapt lesion. Now will the child long
Wintered in man-flesh thirst again for the spring draught
Cupped in clethra's chalice of upturned fresh leaves;
Free his soul to the flight of the careless wing craft;
Rest in the rhythm of ripples where green cress weaves.
There a dark trout quivers behind a brown stone,
Pale trout marks his metal above the jewel sand,
There the petalled shad-blow, delicate, down-blown,
Floats on the image-blue of a heron's cruel stand:
Yet on a spring-time river, sun through the trees' sound,
Life's cup with death runs over, in winter lees drowned.

SO A DAY passes, and a few hours, and a week is gone,
And it is April: and spring corrupts the mind and the heart,
For the flesh moves and is great in these days,
And the thought of Rosemary is as a splinter in moving flesh.
Work, work, play. A day passes and another day,
And Judith grows stronger in my mind and Rosemary is
    less actual,
And a week is fled into the passionate emptiness
Of April without Judith, with memory. Work and play.
So the days pass.
So the days pass as the air blows:
As the air blows through city windows now and the red cur-
    tains move to it,
The old curtains, unchanged, of our house.
This is the air of New York: should it not blow away
Memories and the strange shape of people impressed
On this chair, that pillow, the books in their long silence?

Why is the house unchanged, that has no mistress?
Father is here, and is not here. He sleeps and he eats here:
But these are not the touchstones of use.
Joss is away and away, yet his shape is here,
And my mother's phantom, and a young Tom, a child Tom,
Growing Tom: these are here.
Yet the air blows, full of the good music and brash noise
    of the city,
Through and through, in this window, out that window to
    the ailanthus
Spread in its lank long growth in the yard of many angles
    and shadows.
Can it blow and not change the air of a room?
The room is dark and the walls are gold: many little objects
Are no longer here—yet see:
This table held these, that table is lonely for those, that are
    not here.
It is changed, oh changed, yes, and it is the same:
What shall preserve such matters when the life that made
    them
Is all changed—all gone?
Not home?
This is my home, and the air that blows here,
This is the old air, blowing the old way, ruffling familiar
    shapes,
Sweet with the scent of spring, corrupt with the city smell,
Hinting of flowers: there are no flowers here, in this room:
    none.
Only the moving smell of another spring pressed on the many
    springs
Gone and gone. Not home? Not ever home again?
Change and no change—and a mother's house without her?
Think, Tom: sit in the red chair. Think, boy.
There must be an answer. Shall you not need it?

And the soft voice of Agatha, saying, 'Here's your coffee'; say-
    ing,
'It's balmy out.'
And the gentle voice of Agatha, saying, 'Lunch is ready', and
    saying,
'Have you washed?'
The slap, slop, shuffle of Agatha, tympani to the rung notes of
    china, tea-cup rattling on plate, china-sounds,

Not the clear chime of silver now—but the slap, slop,
Shuffle of feet as Agatha comes, saying,
'Tea's here'; and saying, 'Your hair needs cutting.'

So a day passes and a day,
And Judith is not here, and the tops of the buses
Swing in the old way, and one sits alone
Joss is away and away, and Father eats here and sleeps here,
We talk here, but these things,
These do not make a house to a home again.
The rain pours down in the April torrent, the gutters
Run in the old swirls, and I am alone,
Wondering at the brief span of holidays,
At the emptiness of them, of the fullness of this house,
With Father so rarely here, being out,
Giving only as much of himself as suits his convenience,
Pleasant, amusing, absent, withholding, the cool voice,
And the steps forever turned in their own direction, gracefully.

And always the gentle voice of Agatha, saying,
'Will you not have a friend in?' and saying,
'You to be married! You so young now!'
And the prying voice of Agatha, questioning, asking,
'Have you no picture to show me?' and saying,
'Ah, the lovely face, a woman is what a man needs,'
And adding, 'She's the lucky girl.'
The sound of the rattle of rings as the curtains close,
As Agatha twitches at them and pulls them straight,
White hair in the soft lamp-light,
The light of day gone, as ever, to her touch,
While she says,
'Sure he's lonely, himself alone, a house needs a woman.'
And saying, 'I'm the old bag of bones, but I rattle around,'
And the swish of full skirts and the apron
Forever on the bias, the white cap
On the white hair, over the pink face,
Over the blue eyes and the gentle smile.

And of all places, this is secure,
This is home again, against reason,
Against emptiness, against ghosts,
To the soft voice of Agatha, saying,
'Will you be late home?'

So a day passes, and a day,
Holding within their cup the refreshment of spring,
The good draught of Cottrellton: here the house where Grand-
    father
Could build a peace with the wall of his great words.
Here now is Father, a quiet strength, speaking softly,
Moving softly, steadily,
Causing a change in Grandfather who becomes
Mixture of pride, resistance, affection, annoyance,
Jumbled together in odd restraint: even the curses
Come with hesitation, for now the rich words
Sometimes die in an old man's mutter, or worse,
Turn to a petulance. Now is Grandfather
Older than ever next my father's vigour:
Though his hair has grey now, his face is lined, too,
Though the pose and the poise have the weight of years, still—
They are borne easily.
Yet it is spring and the loved, soft, salt-filled breezes
Ruffle the clouded waters, ripple the puddles,
Cause the pink-tipped birches to lean to the gentle wind.
The hollows are white with the spring-frost of the shad-blow
And the sandy tracks are edged by the early violet,
And all the earth is rich with the idle haste
Of uncharted growth.

And a day passes and a day begins,
Gentle and warm, the sun through the risen haze,
The feel of spring night fresh in the spring morning,
And peace as a shirt to the needing back.
This is a day for fishing. Father and I go,
He at his best, making himself a companion.
Pack up the reels. Flies in a fly box,
Creels in the back of the car. Rubber boots now
Are affectionate elephants' trunks coiled closely
In a jigging embrace. John Ward to drive us,
John to leave us, our pockets all full of oddments,
Sandwiches getting a flavour of mucilin paste,
And a mild aroma of citronella to sweeten
The sweet tobacco. John will call again, night-fall,
Come with the dusk to the great oak where the grey boards

Mark the pile and heap of a man's ambition
Long released.

This is Deer River: the river is Judith.
But Judith is not here.

Judith is not here, but this is fishing:
This is the mood of the moment, before the long line
Runs through the guides; this is the day before one,
All the hours of day, long and long,
Seen through the haze of morning, through the bright lens
Of the unfulfilled, the spring-touched hours.
Pick up this, sling that, carry the rod as a lance,
March with dignity and the heavy step
Of the black rubber boots. And now,
Here is the river. The day begins, the whisper
Of water is good for silence.

A soft breeze, a pale sun, the fresh air of morning caught in
    the shadow of tall trees,
We come at length out of the bright spring day, to the brown
    river
Flowing and rippling deeply between green banks, moss-cov-
    ered.
Now the fingers, grown huge, twist to its triple loop the
    nearly invisible
Gut of the leader, through the eye of the tiny, grey fly: and
    the loops close and diminish
To the knot hidden in the bristling hackles. So! Oil on the
    wings, oil on the hackles,
Make the accustomed motions with skilful pleasure: the day
Lies in the palm of the hand as the barbed fly rests, cautiously
    held.

FATHER: Not a sign of a fly, no sort of a hatch yet,
            What are you using?
TOM: A Whirling Dun, to begin with,
            I shut my eyes and picked it.
FATHER: I'll try a Cow Dung.
            It makes no difference. Begin. We'll start together.
            I don't see anything rising, do you?
TOM: I saw one rise.
            Below that clump of marigolds.
FATHER: That's deep water,
            There's usually one fish there. Go on, you're ready.

TOM: O.K. I'll start. Stay by the bank then, will you?
I've got to cast low under the maple boughs.
I'd hate to catch you.
FATHER: Yes. I'm too big to handle.
A dandy day, Tom.
TOM: Yes, it's a dandy day.
God, I hate fishing!
FATHER: I know. But it's good to do
The things you hate. Discipline.
TOM: Yes. I fish
For the good of my soul.
FATHER: Go on. For the good of your soul.
Not for the good of your tongue.

Slide off the mossy bank now, it crumbles: the distorted black
feet
Rest on the yellow quivering sand that shines below the
brown flood of water.
The water whispers and parts and divides to the pairs of silver
streamers
That grow to the dark columns of legs. The river
Becomes a mirror now, holding the bronze of thin elms, the
soft pink tips of the maples,
The black of the alders, in a web of colour fleeting together in
the soft run
Of its quiet waters.
The wrist flicks now, the cricket-noise of the reel is a good
sound
Against the song of the birds and the song of the bubbling
streamers flowing
Away from the columns of legs. The fly lights on the mirror,
Runs back towards you, the slack in the left hand grows, a
long loop;
Let the wrist snap again now, the arc of the rod is a whip,
bending,
Back and forth and again and again, and now,
The slack runs out and the fly lights on the water, a tiny
grey speck on a silver mirror that moves,
Forever returning, endlessly returning.
So one repeats and repeats: and the columns of dark legs
move,
One step up and another, and the fly rests on the moving
mirror,

268

Jiggles over a riffle of broken mirror,
Lights on the gold lip of a marigold, flicks off, rests on the
    golden image, and then,
Swiftly returns, and again the wrist moves,
And the bronze of the elms crosses the red of the maples in
    the broken riffle, shot with the flare of sky, a silver-blue,
Burnished and moving, cutting the black of the alders caught
    in incessant curve
Of the welt of riffles.

FATHER: Any answer?
TOM: No, come on. Try yours for a change.
FATHER: Right. Here goes.

He slides off the bank. Over the cricket-noise of the reel comes
    the gurgle and splash
Of his progress up-stream. Now he is by me. Now,
His fly is out on the water, and now further and further, the
    cast lengthens, until
With easy skill he has dropped it beside the marigolds, softly.
SLOSH!
It is like a stone dropped heavily, near his fly; the ripple circles
    widen,
The fly floats back.

FATHER: He never touched it.
        Came to sneer.
TOM: I guess so. Try him again.
        He may be foolish.
FATHER: Or I may be more skilful.

The fly whips back and forth, a foot off the water, under the
    maple boughs;
It lights, again off the marigolds, but a fraction further away.
SLOSH!

FATHER: There, by Godfrey! Now if I just can land you.
TOM: Want me to net him?
FATHER: Yes, if you've got it handy.
    Otherwise I will. Hey! George, but he's a fighter,
    He wants to get back of the spice-bush there, the
    devil.
TOM: If he gets round that, good-bye!

FATHER: I've got to hold him,
I hope he won't tear loose. Come here. Ah, now,
That's better, try the riffle.

TOM: Whew! see him go!
If he's too much for you, Father, I'll land him for
you.

FATHER: Be off, or I'll kick you down stairs. He's coming
now, Tom,
I'll work him round to your left.

TOM: A little further.

FATHER: He's got ideas of his own. There. Curse! He's off.

TOM: Oh damn, you've lost him?

FATHER: He's gone. Too bad, a good trout
Put up a good fight. I think I held too tightly
Up by the spice-bush.

TOM: What else could you do?

FATHER: Nothing. It's all in the game. You'll change your
fly?

TOM: I might as well. I'll try a Queen of the Waters.

FATHER: Try a Cow Dung, too.

TOM: No, let's be different,
As long as we fish together.

FATHER: You'd rather split?

TOM: No, would you?

FATHER: No—we can split up later.
I like your company. I am getting older.

TOM: What has age to do with it?

FATHER: Wait and see—
Though it may not happen to you. You've tied
yourself
As Father has, to the agonies of some people,
But you get paid back.

TOM: I hope so.

FATHER: I built a wall
So high and strong that they can't get at me—and
I—
I am caught inside it. Even the gates, now
Rust on their locks and the keys are lost. It's odd:
One sees this and cannot change it. It is lonely.
Perhaps I have seen it soon enough to use
The knowledge for Joss. He's building a wall. Per-
haps
I can dissuade him.

270

TOM: Joss?
FATHER: He's like me, Tom,
          He's not like you. But this is solemn stuff,
          Too solemn for fishing. I am off.
TOM: Good luck.

So the minutes pass and are builded into an hour,
And the hours bloom and are cut by the sharp knife of the
     sun.
Here a fish is caught. There is a fish that will but tease you,
     rolling near the patiently placed fly,
Only enough to flutter the heart, to send the ripples roaming,
     to mix the deep green
Of the laurel leaves with the bronze of the thin elms, the flare
     of the silver sky, the flash of the sun,
Metal to dazzle and blind.
And then, when you are not thinking of this, when the mind
     and eye
Are filled with the visions of fish in the moving water,
Of the little detail of a shad-bush against the thickening grey
Of the bare, close branches of underbrush, suddenly
The sun pours in on the water, the sky is seen uncrossed by
     the bronze branches,
The pale grey twist and strength of oaks is above you, the
     steep bank rises, the brown grass
Droops in a pattern of watered silk to the skirts
Of the patch of scrub-oak, thick grown, leaves still clinging in
     brown defiance of spring,
And a long shelf of sand makes out to the rush of shallow
     water,
And this is Judith, and you, and November dusk,
And the thin, distant sound of metal rings
In memory's ear.

FATHER: I say we knock off here. Let's eat our lunch, Tom.
          I'm getting peckish.
TOM: Oh. All right.
FATHER: Not hungry?
TOM: Not so hungry, really.
FATHER: It's such a good spot,
          One of my favourite spots. It's good for duck, too—
          Worth remembering for the autumn.
TOM: Yes.

                           271

FATHER: Well, how about it?

TOM: Where?

FATHER: Up on the bank there.

TOM: There's a place above, the bank by the Duckling
Pool,
That's a good place.

FATHER: It's wet there, the bank is damp.
This is dry.

TOM: I know. But you see the river.
I like to see the river. See if the trout rise.
It's fun to watch the river. You see the reach there,
Up and down. Here you can only see
The single pool, and its riffle, you couldn't tell
If a fish rose.

FATHER: They haven't risen all morning,
What makes you think they'll start now?

TOM: It's only April,
The sun is warmer.

FATHER: True. But I like this place.
Don't you like it?

TOM: Yes.

FATHER: I like the laurels.
I like the way they grow in their curious islands.

TOM: This is all art, not fishing.

FATHER: Fishing makes me
Worry about my art, it's all so lovely.

TOM: And if you painted, you'd worry about the fishing.

FATHER: Yes, I suppose so.

TOM: Further up is lovely,
And you can worry about them both. The shad
Grows near the bank there.

FATHER: All right. Come on, then.

TOM: Fish the riffle. I'll do the pool above you.

FATHER: Right, but walk around by the bank. The sun
Will throw your shadow on to the water, surely.
And keep away from the edge. It quakes.

TOM: O.K.
I'll meet you up there.

FATHER: Good. Don't be too long,
My belly's begun to rumble.

TOM: So has mine,
With all this talk of eating.

FATHER: And art, and fishing,

272

And never a word of love in the lovely spring time.
Oh well, my belly's my master for the moment.
If we get another one here, we'll cook and eat it,
And you can talk of love. You're an expert, now:
You've caught a woman.

TOM: So long. I'll see you up there.

FATHER: A reticent devil. Go on. And catch a trout.
You've got to feed me if you postpone my hunger.

Skirt the bank, and climb up the rise a little: you may not
    stop here, his eyes would see you.
One could have told once: to old eyes:
But one did not tell. The music of silence
Wove our symphony. The music of leaves once
Wove our love to a curious, sympathetic
Chord of a curious love.
To an old man, loving: yes. To this man, clever,
Knowing and clever: no. Not even the hint,
Not even the echo of heart-beats, heard in the ears,
The drum of the ears, like the soft pounding
Of a dog's tail on the hard ground.
Skirt the laurels, climb down the soft decline of yellow bank
Where love grew, grows, will grow, forever and ever,
One's breath like the rustle of leaves, the song of love
Rich in the secret ear, like the chime and clang
Of the metal music releasing my love to sound
In the words of love.
Skirt the soft long spit of sand, over whose naked beauty
The wings flew, in the whistle of dusk-flight.
Turn the back, for peace, on the peace that moves
The heart to thunder.
Let the wrist move again, let the eye rove
Over the water, let the small fly
Be the tip of skill, on a thin thread
Binding the day to you, the spring day, alone:
For all days are bound now
To the love of Judith.

So the day passes, and the shadows grow bolder, an army of
    shadows,
Out from this tangle of brush, these mingled trees, this rise of
    land, hiding and increasing in the curves of the river,
That is a silver sheet now touched with the blue dusk.

And the tall day gives way before them, dropping,
Breaking its spears of light, till finally
The long shadows cover the valley in a deep blue silence,
And the sound of the birds is become a small and distant
    warning in the lonely air.

I, alone, then.
Father is off and away up-stream, fishing the east fork of Deer
    River.
Time to stop now:
Time to stop fishing, and the being alone, in the dusk, where
    the river says
Incomprehensible things. Where the small sounds
Rustle and rattle in the dry brush, in the dark places,
Where the mind usurps the ear, hearing, distantly, unplaceably,
The metal sound of a wheel on a sand road,
And the image of madness weds the image of love,
And one is alone.
Beauty lies all about: in the sound: in the cool scent of the
    water, the moist smell of the earth newly warmed by
    spring: the green ribbons of sky torn on the sharp black
    branches;
But these are lonely beauties.

So I call: the echo answers: *Father!*
Call, *Whoo-hoop!* and the echo returning
Is the lonely cry of an owl.

There is a good noise in the splash of water
To the heave of boots forward. There is a good sound
To the crash of dry branches broken
Under the hurrying boot.
There is a cheerful rattle of water over a long shallow
Sharp with little stones, decanting
Sky to the wine-coloured pool below it.
But above the shallow, where the good rattle fades to the dis-
    tant rustle of water,
Is a closer silence, for its rustle.
This soft plop: a fish: a turtle? A stone dislodged, and fall-
    ing,— why? In the dusk
Is the sound of the trees breathing, and the thin
Fluting of frogs.

274

So I call again, and the echo answers.
Call, *Whoo-hoop!* and the echo returning
Is a lonely cry, in a silence out of reason.

Make the good noise again in the splashing water
By the progress of the dark columns of boots.
Now he cannot be far: here is the East Fork,
Pale in the green light. Call again.
I may not.
What prevents a call? An echo answer?
Cup the hands and bellow, he's sure to hear you.
I cannot.
Follow the green glaze laid on the brown water,
The solid water of this long, still, deep reach,
Hugging the bank, ducking the whips of the clethra,
The only noise now is the slosh and gurgle
Of the boots in the still water. Stop. The sound now
Is the breath of the trees and the sharp piping
Of the spring-time frogs.

Round the bend to the small clear space
Where the pines reach to the edge of the water
And the ground is brown with the pricking softness of needles
Cast from the dark boughs.
And there:
There is Father, lying, asleep? on the bank's edge,
Feet down-dangling into the water, the black boots limp but
    round;
His rod stands in the water, butt down, tip caught by thin
    twigs.
Asleep?
Throw your rod aside to the brown bank,
Hurry . . .
No sleep.
Sleep is a soft, a pleasant, good word.
No sleep: an arrow
Quivered in the strong heart
Brings not sleep: death: fear
Tells terrible things to fumbling fingers
Touching a slack wrist, near a pierced heart;
Faint light, gloaming, spring dusk,
Lights the white of the sightless
Eyes. Death

Sits in the lax jaw. Fear,
Pain, horror, and fear again. These
Shadows are filled with a vast fear:
Name? Run now, run! No.
The irrelevant thought
Sees a whole life ahead, a whole death
Marred by running. An arrow
Runs swiftly, outruns.
Look now, look here, seek there. Here,
Ten yards, twelve yards, the crumpled
Acid green—heart will burst soon
Of this pounding—green skirt
Crumpled form, dark skin, head
Battered, the dark stain darker
About the dark brown needles—here now, further:
Small form, crushed head, child-form, fear,
Horror and death: and madness—the heart
Hurts now, hurts to each long
Willed beat, unwilled pain.
Say a word now, whisper, speak to Tom,
Say, Tom, grown Tom,
Go, Tom, slowly, go now,
Find John, go slow, the river, Tom: John
Waits below, Tom.
Go now. The water holds
Grey glaze in the spring dusk,
Splash sounds soft, soft, water sounds,
Soft sounds under the heart beats.
Now is distance added by splashed inches,
The soft night rises
Full of the water sounds, and the thin
Breathing of trees and the fluting
Of the small frogs and the splashes grow
Louder as haste lays
Hands on the heart and the heart runs
As the feet run over
The soft earth by the bank now
And the sharp whips slash
The face in unfelt pain and the dark boots
Cover the ground to—help? No,
No help, safety, to tell,
To say, Death:
Not sleep: Father:

And murder, and:
Jake.

Here is the great oak that marks our meeting place;
Here are the good twin lamps and the warm comfort
Of the sound of a running motor:
Here is the solid, living form of John Ward,
Steady John: tell John,
Father's dead, murdered, Jake,
Come!
He says only, "My, my! Steady, boy,
Here's a torch now, take me along there,
We'll just take a good look. Lights is good things, the dark
Is mostly deceiving."
Lead the way back now, swiftly, without running,
Piercing the dark now with the sharp blade of light
Cutting a way here, a path there.
Follow the moss-grown path, now. It swings
In a wide arc through the oak trees,
Past the pitch pine groves, black on the grey sky,
Into the white pines' blackness against the first stars
Of the dim eastern sky. Our feet
Make but a soft sound, our ears
May hear each other and fend
The expected and terrible sounds, unnamed, unknown,
Not reasonable, there, being awaited,
Hid in the curve of the ear.
So the blade of the torch flashes
Over the pine-carpet, and here:
Acid green: the crumpled form of the woman;
And here, so few steps, the huddled
Innocence of the slain child
And the stained, huge
Stone of its death beside it:
And upon both, the pale gold of marsh-marigolds, glinting of
    water,
Fresh plucked, fresh laid, tenderness
On immediate horror.
John says: "God Almighty!" We turn now
To the soft river bank. Here:
This is the place, the polished
Metal bands of the rod reflect the light, the beam
Buries its green shaft in the blur of water,

But here:
Here is no body: Father
Is not here, only
Blood on the dry brown needles, the yellow
Weave of the creel, the grey
Of the felt hat, brown leather,
Upside down, in horror.
Speak now, speak: a babble of incoherence,
"Gone, he's taken the body. It was here, was
Here by the river, the bank's edge, gone now."
John says only, "Seem so. We'll be going,"
And a firm hand seizes my arm and we depart,
Walking slowly, the white light
Turns on the ground ahead. Our feet
Follow the dim path. In silence.
So we move for a great while, till I whisper:
"He was there, John, when I
Stood by Father." A terrible
Fear contracts my bowels, I feel
Faint and ill. His hand on my arm is steady,
He says: "Easy does it, this is for the police,
Easy Tom, easy, boy, you got me here now."
And we pursue the light on the noiseless path
Past the dark pines, hearing only
The thin breathing of trees and distant
Fluting of frogs.

3

It is all over now: these things are long past,
They are long past and gone into
The casts of memory. One remembers
The yellow, tender marigolds laid on the dead bodies,
In the torch-light. One remembers
The arrow's shaft; and the absence of the arrow
And its flesh-quiver, and the horror and fear
Of the memory of the dusk which held
Jake so near, not harming me, not moving,
Breathing softly, surely, as the trees breathe,
But with a dread, mad breath.
One remembers these things as detached
And fearful nightmare visions, unreal,
Believed, and unbelievable.

Father was never found: the search continued
Month upon month. Somewhere, some day,
They will unearth the fine and graceful bones
That harbour an arrow: a shaft
Sent from the distance of the years.
One remembers: the skill, the strength, the reason,
The ruthless path; one thinks
Of the small painting, Maria in her youth;
Of Clare; of shooting; of many little moments
Turned to one great one when the light
Played on a painting, played on a man's soul
Nakedly shown. Oh, one remembers
This and that: but always, he was Father,
Magic word: translating
All the substance of thought to one image
Pressed into childhood; pressed to a love
Deeper than reason, coloured by admiration,
Misted with envy, crusted by resentment,
Past comprehension—still there, still love,
Deeper than reason.
                    Somewhere
In the high, wild and thick-brushed woods
Of Glocester township, they found the great white
Bones of Jake, on a green summer's day,
After two years had flung their hours
On the shores of living: an upreared,
Rag-clad skeleton held by the long, twisted
Boughs of a blueberry. They said,
Died in winter, seem so, died in the snow,
Dead a long while.
Perhaps he had nothing to live for?
One remembers Jake: there is little anger:
Other times and places, other phrases:
Jake won't let nothing harm you.
Jake, the protector: madness must see death, then,
As the ultimate safety?
Saw my father as danger? reason
Flung back years to the old love suddenly
Ended by this agency? Madness: seeking:
Hoping for God and finding only the flesh
To distort even the passion of flesh, and making
Reason to spiral down in a long curve
To this dread fantasy.

One remembers: fear, not anger.
Perhaps, in the snow,
With all else emptied, he saw the end, gratefully;
Perhaps death was his saviour, who dealt in death
So terribly to me, so terribly
To his despite. Perhaps
There is a peace now to the fears that shook
The metal barrow into the guard of love
Too closely guarded.
Now perhaps his eye
Is well nourished by just one glittering star
Following its inviolate far course
To such large motion that its circular
And terrifying orbit swallows
Haste and the fear of haste and breeds
Peace to his madness.

PART SIX

I SAID: no tragedy. I repeat it now.
Tragedy is the terrible awakening
That fears a future, all good life become
Unalterably past. There's tragedy
In the unfutured growth of dismal long days
In dull succession; when the dreaded end
Is not more final than a broken wish
Past human mending or super-human aid.
Tragedy is the small, perverse and rigid
Fate that can always thwart, when to man's eye
All life's distorted by a falser seeing
Than all occasion warrants: it is deadly clipped
Into the long and cancerous dark roots
Of man's dishonesty, roots that have spread their fibres
Down through the willing mind to the blind flesh
And ceased their parasitic life to be
The integers of living.
Death is not tragedy:
Misfortune, grief, the very end of love,
The partings and the angers, these are but
The past of life, and such a past becomes
The dung we spade into the spring-time garden
For richer growing.
                    There'd be some tragedy
For any man whose manhood was not deeply
Moved by the light and dark of childhood years—
Whose years held only the blank images
Of superficial happiness, the empty
Lists of unhappened life: such lives become
But mist and vapour like all rootless living,
Having no clutch on the hard deeps of earth:
Nor ever roots struck down to their dark feeding
But must have bruised against the rocks of pain,
Been cut and twisted by the persistent shards
Of subterranean life that buried long
Its sharper fragments.
                    Single, aloof Josiah

Ends before tragedy: not such a death
As waits in an increasing mortal fear
The long decrease of power, of strength that bore
The heavy armour of self-love. His age
Might have shown rifts to the more hurtful arrows
Of older days barbed with their loneliness.
(Passionate, lonely echo flung: Alone!)

This is my story: the moon of my device
Moves slowly now; the next recurrent cycle,
The lapping circles, widen, but contain
Always the old within the crescent brightness
Of new sharp horns.
                I moved upon my love,
Whose richness is forever and forever
Mine past all tragedy: into it I brought
The fortunes and misfortunes of all days
Whose colour stained me.
              How can tragedy
Harbour within the circle of such life
As but contains the everlasting good mix
Of pain, of effort, of compassionate joy,
Of the consuming hope that sees each day
Become a promise beyond the eternal woe
Of failed fulfilment, promise of greater things
Upon such morrows as will fit the soul
To grasp and hold them?
             What is death that we
Who must embrace it, may not see its skull
As but another milestone in the hard
And grander road we travel by the light
Of human, living love once richly given?

Here is no tragedy, this is my life,
And death itself is but the absent moon
Whose light is promised for another night
And for succeeding eyes.

NOW, NOW! this is the instant! grasp it tight!
Seize fleeting present before it be dismissed

Into dry clarity of the past, while flight
Still wears its veiling of the future's mist.
Present and future pleasantly confuse:
The warming hope becomes the ungrasped act;
It is the grasping that can most abuse:
The fingers tighten, and the past's hard fact.
So love comes trailing promises and hope
Out of a dawn of want, a spring of need—
How swift you bind it with a passionate rope,
Even in binding, it is somehow freed;
Yet there is left the memory and good lust
To sift like jewels from the past's dry dust.

❧   ❧

'THERE IS A time for all things?'

There is a time for the great dry winds of March
Blowing the dust up, the grey ghost of winter:
There is enough dust here to cover me up, and you,
And many others: when it shall settle;
But not now. No. There is a time for this,
For that one, and another, and another:
They shall be covered in the dust, and, in the end,
I also, surely. But not yet. No.

'There is a time for these things?'

There is a time for mourning, for the black of mourning:
For the dim-lit service:
In the chanting of voices and the white and black
Of a priest's robe and the candles
Bright on the gold surfaces, on the accustomed
Faces that sing: memorial tendencies—
But only the wild dust settles, now: no man
Shall shred dust down to the rectangular
Pit of the ending.

'There is a time for mourning, and a place?'

Sorrow and mourning are met now, in my mother,
In a deep meeting.

285

'But sorrow passes, mourning becomes over—
Is it not so?'

It does not pass here, it is black worn beyond reason,
Beyond reason; but now
It is but the time and the place for mourning
Met in one person: worn from kindness, perhaps—
Worn freely, willingly.

'Worn gladly?'

No, it is worn in the whole passion of grief
Dragged from disconsolate memory and upheld
By the long arm of failure.
See!
Here is a different grief worn in the lines of an old face,
The grief that sees,
That senses the importunate end, the untimely
Blight of power; the knowledge
Of long and lonely grief growing—now spared; the vision
Of age persisting in the dropped pulse of life
When the strong pulse is timely over.
So my grandfather sees, not wearing black;
Seeing a time and a place for mourning:
Seeing the days
As the beginning of life for me and for my brother: not wear-
    ing
The desperate colours of a day that's closed
In final night, death, done and over:
Seeing a time and a place.

'And you then, and your brother?'

It is not the same: our blood
Hums to a different tune, though youth
Moves to the same force: youth.
Grief for death is the privilege of age, the sanction
Of an older mind. We move
To a love returned, to a freedom now returned:
Judith for me, freedom for him; our egos
Bent on our life that floods, that floods so strongly
There is no hap for death beyond
A time and a place for death, and a time for mourning,

A person missed—but now and then—not squarely
Over the full day. Oh, the taste
Of the milk of the sun of summer is in our mouths, we taste
The heat of the hot meat of the July day, we drink
The honey of August, fresh to our mouths. We go
Our separate paths.

'And he goes whither?'

Whither he wishes: it is the wine of choice,
It is a heady wine, he has learnt the taste
From the man that the wild dust covers before that man
Could tell him the wine decanted was bitter wine.
It is a fine path he goes in the hot
Suns of summer.

'And you go where?'

I go to my love with a passion, I go with a doubt,
I go with a grief and a hurt and a double mind,
I go with a taste of the wild dust, the sight
Of the mourning woman, the eyes
That have seen the lines deepen, and the ears
That have heard an old man's voice say:
Peace! peace to the past, it is the future
That always matters. I go
To the hard trial of marriage that bends
The bones to its singular use.

'And this you knew?'

There is a time for knowing. I did not know.

'Had you not seen?'

Seeing is not to know. Listen:
I did not know that pain and joy commingled
In a harsh ecstasy.
I did not know the dreams that are woven
Out of another's dreams, nor the guessing of dreams;
Nor the grey light of new day on the doubled sight,
Foretelling uncountable days.
I did not know that spirits could surely merge

287

In the battle of sun-filled hours, the rattle
Of man-filled hours.
I did not know that hate and the hard word
Were but the spurs to the young horse that leaps
In the bridle of spring.
I did not know of the seed nor the seed's power;
Nor freedom lost in the binding of the thin
Cords that save on the mountain and trip in the valley.
I did not know of the use of speech released
By love's release, nor of the small words grown
To dangerous stature and the lips sealing
The flood of the heart with the wax of fear;
Nor the little, ridiculous, delicious
Things that enrich and remain.
I did not know the languor of love usurping
All ambition, being its own fulfilment,
Nor freedom gained in the close winding of thin
Cords to make strong the stored love;
Nor the return of reason from its wandering
Rarest Elysium, to the rich, coarser fields
Of common doing: one by one: together.
And I did not know
The ebb and the flood, the soft receding, the bare revealing,
The lofty mounting of the irrepressible
Waters of love in the long tides
That come and go as the pulse, strong, fearful,
Comes and goes in the winding veins.

'And these matters now?'

They are mine now, I have grasped
The edges of these matters. I have touched
The hem of them, the bordering, I have felt
The pattern under my fingers, I have known
The weft of love to my touch—I am
But now beginning. Listen:

I did not know that pain and joy commingled
In a harsh ecstasy.

Judith all over the house: strong music: upstairs,
Tempting the feet to move: fingers at the grey tie,
The hair to brush again. Brush for Judith.

Brush your heart in place, as you brush your hair—
Sam is looking, you must.
Wear your heart on your sleeve and it will get torn,
Or something, or else, maybe
Someone might spill champagne or lobster patties
All over your nice clean heart.
Oh, the day is Judith,
The day's October and Sam is in October,
But say, instead, in a steady sort of a voice,
'You've got the ring, you've got it,
You haven't lost it?'
But don't say: Judith. And don't cry out: October,
But shut your lips on the words that spell the months
Since once June crumbled into an empty space
Of black and hollow days without a wedding,
Without a father.
Mother is dressed in black.
Mother is dressed in black and Joss in his medals,
And Sam and I, we've got our grey ties, splendid,
And soon will be the ties of marriage, not grey,
Nor black nor brown but golden with little links
Like champagne bubbles or bubbles of pure October
Of bootleg vintage, straight from Canada, yessir,
All the blue sky coming straight from the Northwest Mounted
Whose red coats are the leaves. It's a bootleg day,
Stolen from death and sorrow, from black of mourning,
From Mother in black of a sorrow beyond all reason—
Oh, Judith all over the house like a fine scent
Sprayed in October bubbles of scented air.

Say 'Sam! Damn! It's time that we were going,'
And do a double shuffle with your feet upon the floor.

Now we go down the stairs, the little back stairs,
The dusky stairs, the dusky hall,
Out through the bustling kitchen, kitchen full of faces,
Faces full of smiles and glances: the room
Is papered with smiles and the echo of old smiles.
This room is different: the faces, solemn and smiling,
Only a well-bred rustle; but who breeds rustles?
Oh, Rustles are all well-bred, it runs in the family,
But you must not think like this now. Look!
The jokes go out of the brain and the heart's in a panic,

The room is empty of people, the world is empty—
Only a white-clad image advancing, advancing,
Judith—cry Stop! And run!
But you just stand still.
The legs and the feet stand still and the heart stands still,
And a great fear runs all through and the sweat comes,
And the knees are shaking. Judith in white:
The people's faces are white, great globes of faces
Dim in the room of people.
Move, then, move now!
This is the minister, this is Judith beside you,
This is in sickness and health, to love and to cherish—
Whose voice said 'I will'?
Not your voice? Your voice.
Now the ears hear better, the globes are faces,
The minister seems to be only the Reverend Munson,
Stuttering slightly.
But this is Judith beside you,
This is everything good in the whole wide world
Wrapped in a white veil, and a clear voice saying,
'Thereto I give thee my troth.'
Then a voice and a voice,
The well-bred rustle, the ring from the hand of Allen
Coming to hand the ring from the depths of space,
For a disembodied hand comes now;
And the words run on,
And together we kneel and rise, Tom and his Judith,
Till suddenly over the beat of the words you hear
'Each to the Other' as if it bore a sense
Beyond the words as a flute plays over the gale
Of the short and the long taut strings.

The globes of faces are smiling and some are weeping
Over their smiles. You smile at Isaac Carpenter,
You smile at Rose his wife, and you smile at Mother
But without looking at her, only the corner
Of the eye perceives.

And thank you, Sam, and thank you, Arthur and Edward,
And thanks, then, Joss, get Mother a big drink, will you?
And thank you, Cora, you look like a dream, oh really,
The dress is dandy, I'm glad you like the roses,
And thank you Mrs. Standeven, well, Aunt Rachel,

Of course, I'd love to, Judith her name is Rachel?
The aunt with the teeth?
Oh thank you, Mother dear, and cheer up, Mother,
For Joss will get you a drink, I'm sure you need it,
And hello there, Miss Darnley, thanks for the tea-pot,
Thanks for the soup-spoon, Mr. Waterman, yes,
Grandfather's here, in the wheel-chair, by the window,
Thanks, Mrs. Frobisher, oh, of course I remember—
Your face is as flat as the cards that slap and shuffle,
Your face is as flat as the deuce, and thanks, Mr. Hal-
    lowell,
And howd'ye do, Mrs. Hallowell, howd'ye do
Caroline and Maude—but you've changed your dresses,
For Maude's in green and Caroline's wearing pink,
And howd'ye do, Miss Brown, you are so pretty,
And oh, Mr. Babcock,
Howd'ye do, I hope the music's sticking
Well on the doors for in the music there
Judith and I and love are embedded forever—
She was a Carpenter, now she is a Cottrell,
Leaving the Carpenter's house.

And a great voice calls from a chair, 'I'm looking at you!
I'm drinking your health and Judith's, I wish you love,
There isn't enough around.'
And people laugh:
And music comes from another room and Judith
Runs to the great voice: but she may not leave me
For I run too and the great voice
Cries: 'Good luck! but damn it, Judith,
Dr. Thingummy's here, keep him away,
I'll drink champagne if I choose, and not be lectured,
I've saved these days of life and by God! I'll spend 'em
For you and Tom and the memory of love.'

And thank you, thank you!
And gosh! some people are eating the lobster patties,
But not me and not Judith, thank you, thank you!
Just a few words, and Happy, and Special Day,
And a health to Mr. and Mrs. Carpenter,
(And a health to the waiters at five dollars a throw
Who give you the glasses for healths and for special days)
And then . . .

Put it right in the bag, Sam, and put this
Into the hat-box, and Joss, look after Mother—
And boy, does he look smart in all his medals!
And his uniform makes hollow the sense of Tom
Down for a careless strap . . . and Martin down . . .
And Father down . . . and at last!
Joss is away from the room and Sam is there,
And at last, ah!
Sam is away and just for a fleeting minute:
You are alone.
Music all over the house, thin music upstairs,
Tempting the eyes to cry and the lips to quiver,
Giving the word 'alone' a fearful meaning,
And the world's before you, but not alone,
And then . . .

The paper rose-leaves flutter, the hard rice stings,
The car starts off from the sea of the globes of faces,
From the high women's voices, the deep men's voices,
The wet, sad face of Mother who has no voice,
And you change the car to another that has no ribbons—
Here is the train.
Here is the little, bag-filled, hot compartment,
Here is Judith in the blue serge,
Here are you.
Here is the coat and the hat and the wrap and the rug
And the tickets are in the coat that is on the rack,
And here's the porter, and here,
Here's the conductor, grinning, and you are grinning,
And here's the Pullman man and he is grinning,
And the room is as full of tact as a whale of blubber,
And the wheels say rattle-bang, clatter-bang, switch-points,
And the door shuts and . . .
You are alone—but—
Not alone now, two, for a pale face
Looks at you and the grey eyes look, the dark
Hair is shining under the dark blue hat,
And the white hands
Flutter and are yours now,
And the pale face
Whispers and you
Whisper the same word and the train wheels
Rattle as words grow dim in the long time

Of lips not speaking, lips no longer whispering,
Lips enjoining terror, entreating love.

So in the night-time,
Under the yellow lamps of the war's New York,
Young Tom mounted the stoop and rang the doorbell,
Tom with a bride beside him, Tom wed to beauty,
Peeked through familiar sidelights now unfamiliar,
Saw the white apron, always on the bias,
Saw the dear face of Agatha draw near them,
Heard the door click and open, stood in the shadow,
Said, 'We are here now, Agatha, we are here,'
Heard her cry out 'Welcome!' and, 'Mrs. Cottrell,
Give me your things now, Mr. and Mrs. Cottrell,
I welcome you home.'

Then there is supper and supper is now over,
The champagne bottle is empty, and its bubbles
Gather into the globe of the one lamp.
There is a soft light on the dark red curtains,
The sound of the city, soft.
You say, 'And so . . .'
And Judith says, 'It's an end and a beginning,
And they lived happily, happily ever after.'
You say, 'I hope they do.'
She says, 'You worry. You are mine now, listen,
I shall not let you worry. The worry is over.'
But still you say, 'This house—and others before us,
We must walk carefully to avoid their errors —
But we have love.'
'Have love,' she says, 'what more can anyone want?'
'There is the wicked witch,' you say. She answers,
'There is the prince's kiss.'

And the one lamp is out, and the room is dark,
And the stairs are dark, and this is my mother's room:
But different now, here is a new paper
Clothing the walls, ready now to absorb us,
To retain our image. The cupboard is empty now,
There are no dresses.
The bureau is bare now, there are no little bottles,
There are no pictures here, nor on the mantel
Are any photographs, and the jars and vases,
These are different now, and the flowers they hold,

These are our flowers, for us,
Chrysanthemums,
Dahlias in a blue vase—and here,
These are different chairs and a different table,
The curtains are blue and new and swing in the soft
Air from the back yard, the lamp
Is a new lamp giving
A new light, shining now
On the dark hair of Judith, on Judith's white skin,
On the red of Judith's lips, on the grey eyes
Open to you now, open to you, telling
A new story; these are different eyes,
And these are different, slim hands
And only,
Only the bed remains, yes, only
The bed remains.

Only the dark now, only the dark,
Only the two spirits striving, only
The hands that reach for love, each to the other;
Only the dark, now, and the small words,
And the lips that seek, and
The terrible acquiescence.
What is the dark now in so fierce a light?
What is love now in the dark lightning,
In the noiseless thunder of blood
In the long veins,
The searching,
The pain and the passion and the weak compassion,
The strength that rears
Strength to its search to find
Sharp pain, sharp joy,
The giver and the giving commingled swiftly—
Swift to your love, it grows
Fast to your heart, the pain
Is the knife of the mind in the heart,
Is the fire of breath
That scorches and sears and burns
The dross of your mind,
And the mystery of your love
Is your own possessing, possessing,
Your own . . .
And now . . .

Only the dark now, only the dark
And the sound of breath,
And the taste of tears,
And the crowding thoughts and the dim
Impulse to everlasting
Love and possession and giving and the hurt
Of the pain of the knife in the heart,
Of the mind's knife,
Cutting the old away, for a new heart,
And the tender hands
Now possessing, but only
In the dark now, in the dark—
There is a long time yet
Till the light grows,
Till the day grows,
When love will be seen, for now
There is a trial of love, there is the pain,
All in the darkness.

I did not know that dreams are woven
Out of another's dreams, nor the guessing of dreams.

Lie in the clouds of the night
Where slumber's a distant thunder,
Where the rifts of the day in a storm unite
And the heart is split asunder
By the blade and the edge of self, and the flame of another.
But love lies close to the touch though dark to the sight,
And peace is a storm to cease—dream to smother
Love in the darkling world where love is to fear and to won-
      der.

Judith's a dream—shall you waken?
And you, a part of her dream?
Lift heavy lids, till the dream forsaken.
At the deep, dread edge shall seem
Now the desertion of love, the desperate, dear
Flight to the single world—till flight's overtaken
Soon by the dream that is real, that is clear—
Till love is possessed by a phantom love and at last is supreme.

Softer the sounds of the hours,
The breath of the city is deep,

The wall with its twilight shadow of flowers,
The moments of night that creep
Into the depths of passion replete in the heart,
Till the dream is a shape in the mind, and the shape towers
To the image of love, to the counterpart
Of the inseparable dream that is you . . . that is her . . . that
    is sleep.

Nor the grey light of new day on the doubled sight
Foretelling uncountable days.

Somehow the sound comes
Over the low roofs, and is caught here
In the back yard of many angles, rests here, echoing
Round and round to the vanishing point:
Clip-clop, clip-clop, softer and softer,
Tip-top:
The sound of horse's repeated down-step
In punctual rhythm—only the milkman,
Only the horse and the cart clattering—yet,
Echoed in memory. Grey light
Filled with an echo of old days. Grey light
Seeping and creeping in to the old, new
Room now. Dawn's light
On the dark hair, in the old,
New dawn; the soft sound
Vanishes now and the sound is soft
Of her breathing. Lie still:
This is the first day of many days
Linked in the long, unseen
Chain of the days to come, but lie still:
Breath beats, hoof beats
Echo again at the far edge now
Of the far grey
Angles and shadows of grey light;
Soft breath, dark hair,
Sweet days, old echoes—
New joy! Close the eyes on the grey dawn,
Keep the memory, keep the echo,
Keep the joy that swells as the sounds retreat
Into the soft grey of the dawn of joy . . . but . . .
Lie still: love still
Lies still.

I did not know that spirits could surely merge
In the battle of sun-filled hours, the rattle
Of man-filled hours.

"It oughtn't to be so hot, Tom, in late October—
Just feel that sun!"
                    "I feel it. I like the feel.
It makes me lazy."
                    "Why shouldn't you be lazy?"
"It makes me more than lazy."
                                "Be careful, Tom."
"Because of the driver? He's French. He's sympathetic.
The horse won't care."
                    "Please not."
                                "I feel so lazy
With the sun like a deep warm blanket for our shoulders.
Except for the shadows, we'd need no clothes at all.
Why are we here, and why are we dressed?"
                                        "Look, Tom,
Did you ever see a street that was any steeper?"
"It's steep but shadowy."
                        "There'll be sun at the top.
We'll see the plains of Abraham and the river."
"And then?"
            "We'll go down again, like the King of France.
Down to our room."
                    "Yes. Don't you wish we were there?"
"No. It's nice in the sun. I like the houses,
The people, the crooked streets. I like the noise
Of the wheels on the cobbles. I specially like the jiggles."
"If it was colder, we'd have a robe for our knees
And our hands could hide below it."
                                    "I like the sun.
I love the heat and the noise."
                                "We've got three people
Here on the back seat."
                        "Three?"
                                "You and I and the people.
The people are sitting between us."
                                    "Oh, Mr. People,
How do you do? Do you know my husband, Tom?
He's a fine young man."
                        "Do you like Mr. People?"
297

"He's rather exciting."

     "He's not. He's a nuisance, Judith."

"No, Tom, a fact. We can't be always alone."

"No, maybe not. But tell me, where did you learn
So much so quickly?"

     "I didn't learn. It happened.
Look, there's the river now. That's a fine, big river.
It must be wonderful when that rush of water
Is stilled in ice."

    "You'll never be stilled in ice?"

"I'll melt for you, Tom."

    "Always?"

      "Always and always."

"How do you know?"

    "I feel it down in my bones."

"I wish I were so sure. In time you might find it
Best to sit in a cab and feel the sun
Hot on the shoulders and Mr. People between us
And be so sorry when Mr. People left
And we were alone again."

    "No, never, Tom.
Being like this is fun, and being alone.
Time may make it different, but always fun.
I've seen it so."

    "I've seen it not be fun.
I've seen it be pretty awful."

    "Hush, Tom! Hush!
Take the day as you find it. We'll add the days
After we've had them."

    "No—you never look back .
You always go ahead. The past is useless."

"Hush, Tom, hush! And the buses? The North River?
And the Babcocks' dance and the porch?"

     "Move nearer, Judith."

"No—don't move. Don't move. Look at the view, Tom,
There are the plains of Abraham. There Wolfe died.
There is the big, blue river, way down below there—
Look at the boats—he climbed from there to here, Tom,
Out of the past way up to here in the present.
And still the sun and the shadows are as ever,
So look, my sweet."

    "And think."

     "I'll think of you.

You think of me. We're distant. You're here beside me
And yet you're distant."
                              "You like it?"
                                              "It is heaven,
Waiting for distance to grow less. You'll try it?
Seize the sun and the warmth, my love."
                                        "I'll try it.
But if I closed my eyes, we'd be alone then."
"Keep them open, Tom."
                        "I'll keep them open,
Because you say to."
                      "No—because you'll feel,
Distance will vanish. And the people vanish
And time and Quebec and the driver, they'll all vanish
Into your thinking, with you and me together,
With the sun between us."
                          "Yes."
                                  "Keep silent now,
Think of me, think of me, but keep silent a little."

"It is true, yes . . . Judith . . . I see the river,
I see the boats and I feel the heat of the sun,
And I see the hills in the distance, all so blue,
And love and the people walking. I see you, too,
Out of the corner of my eye."
                              "The warmth
Is heavenly, isn't it, Tom?"
                              "And you are heaven
With the blue air between. Oh, we are going
Down the hill again—as it begins, it's over."
"No, as long as it lasts, it's still beginning.
Just feel the sun!"
                    "I feel it. I love the feel.
But it makes me sad."
                      "And loving?"
                                    "It makes me loving,
But this is a new love, Judith."
                                  "A new love, sweet."
"And it'll be over, when we get to the shadows
Down below there."
                    "It'll be over, Tom,
But look, we've had it. It isn't in the future,
We had it, you and I, and our Mr. People

Sitting so stiff between us. Oh, Mr. People,
How do you do? I am Tom's wife, I'm Judith,
Isn't that nice?"

I did not know that hate and the hard word
Were but the spurs to the young horse that leaps
In the bridle of spring.

That day the wind blew and the waves became great,
Giant shoulders that heaved at the ship and pushed it heavily
Until it quivered and rolled. The tops of the waves,
The bubbling green and white froth of mixed waters,
Would pause for a second, as though they snarled at the black
     side
Of the leaning vessel and then strike with a dull, wet sound,
Turning to the small, many waterfalls of salt torrents
Dropping tempestuously back into the troubled sea
To write white warning letters in indecipherable anger. The
     Atlantic
Had no horizon and the inseparable clouds merged
With the sea and both were grey and greyer until the night
     was there
Without warning: just day drifted into darkness and the
     touch
Of the invisible cool spray.
                              All afternoon
Judith was sulky, and her grey eyes were tired and withhold-
     ing.
She would not take to her bed, she said, "I am quite well,"
And in the same breath, "I have a headache."
She lay down to rest but, when I left her, joined me,
Rising impatiently so soon, and we walked hardly
On the slanting deck whose motion now and then betrayed
Our striding pace. She said she would have no tea,
Refused the steaming cup on the damp and chilly deck,
Went below to our cabin and immediately
Ordered tea and drank there, eagerly, complaining
That it was foul tea and not worth drinking, awful tea.
The cabin was full of the small tiresome sounds
Of the ship's movement. Our voices
Cried above the jingle and chink of glasses, the small rattle
Of wood and metal. She said, "Oh Tom, look. Don't fuss so.
I am not seasick, I am not one to become seasick. I feel

Cooped here, shut in, I want exercise. Look, Tom,
It is beastly on deck, the salt spray thick there, the smoke
Blows down out of the funnels and chokes me."
I said, "All I know is, you are not yourself now."
"What is myself? I don't know. Why should you? Just let
Poor nature take its course." "Just that exactly,
Put yourself to bed, now." "No." "Have dinner there,
You'll feel better tomorrow."
                            She laughed at me:
"If you had had a sister you would be better
At guessing, knowing these things, women's vagaries.
I'd miss you, Tom, and the company, and the dancing."
"You can't dance now, dance on this great, heaving
Floor of the ship." "Oh, this is not bad. I've danced
In a real storm." "We'd fall down."
                            She said, "Oh,
You don't have to dance with me, cheer up. Don't
Look so sad. Is it as bad as that?"
"What is as bad as what?"
                            "Dancing with me, Tom?"
"Don't be silly, Judith."
                            "It's what you said, though."
I thought then, this is a queer day, women are queer, too.
Everything's at cross-purposes, here's Judith
Wants to quarrel with me. Quarrel already. Not I!
"Lie down, please, my sweet, at least till dinner time, will
        you?
You can decide then." "I can decide
While I am sitting up. I don't have to lie down on a bed
To know my mind. I'll read.
Hand me my book, Tom."
                            I gave her the book, gladly.
"Then I'll go out again, for a while. I like the smell
Of the deep sea. I like the taste of the spray coming
Out of the darkness." "Don't go," she said, "don't go!"
"I thought you wanted to read?" "No, Tom, I don't. Damn
        books!
Or if I want to, don't want to read alone here, be alone
In this drab cabin." "All right," I said, "I'll stay."
I sat again, on the edge of my bed, picked up a pencil,
Took a pad of paper, thinking, Write now, write. These
Are the moments alone. Use them. She cried out,
"All right, go out, go out! But don't stay here, only to write.

301

That is worse than out—you sit here and are not here, away,
Both at once, I can't bear that."
She threw her book to the floor, open: it slammed
With a small report; she rose then, seizing my cap,
Jammed it on my head, snatched my pencil from my fingers,
    swiftly,
Flung it across the cabin; grabbed me by the arm and pulled
    till
I rose heavily, being bewildered; pushed me to the door
Saying, "Go on, go walking, smell your beastly sea,"
Slammed the door after me. I thought, Great God!
What has got into her, Judith, the wise and loving?
Temper I knew, but not a useless temper, at nothing:
Temper three weeks from marriage, honeymoon temper, com-
    ing
From the clear skies of love. What had I done?
I walked the deck in the darkness: it was curious,
I could not foretell the motion, nor see the motion, the planted
Foot struck hard on the rising lines of the long boards,
The endless, solid black lines; the foot fumbled
For a lost meeting. The mind fumbled for meaning
In the lost words. The wind blew
Thoughts away as the breath caught in the stiff, palpable
Thrust of the wind, and the eyes strayed into
Conscious seeing of the raw whiteness of ship-lit islands
Heaving in foamy blackness. The mind, the wind, and the wet
World of the wide waste of invisible waters joined now
In a common tumult.
                            All throughout that evening,
I sparred with Judith, holding off from anger, feeling
Troubled and hurt and knowing hurtful thoughts, and wait-
    ing
In a dim undefined excitement for some moment, coming,
    coming,
Some climax to delay. For all things
Were wrong and could not be put right with patience
Nor with forbearance, silence being as great an irritation
As the swift spoken word. We dined, had good wine,
Drank the slow fire of brandy, fresh now to our palates—
But nothing easily done. Red wine or white wine? neither?
Whisky? or shall we have wine? "Oh, I don't care. Oh, do
    please order,
Why should I decide?" Or will you have chartreuse,

Or kümmel, crême de menthe, or curaçao or bénédictine, or—
"What is best, Tom, what is best, decide, man. Tell me."
And chartreuse ordered, it was changed to brandy.
We danced, but heavily, to the heavy music, slowly, our feet
Seeking the arbitrary floor. She said, "It's like being drunk,
And yet we are not drunk. If we were really
Drunk, should we know? We might as well be drunk
As dance like this." So we sat down. She said, then,
"There will be only a little more of the music, drink up,
Finish your drink and dance, we're wasting
Time in this sitting." Or, gaily: "If we sit,
We get our exercise, the chairs move so, we might
As well be dancing." And dancing: "What is wrong, Tom?
Your feet are clumsy, you hold me now so loosely. Have you
Forgotten how to dance since you've accepted
Marriage you were tormented by? Did the pursuit only
Inspire your feet?"

                 But I said little, smiling, grinning,
Flushing a little sometimes, and the more I kept
Silence and all my smiles, these seemed only
New provocation to attack.

                     The music stopped at last:
So she would go out to the windy night to feel the wind
Fresh from the ocean that bore us on to Europe, lovely
    thought!
Yet in the wind of night, her dark hair blew
Roughly and so she cried, "I cannot bear it, it is blowing
Rain and salt spray," and, "Let us go in quickly, quickly,
Before I am destroyed. Why did you let me come out so,
Into the salt spray, you had felt it, I had asked only
For the cool wind—you must have known."
                     And so we came
Down to our cabin, but I left her there, going above again,
Driven away by her who cried, "Must we forever crash
Into each other in this tiny space, can I
Have no more privacy?"
                 Now on the windless forward
Heavily glazed protected deck I stood, and the spray slashed
Often and briefly at the windows, and the eyes blinked
Involuntarily. I thought, We beat
Our wings in a new cage that we have chosen, these bars
Are still too shining, we can see them yet too clearly, time
Will tarnish them into obscurity . . . and we may lose

Fear . . . and the power of flight?
                                      The distant, lost bow
Dipped to the sea and wore a visible white wreath
On its thin edging, and was lost again in the blowing
Darkness and crash of the impersonal waters, now held
To unreality by the streaming glass sheets.
                                      Then I went
Below again to Judith, wondering.
                                      She sat
In the arm-chair by her bed. She wore now only
Her lacy nightdress: the cabin was hot: the smoke
Of her cigarette lay heavily and wavered in the forced
Currents of warm air. She said nothing, but looked at me
Distantly. I undressed for bed. I washed more carefully
And longer than usual. Still she sat there, looking at me,
Silent, unsmiling, removed. I said, "Judith." She looked up
    then.
"Yes?"
        "Go to bed now, it is late."
                                      "It's early yet."
"We lose an hour tonight."
                          She said, "Go on, go to your own bed,
Go to sleep, if you're tired. I am thinking. You can turn
The lights off, if you choose." I said, "How can I sleep
With you there, sulking?"
                          "I am not sulking. I am only
Thinking."
            "Think in your bed."
                          She answered, "It's too hot,
The cabin is too hot."
                      I said, "I'm sorry, the sea is too rough
To open the port. I'll ring."
                          "Don't ring. They'll make it icy."
I said, "All right."
                    She cried out then, "Oh God! Do you never
Ever get angry?"
                    I looked at her. I answered, "Yes. My anger
Comes slowly, lasts a long time."
                                  "It comes so horribly slowly!
If you'd get angry . . . I don't know." She paused. "Oh,
Everything's useless!" She raised her clasped hands high
And stretched her arms up. Then she let them fall down
    limply

304

Into her lap, and her eyes rested on her hands, joined there.
"Go to bed, Judith, or I shall get angry. Child! You are acting
Like a small child."
                    "I wish I were," she said. "A small child . . .
But I'm a woman, now."
                    "You act like a small child, Judith.
Get in your bed." I went to her side; I took hold
Of one arm and I pulled. She slumped down, heavily, resisting.
"Get up!" I said. "Get up, and stop it!" Suddenly
She leaped to her feet and the colour flooded into her face.
She cried out, "Let me be! Take your hands off me, who
Gave you the right to pull me, to command me, to tell me
I shall do this or that? Let go!"
                    I said, "I'll let go, Judith,
If you will go to bed."
                    "You'd bully me?"
                    "If I must bully you
To get some sense into you."
                    She gave a jerk, swift, hard,
And freed herself and faced me and said, "So, violence, vio-
  lence . . .
Or what . . . or is it you, at all? . . . or is it something
I don't know and got into. . ." She breathed hard. I reached
My hand out toward her, but she ducked aside and then,
She raised her arm and struck with all her force and the palm
Of her hand smote my cheek, flat, with a loud flat sound,
And we stood so, staring, motionless.
I saw her eyes turn then from grey to dark, slowly, and the
  blood
Left her cheeks and mounted again and left her, as though
Her blood were her breath. I felt the waves
Of a fierce feeling, unnamed, go through me, as I looked . . .
  maybe anger . . .
Maybe something not so clear as anger . . . something
That stirred and beat and beat and beat in the blood, and I
  looked at her,
Standing now, her hands touching each other, tentatively, as
  though
They did not know each other, but were meeting now
For the first time. And the beat and the beat grew louder and
  stronger,
And I moved then and I reached out my hand,
And I seized her nightdress and I ripped it, one great tearing

305

Rip and I tore it again and it parted and fell and still
She stood so, still . . . not moving, naked, her eyes black,
Her lips parted a little . . . and I reached out
And I laid hold of her shoulders, and I pulled her close and
      closer
Till the thunder of blood in the long veins
Was neither my thunder nor her thunder but the storm
Of our own tempest
And time
Ceased and the overwhelming
Passion of love was joined in a new
And terrible joining.

I did not know the seed, nor the seed's power.

We went one day from Paris to the west
To lunch with a Mrs. Mallory: she had known
My father in old days. I had looked forward
To meeting her because she wrote, and bore
A name made famous by her books. She lived
Only in France now.
                    Toward the end of lunch,
She said, "I leave soon for the south, near Cette,
I have a pretty place at Frotignan
Where I can watch the fishing boats. My garden
Is built for winter. Come and see me there,
If you come south."
                    We thanked her, Judith saying,
"How can you bear to leave this lovely place,
This heavenly house?"
                    She said, "You like my house?
I like it too. In all the years I've lived
(They're getting to be many), I've not seen
A place I loved so. In America
There's nothing comparable. When we've had our coffee,
We shall stroll out—it's chilly, not for long—
But just to see the view from this locked garden.
Mind you, no key to it—it's just December
That locks it up. At Cette it will be warm.
It's sometimes lonely here. My friends, like me,
Are growing old, they like the warmer sun,
They'll visit me at Frotignan, not here,
Not when it's winter."
                    "It seems so mild," I said,

"Does it get very cold?"
                              "Not very cold,
But raw. But I come back here in the spring
When the earth smells so sweet. Oh, the good smell
Of tended earth is different from the raw
Smell of wild land, more sweet, more satisfying.
You've come from a crude country. If you write,
You'd best stay here, in France. Intelligence
Is given peace to grow and time to grow
And is not hurried and heckled by the clock
Of over-energized America."
I said, "Oh yes, I do, I want to write—
But Mrs. Mallory, I want to tell
Of my own country." I smiled at her and said,
"I like its smell."
                              "Why, naturally you do.
It's all you know. You'll write of what you know,
Also inevitably. But learn of Europe
While you are young. Get civilized. Soak yourself
In this source atmosphere. The air of France
Is full of all its history, of its grace,
Its rich and splendid grace. Writing begins
Here with the great ones. What is there beyond
Rawness and newness, ugliness and speed
In your New York?"
                              "Oh, in New York," I said,
"Even if that is all it says to you,
It's not America."
                              "Oh yes," she cried,
"It symbolizes—rather, sums it up
In closer fashion. Can one be an artist,
Having so many things within oneself
To overcome and conquer, in a place
Where men conceive that art is self-indulgence—
If not immoral—where the only standard
Is always, 'Did he make some money by it?'
There can be no artistic standard there."
I flushed and said (although I knew within me
I'd better have kept quiet), "Yet you write
Mostly of us Americans and our ways
But not of Frenchmen."
                              "Yes," she said, "I do.
I have a passion to show us where we're wrong,

To point the moral of our ugly ways.
While here, I see those clearly—I have gained
Time and perspective. Could I see them so
If I were in the thick of it? Where life
Goes on in dull activity? Where disorder
Rules in the place of gaiety? Where fools
Pretending European culture, spend
Their money only on the trappings of it,
But never see its core?"

                              "But those," I said,
"They are a special few. The simple people
Are not like that."

                    "No, only dull," she answered,
"Lacking the dignity and the force of peasants,
Having no other quality to replace
Their lack of dignity save boastfulness
And too much plumbing."

                       I felt a passionate need
To answer and defend: but silence fell
Cold on my need. "Now come," she said. "We'll walk
Down to the garden end. And then I'll show you
Some of the house—as much as still remains
Out of its wrappings for my exodus."
She rose, and we rose too. The soft brown walls
Panelled in pear-wood made a lovely ground
For her white hair, the slim directed grace
Of her fine figure in its greenish tweed.

We walked the rustling gravel garden paths
Between well-tended beds. She talked to us
Of what was there in spring. She made it sound
Rich and enchanting, and the memory
Of Mother's garden seem so poor and thin
In contrast to its settled excellence
Of ancient habit. The pale sun cast down
Its silvery light and turned the distant trees
To a most delicate soft grey, and made
The church across unseasonable green fields,
Against the even striping of dark plough,
Look settled, comfortable, wrapped in air
So palpable it was a mist of thin
Translucent colour. A farmhouse roofed in tiles
Showed brown and red above the golden, square

Stacks of straw hiding stone walls in profuse
And careful husbandry.
                                   She said, "There's order
Even in nature and to bend to it
Makes order honest."
                              Inescapably
Her words called up an image in my mind:
The blaze of maples and the haze of blue
Over untidy corn-shocks, and I heard
The sound of a wild stream through tangled woods
That made the uneven, exciting, undefined
Edge to the field. I looked at Judith then;
She smiled, and took my hand and pressed it hard,
And dropped my hand again.
                                 Then the distant bell
Hung in the church rang out and rang again,
And the clear pitch of it troubled the chilly air
With simple music and was borne across
The pallor of the afternoon.
                              "You hear?
You two young people, have you ever heard
More beautiful a sound more rightly given
In its own setting?"
                          Judith said, "It's lovely.
It is a lovely sound."
                          I did not speak.
But once more, and perversely, swiftly ran
A memory through my mind—not of Rhode Island
But of Virginia, at Sam Allen's place:
I could hear clearly then the deep and slow
Music of water creeping under gravel
Where a creek turned dry eyes to summer's sun
And the rich silence held the purple echo
Of sound the singing judas one time blew
Through the white-petalled woods when dogwoods broke
Their alabaster shells. It was a strange
And doubled memory of sight, sound, and time
To rouse from an old bell and a new voice
Across French fields.
                          "Now, let's go in," she said,
"And see my house." We turned and went within.
It was a picturesque and lovely house
Furnished in a rare excellence of taste,

309

Comfortable, livable, not ever stiff,
Each room proclaiming use. She told its story
Amusingly and clearly, whence that came,
Who sat first in this chair, who learned to rack
His brains at this desk, to pour out his mind
In lieu of tears; who painted this or that—
But always it was French. Her entrance hall
Was panelled with the adult-infant grace
Of grisaille children imitating life
In elegant sophistries of pose. But best
I liked her library with its simple desk,
A workman's room, a few framed photographs
Not idly chosen, the ranks of reference books,
Its cheerful, chastely gay wood mantel-piece
With a fine panelled Fragonard above it
Of lovers who had cast aside their book
To read each other. By the desk there hung
A little water-colour, alien,
Brilliant in colour, simple in design,
Of a grey shingled house beside a beach
Against the green of cedars and a sky
Of clearest cobalt.
                        She said, "I bring you last
To this my favourite room. Here's where I work.
But that's not why I saved it—do you see
Any familiar thing?"
                        We looked with care.
Judith said, "No—I can't see anything
Except the shelf of your familiar books.
Is that the answer?"
                        "No. You noticed them?
They should not be here, all together so,
On exhibition. One's children should remain
Kept in the nursery while the grown-up guests
Are in the house." I was surprised to hear
The tone of bitterness in her voice. I said,
"The water-colour—did Grandfather paint it?
It's like his work, but early."
                        "Yes," she said,
And sighed once, lightly. "Yes, it's early work.
It is my one concession to my birth,
And to my husband. It's his father's house,
Where he was born, and where we were engaged,

310

And where he died, so very young. For this,
These are my children." She pointed to her books,
In the long row. "The man knew how to paint.
He is still living?"

                  "Yes," I said, "he is."
"One cannot think of him as being dead—
Though once I felt that way about his wife,
They made such flaming life about them. This—"
Wrinkling her brows and pointing to the picture—
"It's crude, American, lacking subtlety,
Over-defined . . . but I must always see
Its fierce vitality . . . and admit its claim,
His claim to artistry . . . always remember
The place it represents, the narrow life
So broadly painted . . . Had he lived, he'd be
A fine and handsome man, whose interest lay
In Yale reunions and being kind and good,
And seeing all the values in the narrow
Strictness of ignorance tempered by good heart.
All that is in the painting of a house—
A souvenir, a warning, a reminder
Of a young sorrow—one—from which all sorrow
Could later on be known—be recognized."
She paused a moment and she said, "My years,
And your relationship to the painting there,
Have made me say this. I am old enough
To dare to warn you. Poetry will wither
Under that sky. Children are funguses
That cloud the structures that they feed upon
With their excrescent shapes. America
Is still too young. The man who painted that
Would have been great, perhaps, if he had lived
Under another banner. You must sow
Too heavily against too many weeds
In that fat country. Prune and cultivate,
Choose and select." She looked at us and smiled
And said, "My words will fall upon deaf ears,
But life may teach you, and from bitterness
You'll learn humanity. What one learns of love
Is from its lack and not its satisfaction.
Ah, well—I've said enough. You'll stay for tea?
It will be ready soon."

                  Judith said, "Thank you,

But you've enough to do, leaving so soon.
And we've already trespassed on your time,
And must get back to Paris."

                              So we thanked her,
And got our hats and coats. She stood and watched
Within the curved stone frame of her front door
While we got in our car and started it.
"Good-bye," she said, "and come to Frotignan,
It's warmer there. Paris will soon be cold.
Tell Henry Cottrell when you write to him
I used him for a text but keep his picture
Hard by a Fragonard. He'll be amused
Or weep for my transplanted ignorance.
One never knows. Have children bound in boards
And printed on good paper." She waved to us
And turned and went inside.

                              Late in that night
Judith came close to me and clung to me,
And she was trembling. "Tom," she said, "oh Tom,
You don't believe her, do you? It's not so?
Am I an anchor, and a brake? Is love
Such as our love—oh, say you love me, Tom,
Say it now, quickly!"
                              I said, "I love you, Judith."
She trembled slightly and she said, "Is love
Only a handicap?"
                              "It can't be so."
"Oh no, it can't be. She was terrible,
She frightened me. She tried to put a sword
Between us, Tom. How could she dare—so cold,
Standing and looking at us as though pitying
Our happiness. Oh Tom, I want a child,
I want your child, so terribly, to bear
Your life in mine. You won't refuse me this?
You won't leave Judith barren, and pretend
Those little books are children, with warm arms,
With hearts to beat? We shall have children, love?"
I said, "We shall have children. Later, later—
Don't press me now. I am afraid. But later,
When our good love has grown."
                              "But later, Tom,
Her words may weigh with you." She clung to me

So hard her fingers hurt the shoulder flesh
And I could feel the passion of her thoughts
Like a stored current running over me
In painful ecstasy. "Sleep now, sleep now.
It is all right, our love is still all good,
Don't be afraid."

       "I am afraid."

           "I swear
We shall have children if you want them so,
But later, sweet. Wait yet a while."

             "I'll wait.
Kiss me." I kissed her. "I could wait and wait
If only I could wait forever so,
Close to you."

      "Sleep now, sleep. I am so tired,
It tired me, her words, all the demands
Of different words."

        "I'll sleep, perhaps. I'll lie
Still if you're near me. You can sleep." She let
Her hands loose from their hold of me and lay
Silent and still, and heaved a heavy sigh,
But not unhappily. I thought of her,
The tall, grey woman, and I thought, You dared
To play with life in life and not in words;
You dared to lay your hands upon my life
That least concerns you—or was it jealousy,
But not much daring? But you rouse a force
More powerful than any—you have roused
The essential force of this our newest love
And dared to question its release. And then
A passion rose in me as though I'd caught
The ague of it, and I trembled so
That Judith felt my shaking, and she came
Close to me once again, and seized me then
And wept against me; and I wept with all
The troubled love I knew and yet was happy,
And shook with fear of all the hidden power
That lay within us: that might someday flower
Into our child: or wanted or unwanted:
Or making or yet marring. I thought of days
When in our retrospect we yet might see
The truth of this suspicion that was sown
Into my mind by the chill prophecy

Of that old woman—and across my mind
Stalked one last thought: she's barren, save her art—
If art prove barren too, what then?
                              We lay
Close in the darkness without speech.

Nor freedom lost in the binding of the thin
Cords that save on the mountain and trip in the valley.

And on that December night there would be a big stag party
    in Paris.
Can't you come, Tom? No, I cannot come. I shall be away
    then.
And being away, there was bitter cold mist that covered
The whole country round us, and the town of Verneuil
Was wrapped in it. It was a mist that froze to all things;
And on the second day the sun rose and dispelled it, and each
    leaf,
Each spear of grass, each twig on every tree, the hollows
Under the shadowed sides of stones, sparkled in a white rime
And the stones of the church's fragile high tower were silvered,
And the air was deep to breathe again, and one breathed
Not painfully any longer.
And I walked that town, alone, looking and not looking,
Watching the silver tinsel fade to the glaze of wet colour
Deepening all things; watching the sun dry out the colour and
    fade
The shadows to their monochromes.
I walked here and there, alone, thinking a little of Judith,
    fretful,
Wishing she did not feel so poorly, wishing she could get up,
Sorry she was not here to see the miracle of the frost
And the frost's melting; feeling I should be with her;
Feeling I was alone, and not alone, being surrounded
By the sense of her absence; and wishing I was not here.
And the frost melted in the shadows, and the stone surfaces
Glowed in the blue of the sky.
Over the porch to the church was the prim, neat, reasonable
Carved inscription: TEMPLE DE LA RAISON.
Temple of reason under an unreasonable stone-lace tower
Pointing lightly to a most removed and excellent blue sky
With an over-jewelled finger that yet trembled
With an intensity of feeling.

314

Discontent breeds no reason: inside the church
I saw the iron pulpit and the high windows in stained glass,
But I did not really see them: I saw myself, discontented,
Walking the aisles; and issuing thence, I saw Tom
Walking the grey streets, over the cobbles. It became
An unpleasant sight then: to be surrounded always
By an absence, and yet not real absence, nor (looking now
Again at the square tower that became softly polygonal and
      was pierced
With the lace of its cutting and its ardour) able to be free,
      free,
To have a party or something, or go somewhere, with men
And drink; to talk and drink; or do lots of things; or women.
The sun was not even warm in the chill of the lower air here,
Yet the frost melted and dried, and discontent
Dried up passion and bred
Anger at Judith not here, confined, confining, absent,
Present.
        Was there a solace in old towns
For young men caught in the bored perambulation
Of an enclosed space?
Here was a round tower, a keep maybe; there was an old
      house,
Chequered in brick and stone and flint, handsome, but—
Who in hell wants stone chequers in an unwarm sun
When Paris and the boys and the big party tonight, girls,
Champagne, FUN, *oh God!* TEMPLE DE LA RAISON—
Would one aspire another day to the tower in sense and un-
      conscious feeling, or always
Be the reasonable, be the prim letters, neatly, properly cut
On the face of the weak porch?
These thinkings and feelings were on each side of me:
They walked with me: their voice was the sharp sound
Of my feet on the cobbles; their flesh was the humour of my
      mind;
Their mind was the absent Judith saying that morning,
'Leave me, do go out, do see the town, the sun, Tom,
Has risen again.'
        In what temple of reason
Does dislike breed from kindness, from pity, from illness?
Does boredom rise up from happiness and lay
Dull fingers on the quick flesh, and make flesh
Mad with a hunger for the old fruits, and leave

Only the taste of captivity wry in the mouth?
And I walked that town alone, looking and looking,
And there was no escape till my feet took me, willy-nilly,
To the door of her room, the closed door, and then
Through the hall window I saw the tower of that church,
     reaching,
Up and up in grace and I thought,
I have come back to Judith—Judith,
I have come back.

> *I did not know the use of speech released*
> *By love's release, nor the small words grown*
> *To dangerous stature and the lips sealing*
> *The flood of the heart with the wax of fear.*

"No, not yet. Not for a little while . . . so soon . . .
Ah, must you leave me? Well . . . Oh, God!
I hate to lose you . . . "

The window's a sea of blue, green blue. Luminous. Under-
     water blue.
One swims under the water, hold the breath, but now
Seeing the moon, or not the moon but the ocean of its
     island . . .
But breathe, freely, deeply, through the released mouth, under
     the blue
Water that's air. The blue light gives no light save on the
     white
Pillows. White no-light. Sight. Flight. But flight
Is over now.

                              "I am weary."
"I am happy, are you?"
                              "Fearfully happy,
But I am weary."
                    "Rest then, here."
                                        "No, I shall rest."

There is a time and a place. This
Is a pillow for resting. A time
For resting. The moon
Came up for us. For us? Winter moon.
Italian moons are very good moons, look away—

316

Look away. Why should the shadows of stone on stone . . .
      moonstone . . .
Moon-shadow . . . cornices—be   black,   Florentine   black,
      Medici
Black, or blue, or blue-green under-the-water . . . the moon
Tires of half-shadows, tires of winter, swims hungrily
To the fat shore of spring. Air's cold. Warm here. Soft—
Here, there and everywhere, soft save the shadows,
Up and down the walls they go, pop goes the weasel.
Look away, my bonny, bonny boy. But why? Oh, because
There is only sight out the window, sense
Remains indoors. Beds are sense. Beds
Are sensible. Weary beds.

      "Weary?"
                  "Yes, but lovely now. Stay near."

Weary way, Neary way, whither shall you wander,
Up hill, down dale, or shadows, up moon,
Down shadows, in my lady's chamber.

      "I feel so foolish."
                  "Do you?"
                              "Idiotic
The silliest things, in the head. Just now, just now
My mind is like my tongue and is hung in the middle.
Poor tongue. Hung in the middle."
                              "Let it hang.
I think it's a grand tongue."
                              "Shall I tell you something?"
"Anything."
                  "Well—I love you. And I am tired.
And one is part of the other and the moon
Is part of both. It's dark here, but the window
Is full of light and the light is scared to enter,
It's do damned tactful."
                              "Sweet!"
                                          "It's not like this always."
"What's not? Always?"
                              "Oh. Well. Love is. Always."

No trees now to move in the winds of night,
Now no winds to move in the trees' leaves,
Only moonlight, silent, no sound

Save the whisper of breath, soft drawn, the
Lisp of linen. Always? No, not always.
And the not always is a weight, a heavy, dragging
Weight. To lift it? Here is peace beside you. Love
Beside you. Darkness. Square of light, window
To light the other end of the darkness, the far end,
The far darkness, the rustle
Of distant thoughts,
There is a time and a place. These?

    "Shall I tell you?
            "What?"
                     "Shall I tell you me?"
"Tell me you. Who better? The very best
Thing about me is you."
                "I am not good.
I am not strong. I'm weak. If I get strong,
It'll be your strength then. Do you see?"
                     "Oh no.
Men are strong."
           "And women are weak? Oh no,
It's the other way round."
              "I'm weak, when you are near,
Your hand. Just weak—for a touch."
                "That isn't weak.
That's something else."
        "That's you."
               "That's you and me,
Together—like this."
        "Oh, yes! Together like this."

United we stand, oh yes, e pluribus unum,
Bury your own dead. Bury them. They're not buried.
But don't you shoot till you see the white of the moon.
Bury the rustle of silk, bury the rustle,
The well-bred rustles, the well—ah, no—
The well-bedded rustles.

    "Once on a time I . . . "
        "Yes. You what? Go on."
"Once on a time I went with Father, shooting,
Down in Florida."
        "Was it fun?"
           "The shooting,
That was fun. . . "

318

And there was no moon that week, only the rain
One night, only the rain, what harm?
Oh, what harm telling, a tongue hung in the middle
To bury the dead. Or raise the dead? To bury
To bury St. Edmunds, the berry pickers' union,
Bury blue-berry under the cold, cold moon. Well—

                    " . . . yes, the shooting."
                                        "And what was not fun?
        You're saying it in your voice."
                                        "There were four men there,
        And there was an older woman, and—oh well,
        There were such odd ones there . . . "

But one is dead, death,
Under the wild dust, that one,
Under the thin piping
Of the frogs, and he
Had no marigolds, he had
Only camellias. Now, reach out—
Death and love and the thin
Square of the blue light, these things
Are joined now—but now, now—
What's this now, the hand is
Not lax now, the hand is
Touching and being touched and so, warning, saying:
There is a time, there is a place, and who,
Who shall forgo these?

                    "Come closer now."
        "Tell me the story."
                            "No, it's a long story,
        I have another story now. Yes. Oh, be closer.
        Words are terrible, they are the wasters, wanters,
        The trappers, the . . . never mind now, so . . . be close . .
        Florence not Florida, love, not . . ."
                                        "Not what?"
                                                "Love,
        This is the story, this, and this and this—
        The moon's the time and Florence the place, oh sweet,
        Never remember the past . . . "
                                "Never the past? Oh,
        What should I remember but you, and you,
        And you forever . . . "

And waste not equals want not,
Under the darkness now, under the darkness,
Under the black, sharp, Medici shadows under the cornice,
These forgotten, buried, buried in darkness,
Bury the dead in darkness, cover
The lisp of linen in kisses, present kisses,
Never the past now,
Never the past, oh!
These are the heart-beats of a love or a fear,
Or this is the edge of love or the edge of danger,
The steep, swift edge of danger, sharp as a shadow
Now in the darkness, now
Only in darkness.

  Nor the little, ridiculous, delicious
  Things that enrich and remain.

We stopped in January on the road over Pisa.
He spoke in Italian first, but when we looked blank
He spoke in bad French. "This Ford. It does not budge.
Senta: it doesn't go." He waved in an arc.
"I have even kicked it. And yet it did not respond."
I said, "I was practically born in one of those things
I'll look it over." I lifted the hood of the engine.
"You cleaned the spark plugs?"
                              "No." He shrugged his shoulders.
"Why should they need it? I cleaned them in November."
We cleaned the spark plugs and put them back. We cranked,
Each in turn. It kicked, but it wouldn't start.
Judith said, "Try the timer," to me, in English.
"Madame says what?" I told him. He said, "Dear God!
Do even the beautiful young ladies know
Such things in America?" "Yes," I said, "they do.
They were practically born in Fords."
                                    "Ah! Well," he said,
"This crèche—it has cradled no children. What is this timer?"
I showed him. We took it apart and cleaned it out,
And we added a little oil and we put it back.
We cranked and the Ford started. He had to run
To get into the seat, for the car had started moving.
"Thank you, thank you!" he yelled. When he took his hand
From the throttle to raise his hat, the car nearly stopped
And he grabbed it again. "Good-bye," he cried, "Livorno,

Carmino Cella, stop and see me. My wife
Shall have her next child here. Bonne chance. Arrivederci."
The Ford bucked forward. His tie flew out in the wind,
And his beard waved backward. He called out then, "Hot dog
I'm gonna get home. So long!"
                                We watched him go.
I can remember his beard and his purple hat,
And his bright green tie and his smile, and Judith laughing
And saying "You mustn't say people are born in Fords
To strange Italians, darling. They might believe you."
We never saw Signor Carmino Cella again—
We didn't need to.

> *I did not know the languor of love usurping*
> *All ambition, being its own fulfilment,*
> *Nor freedom gained in the close winding of thin*
> *Cords to make strong the stored love.*

There were fine sights on the streets of Madrid in those days:
The policemen's uniforms, assorted, parti-coloured, gay, opera-
    tic;
The very hot sun and the very clear shadows and the shade
Rich in colour, heady with the smell of the acacias in bloom.
And I remember, too, the coolness of the Prado basement
    (stone-cool)
And the cool colours of the mad Goyas with here a spot of
    red,
There a spot of red, but mostly madness in grey, chilling
By genius, near the chill of stone.
There were fine sights and sounds and smells, and it was fun
To drink tea, expensively, at half-past seven and dine later.
Perhaps at ten, and later again see La Argentina's heels
Tell time by the clock of the heart in the hot spot-light.
There were no mornings then.
There was noon and afternoon and evening rich with dust
In the long shadows of strolling people,
And night a long space, a huge star-pricked room with the
    corners
Grandly lit, and always the sense
Of spring and youth and the sweet, nostalgic, honey-locust
Smell of the acacias dropping to the dark streets like a rain
To feed the plants of passion.
Those were fine days: the sound of Spanish spoken rapidly,

321

Angrily, against quick laughter, the darker faces
Turning to a laugh instantly from the fierce expression of
    anger,
As though one bred the other. We loved all that.

We'd drive, in a low-neck hack, together, at dusk, in love,
Seeing and hearing and smelling and remembering
The wealth of the day: Greco; the concierge who said,
'Jesus! I knew you guys come from New York';
The dry beauty of the Retiro; and always,
Present, moving, the dry rain of the acacias on the Calle de
    Alcalá.

So now, when I smell the honey-locust, a wavering dark lance
Over grey stone walls, against white wooden houses,
In the tangle of choke-cherry, blackberry, catbriar,
I remember this: I remember (over the printed guns, the
    printed thunder of planes):
Content, and happiness, these two, joined;
And freedom from fear, because love had been accomplished
And Judith was, beside me, content, happy, and we,
Hungry for our content;
And freedom, unexplainable—liberty, the possession
Of one's own soul in the orbit of two souls;
And freedom, from care, from ambition, from all other desire,
The mind idle to store, to accumulate, never giving now,
Only receiving: love, warmth, this sudden liberty more free
In the circumscription of love.

There were fine sights on the streets of Madrid in those days:
But then there was peace: and there was always Judith:
And the fertile rain of the distilled acacias.

> *Nor the return of reason from its wandering*
> *Rarest Elysium, to the rich, coarser fields*
> *Of doing: one by one: together.*

We lay on a rug, in a cropped field, at the edge of the Romney
    Marshes,
And the May sun was pale and pleasant, and the shadows
Began to lengthen. Judith said,
"What is the matter?"
                    "Nothing. Nothing's the matter."

"You are so silent, Tom."
                    The winter-killed brown bracken
Drooped on the steep continuous slope. Far below,
The fields, framed in their hedges and the hedge shadows,
Followed each other from green and brown to blue
Little by little, to saffron in the haze that finally
Made an end of marsh-fields in the pale, undefined
Arc of the sea and the sky meeting.
                              If only
These could take words!
                    "You are a good soul, Tom.
You want to be good. You want to be kind.
You wish to have me happy. But do you think
You can fool me now? You put on a smile like a shirt
To cover your nakedness. I see straight through it,
To discontent."
                    I thought: later, not now.
I followed the pattern of sheep in a far field: grey
On a grey-blue field.
                    "You dramatize small things
As well as big ones, little troubles grow larger.
You dramatize marriage."
                    Martin had said that once.
And small fields. One could add words
To words to a pattern of grey sheep and the glaze
Of green on distant, small fields. But not yet.
I said, "Marriage?" without moving or looking.
"I have watched it for days, now. Creeping up.
If you were like my people, I'd know, I'd know . . .
Or partly know. Now I'm baffled."
                         "It's nothing, truly."
There was a church tower, square. By looking
Long in the distance it was clear. Before
I had not seen it.
                    "They said, 'You've married an artist.
That is risky. Artists are funny people.' "
Yes, I thought, it was risky.
Sheep. They should marry sheep. Not sky
Marrying water in the Kentish spring. The shadows
Grew longer: one saw more clearly. The shadows
Defined and clarified. But words were wanting; words.
There'd been a void of words—for a long time. What
Made shadows for words? I said, "They thought it risky?"

323

"Yes, they did. But that's not true and it's fine.
I wouldn't change it. They forgot they'd taught me.
All of them. Father, Mother, uncles and aunts
And fourteen cousins. Married mostly. Not artists.
They all get angry at nothing, and blow sky high,
And giggle after it. But you bottle it up.
They told their troubles; you cork them. You hide your trou-
    bles.
They'll get so big."
                        "I'll write them."
                                        "When?"
I turned. The sun made little rainbows
On the loosened hairs against the dark cloud of hair.
"In time."
                "In time—but what time? I am afraid.
I am afraid when you go away and leave me . . . "
"I haven't left you."
                    The sun was dropping
Into the saffron haze and the haze was pinker, and warmer,
And the shadows longer and longer. Beautiful, ragged
Shadows—the sheep, far off, seemed nearer now. What thought
Had the sheep made . . . or the little fields? Shadows?
    Martin?
There'd been the edge of a word.
"Is marriage too much, Tom?"
"How could it be, too much?"
                            "Too good—for me. Too much
From you for me. A work in itself?" I frowned.
"What are you frowning for?" I thought: these words
Are all new problems, before the old have shadows.
Noon ideas. "Are you waiting for something, Tom?"
"Something. An idea—time—a combination.
Something—or words."
                        "But now, you are not happy."
"How do you know?"
                    "How do I know? It's written
Up and down your face. You look like Daddy
Out of a job on Sunday. You look like Mother
In an empty house, no guests, no one to dinner.
You look like Aunt Rachel with not a soul to talk to.
You look like Cora, while she is sitting, waiting,
For a beau to call her."
                        "Oh, let it go now, Judith."

"And I'm unhappy because you are. You know it.
You know you are unhappy, Tom." I said,
"No!" rather sharply. But inside me
I knew it was true.
                    "That's all."
                                "No more to tell me?"
"Nothing. I do not go where I'm not wanted.
Be alone, then. Go off. You go to silence
Like a distant country. But what you find there—nothing—
Nothing but just more silence, and a face
As hard as your voice."
                        "Don't you be angry, Judith."
"Oh, let it go now, Tom." She mimicked my voice.
She lay back, flat on the rug, and lifted her arms
And put them under her head; and closed her eyes.
So, being alone then, it was not bearable:
I reached over and laid my hand on her breast.
She didn't move but she said, "No! no!" Her voice
Had firmness.
             The sheep
In the far field moved now, suddenly, all together,
Walking from one place to another. I could see
Nothing, no man, no dog, nothing: they moved
By a common impulse, further off. The soft breeze
Was rich with the sea.
                      But now—what now? One drifted
Close to something exciting, moved by the waves
Of the other's making. But in the calm,
One could not drift. One wondered,
Where were the waves? The sun
Was low now, just a blur of light in the mist.
The shadows were long now. But one sat
Suspended, in a void: but the void was an island
And its sea was Judith—Judith and discontent—
Discontent fed on happiness? Time would tell.
Just by waiting? You could remember
The sheep in their shadows, the far fields hedged with
    shadows,
Or in sharp sun? Or in the dusk, would shadows
Grow in the mind, the memory would define
What the high sun had blurred?
But she knew: she had said it: and the sheep now
Were lost in the twilight, and the little rainbows

325

Had fled from the mist of the loosened hair.
Oh, discontent: yes. And love: yes. But wanting, something,
Wanting, and waiting—attending—but beyond love,
Drawn far off . . . and then . . . suddenly:
You must attend the satisfactory dusk,
The rise of evening, the decline of day . . .
So it began . . . so it began, like an echo
Of music once heard, somewhere: line upon line,
Growing, and suddenly there, pausing a little,
Coming in waves, distracting, and two whole lines:
The hours of day all gathered to their sheaves,
The stone still warm from the remembered sun . . .
But not so soon, now, a pause, a fitting together,
A patching; a word lost in the blue haze
Where the sky and the sea met and married, mistily;
Lost in the hedges now, where the dark
Shadows were evening and not fields, no longer
Fields but remembered light—until
It was completed.
                         "Judith."
                                         "What do you want?"
"I have a poem for you—or for us—or for living—
I don't know."
                    "When?"
                                   "Just now."
She sat up slowly. "Say it," she said. "I've been
Angry. It's over. Say it."
                                    I stumbled through it.
"Say it again."
                        I said it, this time more smoothly.
"Lovely," she said. "But now I have two men,
Instead of one." I looked at her in silence:
Her eyes were enormous. She shook her head then, slowly,
"Two people now."
                             I thought: You have
Two lovers, Judith, two lovers. They can absorb
Unhappiness between them. I said, "Just one—
Just one lover."
                         She said, "Let us go home, Tom.
The poem is lovely. Let's take the poem home now,
The honeymoon's over. Life may be exciting. We face
The long stretch of it." She rose. I sat still, hating
The moment to pass. She said, "Get up and come.

Come—if you love me."
       "Oh, I do. I love you
More than . . . "
      She interrupted: "No! Don't say it!"
I rose then and I kissed her. She kissed me, warmly,
Without a trace of passion. We folded the rug, silently.
Then we walked back, away from the dark marshes,
Away from the sheep and the fat shadows
Spilling down to the sea. She held my hand
Like a companion, now.

And still I did not know
The ebb and the flood, the soft receding, the bare revealing,
The lofty mounting of the irrepressible
Waters of love in the long tides
That come and go as the pulse, strong, fearful,
Comes and goes in the long veins.

'And these matters now?'

They are mine now: I have known them:
I have known their shadows: their light:
I remember.

PART SEVEN

'VE CONNED my diaries with attentive eyes:
Out of these pages closely written over
Return realities: they spring as flowers
Leap from their annual seed's so small beginning.
A phrase, dry, factual—but it can hold
The full, rich cosmos of an experience
In its few words. I give you these, in order,
Year upon year—chosen for memories,
Chosen for light that shone from them, as lanterns
Show in the darkness of the common night
When the moon's buried in its far shadow-death
Nor yet heeds resurrection.
                              These betray
The flights and falls—but nothing flies for us
That may not tumble to its hurt. They give
The growth and reason of two souls—not all:
But here a little, there a little. So now
Your eyes may grasp the meaning, see the tide-flow
Always inexorable, always moving on,
Or high or low, or neap or in the slow
Midsummer's mean. Yet always moving on.
Out of a decade's richness, these few, poor,
And flawed small jewels: because we wore them once
To sharp remembrance: because the words
That once recorded them in heat, have kept
Internal warmth and have not cooled and cooled
Into historical chill.
                    No longer I:
It is we, now. Not only Tom, alone,
Fretting his way to freedom, doubtfully,
But two, with doubt uplifted into hope,
(A grander scepticism) holding on
Each to the other toward an ultimate

And timeless fusion.
                                      Read. It is our tale
From which I am at last inseparable.

O MOON-LED woman, on whose moving tide
The waves of living heave and stir and pass
Letting your passionate flood again subside
To the still sanity of a looking-glass,
What sun-bred power may disallow the brief,
The four-times-seven circuit, wax and wane,
That cloaks in mercy the remembered reef,
Bares petty ledges of forgotten pain?
Who sails your waters cons your almanac,
Foretells your moon on its meridian bar,
Setting his drift forever to your track,
His course on one immutable high star,
Knowing the ebb that's but impermanent death,
Knowing the flood that is love's very breath.

THERE WAS the June day, a long work done,
It was to show to Judith: the need to share
Now was a strong compulsion. That day heat
Flowed from the bare street
Under a cruel, westering sun
And I breathed the damp, dead in the moveless air,
And I sat inactive, alone . . .
And thought of the false name
Of the one poem, *Portrait of Mary*—the poem was pain
And joy together—and must be shown.
And then, toward evening, the sky was no longer fair,
And the weather
Turned to storm in a green glare
And the city grew blue-dark and the bright flame
Flashed to the northward and the sweet rain
Poured on the streets and the wind blew

332

Cool from the west and the light grew
And sun shone again, as the storm was done,
And the leaves in the yard dripped and glistened, the breeze
Brought new life. But still I remained alone
Waiting a little, lacking a whole faith,
Excited, afraid—willing still to postpone
The moment for showing, sharing more
Of the work I laboured, this child I bore;
And I ceased from thought. And bathed,
Changed to fresh clothes to dine.

Agatha served us both under ailanthus trees,
Under long, pointed leaves the level sun
Turned to enamel against the storm-fresh sky
And its cobalt dome,
And the dark fine
Red of the old brick houses.
                              And dinner done,
Into the house grown cool (the house grown home
To my incessant wonder)
Judith and I, at last, hearing the far
Mumble of distant thunder.
I went to the desk and took the poems: a try
For the casual voice: "The poems are finished and ready,
I've called them *Love and the Evening Star*.
Take them and see. I send them out tomorrow.
They are for you—no—they are yours and mine—
For this last night." My hands, unsteady,
Dropped them into her lap. "There are one or two
That you have not seen. *Portrait of Mary's* new."
She cast just one quick glance at me,
Smiled and then touched the sheaf
With the tips of her fingers, her beautiful fingers.
She said, "I ought to borrow
Somebody's brains to help, for see,
I am so ignorant. Ignorant! What a grief!"
She turned to reading the poems. I could but look
Hard at her face: she was holding my work, my book:
She held the flask of joy and the sword of sorrow . . .
While the smile lingers
(And the seconds grow to a thousand nights and days)
There is no need of speech for the smile is praise.
She spoke: "Must you have my judgment, now and here?"

I nodded. She sighed, distressed.
"You ask your wife to lift a terrible weight."
Silence. I waited. My heart beat in my breast,
For the one poem, the one . . . and the time so near . . .
Would she understand—and so, would she like or hate?
But all the poems . . . indivisibly part of you . . .
But this was the best, it grew
From the thought of Clare
And the agony that severed
Life from a picture and saw the picture there
Separate and entire.
And so in the cool evening I endeavoured
To hold excitement into its silent bounds—
But this was I; naked; exposed at last:
The look in my father's eyes, his dire
Need of an understanding—of that past,
His need (no lover to share?) was my need now.
The distant sounds
Of summer's thunder coloured the quiet room,
The curtain's billow and bloom
Was a ripple of flowered green in the yellow light
Of the single lamp . . .
                              And Judith read, for a long time . . .
And paused—
Lifted her eyes, they were grown dark,
And sighed and read again. I knew what caused
The small and shadowed line, the mark
On the smooth brow—
And now:
"That is both terrible and hard and cruel,
Who would believe you, Tom? You write
Words like the cold shine of a cut jewel—
And yet—I'll remember."
                              There was nothing to say.
"Must you use this, Tom?"
I said, "I must."
She murmured, "Love—in a hateful fashion."
Silence. She read. And I saw the curtains sway,
Sway in the new wind in the old way,
But green, for red—green for the red like rust
Over a house once.
                         She finished. I watched her rise.
She gave me the poems. "Take them. They tell of passion—

Poor, young Tom! Twice shy, twice bitten!
Marriage and love! Is there hard surprise
Now in the knowing?"
                    "No." I touched the sheets
Of the crisp new paper. "This: for you it was written—
I wrote the spell, it has exorcised the dead:
I was troubled, once. Now they are only cheats
And you, reality. So much—in this.
Do you like them—Judith?"
                        She looked at me again,
Leaned on the table and tapped it with her thumbs.
"The poems are you—and I love you. Let's go to bed.
There is nothing matters, nothing—except your kiss—
Will you exorcise me, too, when the time comes?"
I kissed her then:
But the kiss was empty—except for fatigue and pain.
I heard the thunder grow, and again the rain
Beat on the glass,
And the lightning lit the streets with a ghost's glare
And I thought, the ghosts rise and the ghosts pass—
But what she thinks and feels I may not share,
For all that I've learned of love in all my growing
Is: love is a bliss and a doubt beyond all knowing.
And I took her hand, and divided we climbed the stair.

2

That day was the last of many days I waited;
And waiting, so I foresaw a worse than the worst:
The book of poems would be sent back, scornfully,
Or with an absence even of scorn in the white
Printed refusal.
There had been three now, though all with letters:
Not quite, yet . . . almost . . . another time . . .
Interesting, but erratic . . . not commercial . . .
Over-conventional . . . they are small in scope . . .
Beautifully written, but not with a real passion
Felt, experienced . . .
                    Not with a passion felt?
Not with a passion told, or communicated—
But what did they know of feeling? of my feeling?
Did they know of Clare?
Did they know of Rosemary?

335

But there was no comfort in thinking of Rosemary:
There were the echoes coiled, that sprang
Like Jack-in-the-boxes out of an opened lid:
Even if you write lousy poetry . . .
There was pain. And pain could be a panic.
Do? Oh, do nothing . . .
But, Nothing—that was for fools, that was for sluggards,
It wasn't for talented, bright young men—
For failures, people who couldn't . . .
And the short story?
Nearly done—that somebody else had written—
How had they thought my thought, stolen my setting?
Do thoughts blow out on the air as pollen blows
From the wind-sprung flowers?
But there was so much, so much!
So many things to write, and who—
Who would take them? And without other eyes,
Were they alive?
Oh, try to comfort yourself with the dead past,
It is no use, it is still dead notwithstanding.
Some are heard—but some have oblivion
For the clothes of life, for their final winding-sheet.
And the past is not you, but the present is you,
And the future holds your hope, as a palm holds
The dormant root for planting.
It might not grow?
Ah, that was a hard day, that last
Day of waiting, when the crisp, cool, autumnal
Air of the city made one's body feel
Alien to the sorrowing mind. A hard day,
Full of hard thought . . . Crossing a crowded street,
A horn blew at me and I jumped and turned,
And it was a negro in a long, glittering
Black car, red leather lining and metal shining,
And he blew the horn, loudly.
In spite of myself, I cursed him—though he blew
His horn to save me, to shatter the hard dreams
That should not live on the November streets.
I thought, He is a negro, a damned negro,
He blows his horn at me! and all my white pride
Roused and was angry. And then I was ashamed.
And I thought, even in this, you cheat, you cheat!
You lie to yourself:

For either the anger's a lie, or the being ashamed
Is a poor mean lie to cover dislike, to cover
A truth you will not admit.
And I walked and wondered:
For how could a man write what the heart knew
If he buried knowledge under the leaves of lies
Grown rankly and unpruned?
And I went home, then,
But as I opened the door I thought:
Keep this from Judith, for God's sake do not burden
Judith with all your sorrow and disappointment—
And again, I wondered:
Male pride? the man comes home, he can have no failures,
Always the man successful, the hunter returning,
The good provider, the giver, the protector,
The man to his woman—but of this,
What concerns you whose poems may be now returning
Unused, unwanted—just for kindness or mercy?
Or for your arrogance?
And what horn will shatter
The dream of your own pride, now?
And I shut the door on the thought and the long waiting.

She came to me as I stood at the closed door.
"Look," she said, "it's awful—I've done something
Frightful, dear Tom, do forgive me.
I opened this letter from Fuller, oh, by mistake—
I read it, too, I shouldn't, Tom, I'm sorry,
The horrible letter!"
I looked at her and I thought,
Your eyes are like the eyes in the fairy-books,
As large as platters. I wish you could make gold
Out of a burden, like the magical witch.
I said, "He has sent them back?"
She nodded in silence, and she held out the letter.
I took it and pushed it into my pocket, gently
Into the dark of the pocket.
"No more of these then, for the present, Judith.
I'll put them away. And now I'll begin the novel
With my mind all free."
It was someone else was talking, it was not I,
I didn't consider the words, they came
Out of my mouth and hardly in my voice.

"We can forget them. Later I'll surely use them."
She said, "They will ask you for them, they'll beg you for
    them,
And then you'll use them. Yes, the time
Will someday come for that. It will someday come—
And I love your spirit."
I said, "I have got no spirit. I want
Only my tea now."
She said, "I can love a man, Tom,
That takes his trouble. So always take your trouble—
Including me." We laughed. It was over thus:
The days of waiting were over. But for Judith,
She was near then; and the troubled thinking,
That was over, with Judith, so very near
And the days all to come: oh yes, to come,
The days of waiting to come, and the days of trouble,
But to us: together.

IS THERE a foreign rancour fits your soul?
Your hates may feed upon an alien hate?
Or may you make an indignation whole
That is not rooted in its native state?
Shall you then swing an axe to cut a tree
That grows across the marches of your land,
And having cut it, of its wood make free
And build a fire to warm the axeman's hand?
Your own antipathies, are they so strong
They may not soften to the shape of like?
If you behead them, can you right the wrong,
Replace the head you stuck upon a pike?
Oh, let the hatreds and the rancours grow
In their own soil, and let their growth be slow.

THIS WAS a singular, mixed up day: that morning
The letter came from England, and it said 'Yes'
Handsomely, grandly! to a long poem submitted.

338

Can you remember the first poem that you sold?
Or the first story, or the first car, or bond,
Or the first gas-range? And how the whole world seemed
Suddenly on your side? a world just waiting
For more of what you, especially, had to offer—
And how the shut doors and the testy Noes!
The printed slips, or the bored, young, over-sceptical
Third vice-presidents were forgotten, or beaten?
That was the way I felt: for one of the poems
Had been in the sheaf that made up the book rejected
Four times running.
           I sat for a long time then
Holding the letter, up in the small and bare
Top floor room, the room that had been a nursery
For Joss and me. I didn't want to tell Judith,
Not for a little: I wanted to think about it.
I stared out the window, through the long, bare, unsightly
Structure of the ailanthus, up at the north sky
Full of dark February clouds; at the thin and spiny
Spire of a church that poked through a gap in the buildings
And lay against the great and red blank wall
Of a storage warehouse. It seemed so dull and ugly!
The room, too—that was ugly. We had not changed it,
The paper peeled in spots, and the old scars
Of our young playing seemed scars of a hard past
And not of pleasure.
           I thought of the fine room
At Mrs. Mallory's house. And I re-read the letter.
'Send us some more,' it said. Ah!
                But not America.
No, America'd said, and no, and again no,
They're not commercial, almost, another time.
Another time? But the poems would go then to England,
The stories, the novel. Not here . . . *where the only standard*
Is always, 'Did he make some money by it?'
I thought, You learn by time, by having it happen:
It's hard to believe when you hear it of someone else.
The poem had gone to England in desperation—
And why not we? but not in a desperation,
No, in sensible flight from the crude, denying
Harshness of here. And sell the house or close it—
Live in a beautiful quiet house, with a garden,
In a world that let you alone, that was not noisy,

339

That could say 'Yes' to a poem, where cultivation
Was ordered to let the spirit free from the trammels
That this swift, bustling, active life laid on you.
I heard the wheels of the elevated rattle past
Even through my closed windows. I felt a glow
Run through my body at the mere thought of leaving,
Leaving this room, this house, this fearful city—
To get away, to be free!
                              I rose then, eagerly,
Taking the letter with me, to show it to Judith,
To find her, tell her, and share with her the excitement
Of fact and of plan.
                        I found her at her desk,
Her dark head bent to the task of writing letters.
I said, "Can I disturb you?" She raised her head
And answered, "Can you! There's nothing I'd like so much.
I do hate letters! I write such awful letters—
But maybe because I loathe them so."
                                    "Yet Judith,
You like to get them."
                        "Oh yes, I love to get them."
"Here's one you'll love then. Here is a perfect letter."
I gave it to her. She read it. "Oh Tom!" she cried,
"That's simply wonderful. Darling, I am so glad!
But I was sure you'd do it. It just takes time."
"Time and place," I said. "It has taken England,
After so many nays in America, sweet."
She said, "It has. But it's only a matter of time.
Stick to it, boy, and someday you'll have diamonds
To cover me with—or literary diamonds,
I'm not particular."
                        "Listen," I said. "Your father
Has had to cut your allowance. This New York living
Is damned expensive. The house needs doing over.
The rooms we didn't do up are quietly rotting;
Upstairs the paper is peeling. And all the plumbing
Goes to the devil if you say Boo! to it, softly.
Let's sell and move."
                        "But I like this house, it's ours."
"I'm glad you like it. I like it because of you—
And a little for Agatha, and a little from habit,
But I'd like to get out and go."
                                "Go where?" she asked.

340

"To England. Live there. It's cheap, with lovely places;
They'll print my stuff. I guess Mrs. Mallory's right.
We can live like princes for what it would cost to fix
This ancient relic as we should like to have it.
But above all we'd be free."

                    "Be free of what?"
"Oh, the noise, the ugliness, and the fearful pace,
The nervousness and the long, straight, endless streets,
The stupid chatter, the petty, bigotted talk,
The second-hand opinions, the bootleg drinking,
The small, cheap, rich, uncultivated people,
And the editors who say No, it's too conventional,
You didn't feel it with passion. To hell with them!"
"It's funny," she said, "a success has made you bitter,
But a failure made you strong."

                    "A success? It's made me
See that the stuff I write is no use here,
And I'd better pick up and go where it is some use—
Not sit here, missing."

                    "But sitting here you succeeded."
"Succeeded elsewhere."

                    "But with an American poem."
"Art has no boundaries. Not real art."

                    "If that's so,
Why do you have to go from here to there—
Over what boundaries?"

                    "You confuse the issue.
I speak of living and writing, not of subjects."
"Yet this is what you know, Tom. Can't you see
This is the stuff that feeds you?"

                    "It feeds me thistles."
"You can digest them."

                    "No, I am no donkey.
I shall grow fatter on the English hay."

                    "Yes,
Maybe you would. Fatter. Perhaps complacent.
You wouldn't want that?"

                    I cried, "I want to be heard!
Is it too much to ask? Damn it, is that too much?"
She said, "Don't shout. I hear you."

                    "Oh yes, you hear me.
Your ears hear, but they don't absorb the meaning—
Or else you don't want to go."

341

She scratched her cheek
With the handle of her pen. "Yes, that's the answer:
I'd hate to go. I love it here. It's exciting.
The people excite me. And it excites you, too,
I've watched it happen."

"Not now. It bores me now.
I've lived here now too long."

"Go west," she said.
"I'll do that with you."

"The hell with the west. I'd hate it.
It's not my sort of thing. And I'd hate the people,
With their thick voices."

"The way you hated Martin?"
"Oh—that was different."

"Why?"

"He was not like many.
He was a case apart."

"But we're all apart
If it comes to that," she said. "I am. You are.
But I'd hate England."

I looked at her. I thought,
This is what happens: so you are tied and bound;
It is so you shackle yourself to another person
And all her limitations; an obstinate girl,
A girl brought up with a father who deals in woolens,
A foolish, kindly, bustling sort of a mother,
A dull and Providence background. How can Judith
Have learnt to know that the artist has got to be
In his own air, and the air must be his choosing
Or he is suffocated under the thick and drowsy
Mists of this breathing?

She said, "You hate me now.
I see you hating: now for the first time, hating.
It isn't pleasant. Because I have disagreed?
For the first time disagreed?"

I heard an echo,
Clear and concise, a man's voice, fine, but angry,
Speak through the high, hot sunlight: *Throwing away*
The grand good moments of an artist's life,
The moments that excite, that feed the mind,
Let loose the powers.

Against all reason, then,
It made me angrier than I'd been, a feeling

Of being trapped into a well-sprung trap,
Of moving forever within that endless circle
Whose one circumference is a woman's life
And is all women's lives. You break the circle
If you want freedom. But not yet. A little—
Perhaps a little longer—but not now. No.
Now say nothing, for any word you utter
Will weigh beyond its measure, may not be lifted
Easily to displace it—such words are stones
Flung to be hurtful. I had seen these, too,
Under the hot, high sunlight.
                    And yet, I spoke:
"We are free now. And yet you balk at moving,
Balk at the knowledge there, of another world.
Freer than we shall ever be, ever again—
After you have those children you want so much—
They'll tie you down. Oh yes!"
                      I turned and left her:
She sat at her desk and did not move. Her face
Was fearfully white, and her lips were a drawn line
Of red, and her eyes were large, and her hands held,
Both together, the slender tip of her pen.

2

That day we didn't speak more, save a word or two.
I was still angry, an anger that had outlasted
Its own unreason. Judith was pale and quiet;
She might be angry too: but I couldn't tell.
We dressed for dinner and drove to the Harrison's house
Together and silent in the dark of a taxi
Where I could only see her face as the lights
Flashed across it, or when her cigarette
Glowed for an instant. I thought, it's a stupid dinner,
Harrison's dull and his wife is kind but stupid,
And the sort of guests they have are all of a piece:
Just nice, well-mannered, stuffy, conventional people
With a passionate hate for Wilson, a love for France,
And a good, rich taste in food. This sort of thing
Was what I should fly from if I went to England—
But there—it was best to let that go, one's anger
Would rouse again, and it wasn't a place to be angry—

Or anything, maybe, except a trifle bored.
But Judith would like it, Judith liked all these people,
They were her kind—and perhaps I wasn't her kind,
And it all was a fearful error, a long mistake
That we'd taken two years to find—but those two years,
There'd been happiness . . . but I stopped, too proud
And still too angry to lift her weapons for her
In the face of silence, her silence.
                                        The driver stopped
On the wrong side of the street. I told him so,
And pointed the house, and I said, "The even numbers
Are always south, have been for a long, long time.
You ought to learn that, it will help you find them."
He drove to the right house then, and as I paid him
I thought: the taxis in London know their way,
And a hell of a complicated sort of a way,
But these dumb clucks don't even know the numbers
Of regular streets. So we went in to dinner.
That was my mood and my mind when Mrs. Harrison
Said, "There's a friend of yours here, waiting to see you."
And pointed. There by the fire stood Evelyn Leighton.

There were a dozen people who came for dinner,
But I don't remember them. The impression is gone,
Or never was made. But I remember Evelyn.
I can remember a small man—a small man!
Who had loomed so large in the dark and dusty hall,
Whose voice was large, and whose anger was so large
That it sounded still in my ears. And smooth white hair,
Neat but sparse, all brushed straight back from the forehead
Away from the face which was too big for the body
That now seemed doubly small. A dapper man,
With pearls in his shirt-front, a beautifully tied white tie,
The tip of a thin, thin handerchief out of the pocket,
And shoes that shone on small and feminine feet.
And above all the wide smile and the still eyes
That once denied each other. But he was small—
That was the greatest shock: I towered above him.
Before I knew it, he'd seized and shaken my hand
And he said, "How are you, Tom? It's a long, long time
Since last we met. And now you're a man and married.
Is this your wife?" I presented him to Judith.
I said, "This is Evelyn—cousin Evelyn Leighton."

344

The words had a painful echo.

He said, "Hello.
I'm glad to know you. I've known your mother-in-law
Since we were children. We're only distant cousins,
But kind of Tom to remember. How is Maria?
I've sort of lost touch with her. Lives in Providence,
Isn't that it?"

I said, "She is with Miss Darnley.
They share a house together. Have done, since Father's death."
It wasn't the truth. I wondered if he would know it.
He said, "Oh yes, I remember Ethel Darnley,
A determined sort of a body, a fidus Achates,
Or how would you make that feminine? or would you?
But Maria was always kind to the wrong people,
She'd just be kind to Miss Darnley because the woman
Hadn't too many friends. Is your mother well?"
"She's well, I thank you."

"That's good. I must write to her.
It's rather disgraceful. And you, what are you doing?"
"Writing," I said.

"Ah, writing, indeed? Not painting?
You haven't followed Josiah and Henry Cottrell?
Perhaps that's wise. Got anything published yet?
Though it's early for that, I know."

"I've a poem to be published
Soon in the London Century."

"So? in London?
Good, that's good. It's a good way to begin.
They're slower here, at the moment. But you'll get on,
If you stick right at it—if you have half the talent
Your father had, and your grandfather had it, too.
But that's a weight to lift, I know, I've seen it—
Too many parents, too many predecessors,
They think that you'll be like them. Well, let 'em think so,
But stick to your own line, and they'll find you out,
But slowly, slowly—you've got to have guts, to be patient.
I'll see the number—the Century? I shall watch
To see when it comes. I take it. I like their poems.
Ballinger's got an eye for the coming poets.
It's nice to see you." He turned to Judith and said,
"I think we sit together. That's fine for me."
He lowered his voice to a whisper and said, "These people
Usually have old trouts, and I don't like trouts.

345

I may be old, but I've got an eye for the girls,
And I hope to keep it. At dinner perhaps you'll tell me
What you would like to have for a wedding present—
I'm a rich old bachelor and it is overdue."
He bowed and he moved away. He left us standing
Still together. She said, "He is nice, your cousin.
I hope you get the lovely young woman in red,
And not a trout." She giggled. I looked at her,
She was gay and smiling, the colour up in her cheeks,
And I thought, How can you do it, how look like that?
And what will Evelyn say—to my wife? to Judith?
But this was an odd new man, and I didn't know.

I couldn't see Judith during dinner. The flowers
Blocked my view of her and of Evelyn Leighton.
I talked to the women to right and to left, a little,
Because I had to. It has all gone from memory.
All I remember now is the troubled thinking
That flowed through my mind in back of the spoken words:
The ghost of Evelyn as the small boy knew him,
The memory of Mother, the hurtful anger
Flowered that morning, the memory of Father
And his words come to the surface to torment me,
To make me wonder, to doubt the rising anger
That seemed so righteous until his words arose.

But this I remember:
                        After the ladies left us,
The men all gathered together and drank champagne
That was bountifully provided. And so the talk
Turned to prohibition and bootleg wines
And where this one got that and the other one, this,
And of whisky over the border. And Harrison said,
"I'm going to live abroad if this keeps up.
With that big, handsome, small-town fool in the White
     House,
We've nothing but trouble here—and nothing to drown it.
Everything's so unsettled. So many strikes.
Life is too damned expensive. The country's going
Straight to the dogs."
                        And somebody said, "That's right.
I wish I hadn't come back at all. Six months here
Has soured me, too. And at that, it isn't a country,

346

It's just a conglomeration, forty-eight nations,
And nothing to make them tick. Except the war."
"Yes, the war did it," Harrison said. "But now,
The war is over. You're right. It isn't a country,
It's just a mess. It's crude, and vulgar, and wild.
The other evening, a damned intelligent Pole,
A hell of a nice chap, asked: 'What is America?'
And by George! no one could tell him. Several tried to,
But Lord! they couldn't succeed. It's too amorphous."
"It usen't to be," said another man, "long ago—
This was a nation, you knew where you stood then, yes.
But now! Where are we? A mess, a horrible mess,
With bigotry and the Ku Klux Klan and foreigners,
And labour crazy, and farmers all gone dickey,—
Even the arts are mad—or a rotten copy
Of somebody else's work."
                And Harrison said,
"Do you think this ever will be a proper nation,
Something you can define?"
                  "No," said the man.
"It'll break up first. And I think, by God! I'll leave it
Before I'm too old to settle down somewhere else."
There was a pause then. Evelyn cleared his throat.
"You ask," he said, "if America is a nation,
And how to define it. I should like to try that—
If you'd like to hear—was it just a rhetorical question?"
"No," said Harrison, "oh no—go on and try it.
I'm sure we'll listen?"
              "Yes," said the other man.
I said, "I'd like to hear it." He turned to me
And said, "Ah yes, you're young. You haven't yet seen
The country slide down hill, like the rest of us here.
You'll give an ear to an optimist like Leighton."
I wanted to say, 'You're a patronizing fool
And your mind's as shut as a clam when the tide is out,'
But I merely smiled. Then Evelyn spoke. He said:
"I've travelled plenty. Abroad. I've been lots of places.
All over Europe, England, Italy, France,
I know them well. And Spain. I've been east as well.
I lived in China awhile—before the war."
He turned to me and he smiled and he said, "I went there
Shortly after your mother had left New York.
But I got restless. I didn't know my own country,

And so I toured America. Slowly. And many times.
I've been in forty out of the forty-eight states—
Can you all say that?"
                              The other four men just shifted
About in their seats and muttered, but didn't answer.
"I've known the east since boyhood, the whole east coast,
But as one of our sort knows it—the pleasant houses,
The fine deep harbours of Maine, the friends at Charleston,
The fishing in Florida, and the Washington balls,
The hunting down in Virginia and Pennsylvania,
Hot Springs—oh Lord, we've been there, all of us here,
Over and over. But all of us know one thing:
It's not America—only a tiny fraction.
I've motored about the country and talked to its people—
I've heard their stories. I've listened to men in Georgia
Cursing the North as though it were 1870,
But they cursed in American. If you chose to argue
They thought you were just another God-damned Yankee,
But they listened—and disbelieved. I've heard the Swedes
Up Minnesota way, the farmers, grumbling—
And the Poles grumble, who live around Milwaukee,
And all the shoe-factory workers, at Lynn, all foreign,
They all grumble, but—they stay here and grumble,
They don't go home to do it. I've seen the West Coast,
I've been in Idaho and Montana, talked there
To the men who filled my car, and the men by the road
Driving their cattle from one wide space to another,
And the men in the little, dreary, dusty villages:
They're not alike, but they all misuse one language,
And say that the times are hard, but perhaps they'll better
If so-and-so gets elected—and have ten ways
Of pronouncing his curious, Czechoslovakian name.
I've been with people who lived their lives in the Big Horns
And didn't know the name for the wild lupine
That covers the hills in June. But they knew their neighbours,
They knew their cattle and every inch of the country—
And they all cursed Washington and the cattle market.
I've been in places where 'Thank you' got a 'Thank you,'
Or where it got a 'Yep' or a plain 'O.K.'—
Or 'Surely' or 'Come again' or just 'You bet'—
They were all the variants on a single theme.
And sometimes I hardly could understand the lingo
But got the drift: they were cursing as you were cursing:

348

The state of the nation. I drove a Rolls-Royce once
Into a small town in eastern Colorado.
The comment there was, 'I bet she eats up gas.'
In Vermont they said, 'I'd care to look at that engine.'
In Arkansas they said, 'It's mighty lovely,
But I bet she costs to feed. My Ford gets twenty.
Y'all'd never git over our roads in that.' They didn't
Seem to look up or down to the man who owned it.
I've talked a number of times to the men in Pittsburgh,
The steel-mill men, who were cursing worse than the farmers
And that takes doing. I could see they didn't like me,
I wasn't their kind, but I needed no introduction
To drink at a bar with them, or to hear their troubles—
I didn't need anything. I have been in the Black Hills,
I've heard the cattle men curse at the agriculture,
And say that the country was only fit for grazing,
While they bought up the little pieces that failed to go
Because the weather was good one year in five.
I've heard the men in Nebraska, men who lived
In the great dune country, looks like a God-sized golf course,
Curse at the meddling east. They meant Ohio.
I've seen the plains of Kansas and held my breath
For the new sky showing forever over the next rise,
And heard the hard, dry, matter-of-fact men there
Talk hours and hours about one special hog
And what was the matter with it.

                                    You see, I've travelled,
Looking to find America, never finding it,
Finding another phase, finding the south-west,
Finding the artists lodged in a place like Taos
And covered with silver and skin-deep Indian culture;
I've tasted New England fresh after California,
The size of one and the sweet smell of the other.
I couldn't find America—it's too big.
I found but one small thing, and I've held it to me,
It gave me pleasure, I've treasured each fresh, new finding,
Over and over, wherever I chanced to be,
An idle, elderly, well-to-do, curious man
Seeking his country as though he sought for a friend:
Wherever I went, whomever I chanced to talk to,
They all and always said one thing. They asked,
'How's your part of the country, how are you doing?'
And when you told them, 'It's tough,' they said, 'That's bad,

But we'll pull out of it, Mister.' *We,* they said.
They didn't say *You.* That's all I needed to know.
It's why I travel—but in America now,
Three thousand miles—and never a visa needed."
He ceased and he smiled.

                          An elderly man said, "Ah!
Very instructive, very. I wish I'd travelled.
Never had time to."

                          Another said, "Well, Leighton,
You've been about a bit, I must say that.
I went to Chicago once. Yes, and then St. Louis.
It must have been ninety-seven or ninety-eight,
Interesting, yes. Though I can't say I liked it.
A little bit loud, Chicago."

                          Harrison spoke:
"We'd better go up now, friends, and join the ladies.
They'll wonder about us. We'll tell them that Burton Holmes
Has given a talk, or travelogue, doesn't he call it?
And very interesting, too."

                          We rose as he did.
Evelyn came to me and he said, "Well, Tom,
I've talked too long, I expect." I looked at him,
Smiling in spite of myself. "I enjoyed your talk.
It's done me good—at a psychological moment."
I wanted to add the thought that flashed through my mind:
'Can there any good thing come out of Nazareth?' Then
We turned and I let him precede me out of the room.

3

The dinner broke up early, like all dull dinners,
Shortly after the men had joined the women
And they'd yawned their way each through a glass of water.
And then, before I knew it, we both were home,
And suddenly face to face in the big bedroom
Full of our own things now.

                          She was looking at me,
Moving her lips a little, as though she tried
To command the words that wouldn't obey her will.
She spoke at last. "A horrible day. Yes, horrible.
Morning and afternoon and now, the evening."

I said, "What happened to you, at that dull party,
That you'd call horrible?"
                              "Oh, that man," she cried,
"Your Mr. Leighton, your cousin, Evelyn Leighton . . ."
She shuddered a little and stopped.
                              "What did he do?"
"Do?" she said. "He made love to me all through dinner,
He pawed me, Tom, he put his hand on my knee,
He—oh! I didn't know what to do, or to say,
I hated to make scenes—and I hadn't the spirit,
After this morning."
                              "God!" I said, "he didn't?"
I couldn't absorb it yet, but I felt ashamed
As though it were I that had caused it.
                                        "Oh yes, he did.
And more than that, he talked to me of your mother,
He told me she'd broken his heart. He even hinted
He'd been her lover, and how he had healed his hurt
By exercising his charms on so many women—
But he had no charms for me—I thought him loathsome,
Loathsome and horrible—and he tried to use
His wedding present idea as a sort of a bribe
For my complaisance." She shuddered again. The tears
Stood in her eyes, and then she began to tremble,
And every quiver that passed through her young body
Was like a knife in my side. But I knew my way
And I tried to take it. I said, "It was all my fault.
I have been horrible too. The devil was in me.
I've hurt myself because I have hurt my love.
And the one thing that I love."
                              She began to cry,
Softly, standing, her hands clenched tightly together.
She said, "I have tried so hard, not to be crying,
All day, not to be crying."
                              I said, "Forgive me.
It was a bad dream, only. It is all over.
What does it matter where we live or how,
So long as we're both together?" I moved to her
And took her into my arms. She let go, then,
And sobbed and sobbed and I comforted her with broken
Words and the little disjointed touch of hands,
But my heart was full of shame. And at length she spoke:

351

"I'm better now. It's over—except for England—
And the little books for children."
                                    I said, "Not books,
But flesh and blood will be, all in good season,
And we shall live where the roots were first well planted—
That was stupidity, out of a discontent,
Born of the moment, silly, it will not last.
There's only you and here that really can matter—
I shall grow rich from these."
                                    She kissed me then.
I shall not forget that kiss, not ever forget it:
It brought sweet darkness, it banished the cruel light,
It said forgiveness, it severed a mood and bred one,
It filled the room with the comfort of silent echoes.
And later we lay in the dark and in our silence
When the tide of love had flooded and ebbed to peace,
And I heard her whisper, "Tom—Tom, what did change
    you?"
I said, "It was love for you and your own good sense,"
But I thought: keep silent now, nor breathe of Evelyn,
Nor the many words he spoke, nor remembered visions,
Nor the dusky hall, nor anger out of old anger,
Nor the good thing from Nazareth. There was a time,
There was a place for these, but now and only
A time and a place for silence to nourish love.

HERE UNREALITY is more real and true
Than should be with this shadowed, boneless, blind,
This two-dimensional ghost to frighten you
With three dimensions of the fertile mind;
Here troubled passions, having once been dead,
Their pictured emanations exorcised,
Arouse and speak as though the guilty bed
Squeaked in the night that guilty love devised;
Here is the very taste and sound and smell,
The mad dark's tangible, its desired sight
Sprung from a brush that only death could quell,

352

Where only death could recreate the night:
Here is a lust, unbonded by its locks,
Forever caught within this paradox.

1   1

"JUDITH," I said, "I think Joss is a bastard
Not to stop for us. It's a hellish place
To try to get to."
                    "Don't be mean," she said,
"He wants to be with Molly. We felt that way
When we were first engaged."
                              "It strikes me funny
To think of Joss in love. It makes no sense.
I can't believe it. Well, there it is. We'll go
Up by the subway and then walk across—
If that suits you?"
                    "O.K." she said. "It's fine,
If we're together."
                    She put on her hat,
Gathered her bag and gloves and we went out
Into the clear grey of the autumn weather.
We took the subway and our trip was done
High in the hundreds. We walked over west
To the great storage warehouse where were housed
Many of Father's things. Quite near the door
Was parked the smart and shining little car
That Molly Breen had given Joss, a present
When they became engaged. We looked at it.
"What will she give him when he marries her?"
"A fortune," Judith answered, "But what else
I cannot tell."
                "She has no brains," I said,
"And not much breeding."
                        "Stupid women make
Pretty good wives." She laughed and took my arm.
"Isn't it true?"
                I said, "When you are stupid,
I shall divorce you."
                     Then we went inside.
A short man in an apron, known as Joe,
Led us down many long, cool passages,
Past wire doors which opened on the latent

Trappings of use—as though all life lay coiled there
Like a great, strong, and idle length of rope
That once had bound and held. It was so quiet
That our feet stirred the echoes that were dust
A long time settled. At the very end
Of one dark corridor, a gate stood open,
And the bright light of an electric bulb
Made sudden emphasis. Joss was standing there;
Beside, stood Molly, a girl of medium height,
With pretty blond hair, and a childish face
That seemed as though it always might be so,
Aging to lose its freshness but take on
No structure from its age.   "Welcome," Joss called.
"I'm glad to see you. We were both bogged down.
We don't know where to start. It's like a game
One doesn't know the rules of."
                                "Hi!" I said
"We'll let this man—he knows it—sort it out,
Put all the obvious studio stuff one side,
And let us have the textiles and the pictures
Out in the hall here."
                      "Good," said Joss. The man
Nodded and said, "That's right. It's easy done."
He went right at it. The two girls stood outside
And talked together. Joss and I looked on.
The man worked with surprising speed and soon
The hallway was all stacked with pictures wrapped
In their protective paper, and a trunk
Stood open. I said to Judith, "You and Molly,
Go through these fabrics, if you like, and take
What things you want, divide them up between you.
They do no good here."
                      "Some of them are fine—
Beautiful things," said Joss. "Poor Father had
A good and most expensive eye. Look through them,
You want to, Molly?"
                    "Yes," she said. "What fun!
It's thrilling—just a grab-bag." Judith smiled.
Then our own work began: we stripped the paper
From canvas after canvas. So re-lived
The paintings in the light: their colour filled

The drab and hopeless corridor with life,
And memories of the man who painted them
So keen and vivid I could not judge their worth
In this emotion of remembering
A place, a time, the image of a hand
Moving to strike their colour into flame
Over a surface. The living hand was close:
More real under the brutal fact of death
Than when it lived and moved.
                       Then Judith spoke:
"See this, Tom, it is lovely. Molly says
She doesn't want it. Unless Joss does, it's ours—
It is so beautiful." I looked around.
She held the corner of a huge great piece
Lying in deep folds of its blues and greens,
With coals of orange burning in the ashes
Of a grey background . . .
And the long, and rippling
Folds ceased to quiver, and were still, and covered
The door that waited.
Ripple of patterned cloth in a north light,
Persian pattern falling, the sound of steps
Rap-tap-tap on the stairs,
The heart beating.
               "No," said Joss, "You take it.
I never liked it much. It's hard to use.
Very fine in the studio. No, you take it."
Judith said, "Don't you want it?"
                        "Yes—oh yes.
Take it, of course." I did not look at her.
I didn't want to catch her eye. She'd see
Something too much.
             Nothing too much, they said,
They were wise old birds, the Greeks.
                      We just went on,
Working again. I heard the sound of words
In Judith's voice, in Molly's. I heard Joss say,
"Here is a honey! Boy, is that the berries!
Let me have this one." I glanced over at it:
A picture of Rhode Island—swamp azalea
Bloomed in bog-meadow against the lavender
Shadows of maples toward an evening sun.

I said, "Yes, take it." That was mine as well:
Bogs and their meadows and wide maple trees:
They had not been his, only, as a tall
Grey room can so belong.
                              And the time passed,
And this was almost gone from consciousness—
Till Joss cried out and said, "Ah, here's the nude,
Now we shall have a fight!" He stood the picture
Carefully on the floor, and propped it up
Against a packing box. The yellow light
Fell on it justly. Even that bare, bleak,
Unshaded lighting could not harm it. No.
But could it harm me, now?
                              They gathered round it.
The man called Joe gave it one hasty glance
And moved away: embarrassment was plain
In every motion. I said, "You take it, Joss."
He looked at it. "I'd love to—no denying.
By God, it's beautiful! But—it seems to me—
Somehow, it's rightly yours. You saw it first—
He sent me off. Remember?"
                              I remembered.
Judith said, "Oh, it's wonderful. Oh, yes,
Do let us have it!" Then she turned to Molly.
"And you?" she asked. But Molly shook her head,
And giggled and she said, "I guess it's good,
But Heavens! where to hang it? Everyone
Would say such funny things, now wouldn't they?
If it just hung, well, in the living room."
Joss said, "You take it, Tom. It frightens Molly."
I thought: it frightens me. And you can't keep
Ghosts on the wall with comfort, day by day.
I exorcised you once: but now you have
New life to trouble me, because of death
That supervened. You'd whisper at me, yes,
Sibilant whispers like a rain at night,
Soft suspicions sprung from a locked past,
New discomfort.
                      "Put it aside," I said.
"We can decide it later."
                              Judith took it:
She said, "I'll carry it to that window, Tom,
I'd like to see how daylight makes it look."

356

She lifted it and bore it a long way
Down to a window. Of my need I turned
Back to the task of sorting.

2

And then . . . it was all over, and this was sorted, and that,
Here for Joss, there for me, and Judith liked these,
But Molly wanted those. We had made
A use for a dead past: or perhaps
The past is not dead while you still can use it—
Or while you must.
But Molly and Joss were gone now, the shining car
Climbed and grew small to the east. And Judith
Sat beside me and the bus swayed,
And the trees still bore their brown-green leaves,
The river ran its full life, and the boats
Drove their barbed furrows in the grey North River—
But there were no lights then, and no stars:
Only a grey sky.
But still I wondered
(Hearing the thin bell as the two dimes
Were clutched by the metal of time):
It is not *if* now, not *if*, but only:
How?
And after a long space of silence, Judith spoke,
Saying, "Tom, I saw the name on the back,
Clare on the back of it."
I watched the boats on the long, troubled water.
She said, "And still I want it."
I did not speak but I looked at her,
She was not smiling, now, not really smiling,
Only the curve of her lips was upward, faintly,
And we were married, and these lips,
They were for winter and summer, they were for spring
They were the autumn lips, the day-time,
The night-time lips, and for speech, and smiling,
And for our kisses: that had not ceased, nor grown
Weary or stale. The bus swayed
In the old way, and I said,
"You are a fine person, and I love you."
"That was the name?" she asked.
"That was what you said? the one word

357

Spoken so strongly, where the poor girl
First saw her lover seeing another lover
In the dark of the room?"
It was the day-time, and the grey sky lit
Everything into clarity and I said, "Yes."
"These are old things, Tom, so now be wise:
They have not made wise, but too tender, feeling
Always the sharp spur of the old fear
Grown in the past. See, I am not fearful.
Marriage and love—they are not hung on a thin thread
Always in peril. We have woven
A strong cord, now. We shall make it
A great rope. See, I am not afraid.
I just love you: all that you are, or may be,
And, see Tom—all that you were." She paused. She said:
"Was she so lovely?"
I took her hand and I laughed.
"Good!" she said. "Do laugh. It is good to laugh.
It was a cruel—or an impertinent question?"
"Yes, it was both. But Judith, she was lovely,
Lovely to look at. Clever. And hard. And quick.
It is all over."
"Yes," she said, "it is over, it is done with—
Now we shall hang her."
"Yes," I said, "we shall hang her
Higher than Haman."
"Listen to me, Tom. Every time I am angry
I shall say 'Clare' to you—but you must not mind it.
It is too good a weapon. Oh—too good a weapon!
Naked and beautiful and clever, and—then—
She was before me." Then her voice broke,
And the tears came to her eyes. She said,
"I hate her." And her fingers gripped mine
Hard, till they hurt me, and I said, "I love you."
"Yes," she said, "you love me, and I, I love you.
And she—that—it is now all over."
The bus went, swaying,
Down the long Drive, and the great North River flowed
Steadily southward and we sat together,
Close together. I thought: two separate persons—
Much you may know, but little do you know,
Little may judge: for if this is now over,
What have we then begun? Or what are you?

358

Who laugh and weep in the same breath. Or I,
What am I now to you? Who knew me well—
But did not know these matters, nor the flesh
Painted in candle-light,
Nor the long, whispering night—
But know a little and may still laugh and weep
In the same breath, knowing me—but not all of me
That now is but a little more known. Yet,
A phase is over, a new phase
Begins and still we are together, and may be so
Through many phases, having mastered these
That film on film, disclose us, showing us
Little by little, even to lovers' eyes,
Little by little—but never the whole man,
Nor the whole woman.

AGE IS IN DEBT to death, and death shall sue
If age outrun the issue of its bond
And having spent the years that were its due,
Grasp at the hours that still lie beyond.
There's but one termination to such suit
For in the end it must be wholly paid:
Down from the tree shall drop the ready fruit
Though the long season's ripening be delayed.
And yet—and yet—in death there is a seed
That bears the promise of another growing,
A further pith on which a love may feed,
A further leafage of a stranger sowing:
Finality itself is but a phase
If death in death plants love for all its days.

AND THEN it was nineteen hundred and twenty-four—
And the telegram came on the twentieth day of August:
Some dates are not forgotten. I shut the door
And read the yellow slip in the dusk of the hall.

It came from Joss. It said, 'Grandfather is ill
You had better come down at once.' I read it again:
What was Joss doing there? Oh, yes, in Father's house,
Summering there. I heard the city sounds
Out in the hot streets; the sound of Agatha's tread
On the bare pantry floor: these sounds were home,
These sounds were the new life on which I fed.
I thought: it is hard to think where the thought is pain,
To whom will you turn for wisdom, if he is dead?
I thought of the small boy curled in the large chair
With trouble turned to the joy of a voice's sound,
I thought of the young man bearing the sorrowful ghost
Of a friend to be blessed and buried in comfort's ground
By the deep words of courage and wisdom joined.
I thought of the great flood of his love, like rain
Shed from the bowl of the hills to the channelled river,
Washing all petty grief to the clean pain
That's worn to honour.

           Then Judith came down the stairs.
She said, "What's up?" I showed her, nor spoke at first.
She read the telegram and she cried, "But this,
It may be nothing." And yet—I believed the worst
As one braces against a shock in the hope that time
Will prove you wrong and the fears will soon disperse.
I said, "We must go, at once, he is very old."
She answered, "Of course we shall. We can pack and go,"
And she laid her hand on my arm and she said, "Let's hope.
Let's not anticipate. It is better so.
My heart is heavy for him and heavy for you,
But he's got the strength of ten and he's got the will,
And that's what matters. When we arrive there, Tom,
He may be better, or we may find him well."
I said, "You're sweet," but inside myself I knew
This was a sorrow it would be hard to share
Even with Judith.

           We packed and we caught a train.
I tried to read: it was useless. I could but stare
Out of the window as the familiar land
Rolled in the hot sun and the summer's glare
Past the window. I drifted away and away:
I smelt the pungence of the green, crushed sweet-fern,
I heard the song of the thrush in the pretty hollow,
I saw the scene and the man, and I watched him turn

Enquiring eyes to mine as he cursed and spoke,
And the words were shafted words and were driven home.
I was a long way off when the train drew in
And I felt surprise when I found I was not alone.

Joss did not meet us. We hired a car to drive
The long six miles from the Junction by Chog's Cove,
Along the reach of the summer's green-rich shore,
And every inch by inch of the way we drove
Was filled with memories, come to the surface now,
Fresh-seen, new-known, and the memories were of love
Sprung from the old man who had made me see
The way I travelled.
           And then we were at the door,
And Charles to meet us, but no great voice to cry
'Welcome!' as though all welcome must be a glory.
We waited below in the long-dear living room,
And I saw a nurse in white going up the stairs.
I asked, "Where's Joss?" Charles answered, "He'll be down
    soon,
He's up with Mr. Cottrell, he is, up there."
"What is the matter, Charles?"
               He said, "Well now,
Just nothing the matter excepting his age already.
It's just his years, Mister Tom, it's just his years,
He's feeble and old and he ain't been right in his head,
He took sick sudden, he don't seem to know no body,
He lies asleep all day, so small in his bed,
Don't know Miss Molly, don't seem to know Mister Joss,
I sometimes wonder, indeed, if he knows me,
For all my years. The doctor says he's dyin'.
The only once he's spoke real strong and freely,
Instead of a mumble, he asked for you to come."
I said, "Can I see him soon? Should we both go in?"
He paused and he said, "Well, yes. The doctor says
There's nothing to help or harm so far as he knows.
Perhaps he'll recognize you and perhaps Miss Judith,
And if it gives him happiness, ain't that enough,
With the end so near?"
             I heard a step on the stair
And then Joss joined us. He said, "My God, it's tough
Having the old man ill, and unable to know you.
I'm glad you've come. Alone, it's been pretty rough.

361

He's wanted to see you, he's asked for you both. Go up.
The doctor says it can do no harm. Not long—
Stay for a short while only. But be prepared:
He will not know you. His mind is back in the young
Days of his marriage. It's lucky you came so quickly,
Tomorrow may be too late."
                              I said, "How does he look?"
"Awful," said Joss. "So little and white and shrunk."
I thought of Grey Hen leaping the Seldom Brook
With the small hunched figure atop, a part of the horse:
He was little and shrunken then. I said, "Let's go, soon."
So Judith and I went up the familiar stairs,
Down the long corridor, past the old blue room,
Up to the dark closed door, where I used to knock
To rouse his voice to thunder. Now there was none.
We didn't knock; we entered. The room was dark.
A figure in white rose from the window-seat
And rustled toward us. She whispered, "You're Mister Tom?
It's no use now, your grandfather is asleep."
The little, hunched figure lost in the great wide bed
Stirred as she spoke, and he said in a husky voice,
"It's a blasted lie. I'm as wide awake as a bat.
I've waited a hell of a time for just this boy."
The nurse looked at us and fidgetted with her hands.
"Get out," he said, "for I'd be alone with them."
She stood for a second. I said, "You had better go.
I'll call if you're needed." She turned and left us then.
My eyes grew used to the dark. I could see him now,
Looking at us and smiling. He said, "She's a gem,
But the time is short. And my strength is short as well.
I wanted to see you, Judith, and say good-bye.
I've been hoarding my powers for this. You're a fine young
    girl,
You make him a damn good wife and I know you try.
I'm sorry you've borne no sons. But there's time for that.
I'd be pleased to know that you named one after me—
My wife would have liked that, yes, she'd have liked you too.
Now go, young Judith. Leave us together, please,
I want to see Tom alone. Be good, be kind,
Be gentle with him as long as he's good and true.
I'd kiss you now, except that the idiots took
My teeth away, and when I was young I knew
Nothing so horrible as a kiss from gums

362

In an old man's face."
                    She said, "But if I kiss you . . ."
And she leaned across the bed and she kissed his cheek,
And she said, "Good-bye. We shall meet—we shall meet some
     time."
He said, "Perhaps. But I'm taking no bets on that."
Then Judith left us, weeping. He said, "My line
Is run to the reel's end." His voice was low,
I could only hear by an effort. I found a chair
And drew it up to the bed, and I leaned over
Close, close to him. He said, "When the end is near
You somehow know it. Listen and do not speak,
I've more to tell you than I shall have strength to tell.
Or time. Or time. A terrible tyrant, time."
He ceased and over the silence the sound fell
Of the waves on the hard shore. He sighed and spoke:
"I've left the house to you. It's as old as hell
And not convenient. Change it. Never be bound
By what went on before you. I've left Joss money,
More than to you—he has your father's house,
And he thinks he's rich with that stupid little monkey.
But that won't last. She loves him. There is no love
Can last with such a person as Joss. He's hard.
He's like my Jo. He's scared to be vulnerable.
There is no way to protect the loving heart—
By love it grows and beats, and by love is wounded,
By love it is laid bare, and the more you love,
The more you're open to all the scars and wounds
Of the real living. To keep his head above
The waters of pride in which he swims, he'll need
Money—and that won't save him—for nothing saves
The man who is prideful alone, excepting death
Such as Jo suffered." He ceased and he closed his eyes,
And was silent so long that I rose from the little chair
With the thought of leaving. He spoke. "Sit down. Man dies
But once and he's lucky to have the one he loves
Near to his latest hours." He ceased again,
And I sat. He raised his hand and he touched my own,
Lightly: his crippled fingers, swollen and bent,
Tapped on it, lightly. He said one word: "Remember."
He opened his eyes. He was not smiling now.
"The time grows short. I live on the edge of death,
And the riddle of death is hard, for I do not know—

I do not know. Sleep? Or another phase?
Remembrance alone can comfort. I'd live in you.
Remember and don't forget. Not every day—
But now and then remember, let love revive,
Carry the image up to the conscious light,
Say 'Thus and so he was, while he was alive.'
And so mortality is postponed. I fear
The swift oblivion if it is only sleep,
With Cesca vanished because I've vanished too,
Who kept her memory green in the great deep
Wells of remembrance. Funny. A bent old man,
Tired and crippled, and hates to approach the end,
Because he's afraid of it. I have faced my life."
He stirred in his bed and his voice grew vehement:
"Remember me, remember! It is not much.
Your memory is the buckler that may defend
Me from the sharp sword of oblivion."
I found my voice and I said, "Could I forget
The one I have loved so long?" He sighed and said,
Now in a whisper, "Death is the end of debt.
Then we shall meet, or then we shall sleep unknowing—
It doesn't signify. Cesca is very near.
My son is nothing, he is apart, apart—
To the devil with him, we never could rightly hear
Each other's meaning. Only the voice of my wife
Telling me—something—something. And Joss is gone,
Gone like his father. And only Tom remains,
The boy with the skinny knees, and the deep, long
Eyes of love in his head. He can leave me now:
I hear my wife, she is singing. You hear the song?
She wants me. Leave me. Remember me, but leave me,
For I am with her now." Then he closed his eyes
And lay quite still. I rose, but he did not move.
I went to the door and I touched the knob. He cried
Suddenly, loudly, clearly, "God damn the end!
Love is a bliss and a pain, and love's end is sorrow—
What does it matter? Love is the one preserver,
Gathers our yesterdays when there are no tomorrows.
This is the Harvest, by God! and I say 'Thanksgiving!'"

He died in the night, sleeping. Perhaps he sleeps
Deeper than ever now. But I do not know.
I know that my pain was fierce and long and deep,

As love must have it, till day on living day
Turned all to memory, making remembrance sweet,
Never forgotten. No. For he lives in me—
To forget were death, where death is not yet defeat.

SEE, THIS shall be your seed, your very own,
To plant in hope, ambition, and in fear—
Within such boundaries a long time grown
It shall at length be cherished and be dear,
And it shall meet the harvest at the end,
Grown to the ripeness of its golden grain,
And being seed, again as seed may send
Another growth to its insistent pain,
And over it the moon shall wax to all
The circle of its light and fade and go,
And over it shall come the cloudy pall,
And on it lie the sleep of winter snow,
Till cycles finish and your seed is done
And only love remains beneath the sun.

↗   ↗

I GIVE YOU of a later year, the sweet
Moment when love turned innocent again,
Finding a flower-bordered path with feet
That stumbled long
On the more rocky paths of adult men.
It shall be yours whenever you remember
The April song
Over the frost-laid stillness of November.
This you shall see:
Judith and I one autumn afternoon
Sit happily where broom-sedge waves its silk,
Watch the last sun-lit levels of the sea
Knowing that soon
Dusk will enamel mother-of-pearl on milk
To turn the ocean to another cloud

Above whose edges shine in their degree
The golden stars that houses wear by night,
And make the whisper of small leaves be loud,
The scent of bay a wilderness delight.
We do not speak: we follow each our thought
More easily for mute companionship,
Till all the nerves that life makes tense and taut
Relax and the dreams slip
Into the way of peace.
And so the day at length recedes and dies,
The heaven girds on again its jewelled fleece,
And Perseus lifts his weapon to the skies,
And the wild geese,
Sharp compass-needle of the season's change,
Point from the North Star, the magnetic iron
Rung to a strange
Music as they drift under far Orion.
And Judith speaks:
"Now I must surely tell. My time is past.
The days have grown into the shape of weeks:
I have been waiting, for I was not sure.
But now, at last,
I know I bear a child, beyond all cure."
I say, "We wished it so."
She leans against me with a lowered head,
I feel her sobbing, quietly, steadily.
She whispers, "It has been so long, and oh!
I was so frightened that it might not be,
And now, instead,
My only fear is that you lie to me."
I say, "I do not lie.
This is the moment to which I have grown,
It is the truth.
Out of the fright and ignorance of youth,
Has come a love that is not quick to die,
That seeks no more its solitary zone,
Nor life alone,
But is content with you—and yours."
                                      Her sigh
Shakes her to trembling. "Truly? It is true?"
"Of this, my love, I could not lie to you."
She says: "Then it is bliss," and speaks no more.
We sit, together, silent. The stars climb

Slow to their brilliance, the far shore
Lost in soft music, lost in time.

2

So a month passes, and a few weeks, and a season is gone,
And the days go by, one by one, in a long procession,
And it is April: and spring troubles the mind and the heart,
For the flesh moves and is great in these days
With Judith's time so near;
And this is a joy to me, and this is a fear to me.
So the days pass.
So the days pass as the air blows:
As the air blows through city windows now and the curtains
        move to it,
The green curtains of the moving flowers, of our house.
This is the air of New York: should it not blow away
Fear and the strange dread, should it not comfort,
Where Judith needs no comfort, but only I—
Only Tom is fearful?
This is my home, and the air that blows here,
This is the old air, blowing the old way, ruffling
Familiar shapes,
Sweet with the thought of Judith, the touch of Judith,
Hinting of flowers: there are flowers in this room. Yes.
And the moving smell of one more spring pressed on the many
        springs
That are past and gone: where fear grew: but not this fear,
Nor this tenderness, this concern,
This whole immersion in the life of another
Whose life is doubled, as fear
Doubles in the spring days, when the flesh
Is great with change.

And always there is Agatha, of the loose slippers, saying:
'Make her lie down, now, make her rest,' and saying,
'Keep from the stairs, dear.'
And the soft voice of Agatha, saying, 'Let me do it,'
The apron twisted, the white hair, and the gentle voice,
Asking and questioning, but forever saying,
'It will not be long now,' and adding,
'You're the lucky girl.'

So the days pass, and the hours, and always,
There is a peace and a tumult:
There are the eyes of Judith, wide eyes, larger than ever,
Full of peace and serenity, and the good smile,
And the look of accomplishment, the static
Look of the day fulfilled;
Or the swift and sudden
Flare of the temper, the new wish,
The immoderate
Need for attention, for this and for that, or the other, the cry
Of long discomfort that fades now
To the serene smile, to the placid, empty
Happiness of action inactive, and the wide eyes,
Large and beautiful, saying, always,
'Be kind and love me, be gentle,'
Saying, 'I love you,' and the smile that speaks
Soundless sentences that mean:
'This is for us, but I
Am the doer, I am the doer, I make,
It is the flesh now, only, the mind
Is far and away.'
And within me there is a voice crying:
'I began it.' But this
Is a two-edged sword, it cuts toward pride and it cuts
Into a terror; upon its blade is written
'This is the way and the means, be glad;
This is a joy and this is the deep of joy
And this is a proud matter; and this
Is a chain for a new binding, a manacle
Wrist to wrist, to be broken
But never released.'

And the days are born and die and the night
Is but a companion. Darkness
Harbours the whole thought, the misted thought,
The unspoken fear, the dim-seen, half-believed
Fear of the days to come, the passion
Never to be again? Or sleep,
In a long, endless sleeping? but now,
It is for comfort, for the familiar, small words, but only
As a companion now. As a companion?
The mind is off and away, in a flash, roaming:
The traitorous mind,

The Judas-mind, the Benedict-Arnold mind,
Betrayer, traitor:
She sleeps, while the mind betrays her—
For the flesh was great in those days and the air blew
Spring through the window and fear loosed hold
On the abstinent mind, alone in the dark, no longer
Only a true companion.

Then the pain came. But this is all confusion:
The telephone call, and the doctor, and the car,
The elevator-girl in a dress of white,
The linoleum floors, and the smell
Of anaesthetic. And many hours
Pass in a night and grow
To the grey dawn. Beside you
Is Mrs. Carpenter, a smile in a blue dress,
A head that nods on a double chin in a chair
While the breath whistles a little, we knew her well,
Her name was Cranston, Rose,
Her sister, Rachel, yes, the aunt with the teeth,
And thank you, thank you, this is a comfortable room,
The magazines are old and the night is old,
And where is the doctor?
But a long time passes.
And Mrs. Carpenter, now, is silent, and you
Are silent, too: there is nothing to say, just wait.
Wait, and do not think, for the thoughts breed
Fear like a terrible ague in your bones,
And you see Death:
Death in a long white coat, Death wearing
A mask of gauze, and you see
Your name on the ticket he holds and he says, 'You gave
Permission for me to come. Your body, now,
Is paid at the cost of your mind.
Did you not think?'

You say to Mrs. Carpenter, 'I must know.
I cannot sit here, waiting, and not knowing.'
She says, 'Be quiet, they'll let us hear. Sit still.
It won't be long.'
But there is no comfort here.
And the minutes pass.
You hear a cry, muffled, a long way off,

Door upon door subdues it, but what subdues
The spirit that made the cry?
Outside in the street are the early sounds of a city,
The click of heels in the early-morning walk,
The springtime small-boy whistle, the treads of tires
Sucking the watered streets in a whine and a hiss.
But it grows too long. You rise and you seek the door:
There is a long hall, and a small table,
A shaded lamp and a ledger, but no one there.
And the polished floor reflects you and makes no sound
To the frightened footsteps.
And a door opens, and a man in white,
Clad like the image of Death—but it is the doctor,
It is only Doctor Fellowes—comes out of the door,
A voice that you do not know says, 'How does it go?'
And before he can answer, a nurse comes out, she wheels
A table all covered in white, and another man,
And another nurse, and they look at you, and they laugh,
And they say, 'By George, you'd think he was having it!'
And they make cheap jokes not suited to agony—
They are only funny again when life has made
A life from a life and laughter
Grows from the life again:
It is gone now:
It is far off, it is gone,
There is only
The passionate need to know.
But they say, 'Go back, we shall let you know. In time.
You've got no business here. There is nothing to do.
Go back and wait.'
And wait? A terrible word:
The woman waits for the man in the days of war,
And her mind must conjure the image of life and death
In that long waiting:
And now, I, Tom,
Must wait in a small room, in a grey light,
And conjure images.
And the minutes grow
To an overwhelming hour.
And then—

It is all over now, it is all over.
Here are smiles and messages, here is hope,

Here is a bundle of life, it may be yours,
It does not matter, it is a son,
It is a chain and a binding, it bore
Terror and pain and fear, its time
Is not begun for you. But there,
Sleeping upon a white bed lies your life,
A pale, pale face,
The dark hair bound,
Life sleeping but still a life,
And the hope of the days and the long
Reach of the days past, gathered
Into a sleeping woman.
And for a moment
You are alone—and then—
The moment is past, and what did you do, how
Did you seize the moment? Nothing?
A space of time?
A thought? Not any. A mood? It is gone and gone:
It shall remain as a clear void until
Life shall refill it, fiercely, and forever
It shall be cherished then.

Is the fear over?
The fear is gone a little way off, it waits
Forever now, attending. It shall grow dim,
But not forgotten. No. Remember love,
And remember fear. There is no oblivion
To hide them in.

But it is the sunlight now,
And Mrs. Carpenter kisses you and she cries,
And you comfort her, now, when happiness is so plenty,
Who could not comfort you. And you walk
Down the long, silent corridor, past the desk,
Down with the girl in white in the wide car
Past the green doors with the big white numbers
Till one door opens, and then,
There is the day and the street and the life of the street,
And you go out to this,
And you walk in the day, fast, as if you knew
Whither your steps were leading and not blind
On the numberless streets.
You say, 'By God, I'm a father!' and you say,

'By God, I'm hooked now, and I'm chained, I'm chained!'
And you say, 'By God, I love her!'
And love sweeps up
In a huge rising tide and a vast wave
That is green and pure and strong in a noise of thunder,
It bears you up and up—and this, oh this!
It is not for always, but only now, but this
Is yours forever and ever.

I SEE YOU still, as once I saw you stand:
You struck a spark that lit my blood to flame,
Yet I have never touched you with my hand,
And more, I do not even know your name
Save that it's legion and is dear to me
For all such moments of brief ecstasy.

And you I see, and I remember you,
Who wove into the pattern of my life
A thread that was not strong and was not true,
And I have cut it with a sharper knife
And pulled it forth—but there, where once it wove,
Is yet the empty space of empty love.

AND THIS November day I remember, being the first day
Judith and I had hunted at Sam Allen's place, close to the
       Blue Hills,
In this our first Virginia hunting. Yes, it began there
And seven years later it ended there, but not yet, not yet. Oh,
Now we were just beginning.
And I remember Mrs. Fenimore, Sam's mother, a big woman,
       a grand woman,
Who hunted grandly and should have drunk hard and
       smoked hard
And sworn like the rest of them, but she did none of these
       things.

She lived happily in a huge house that stretched way out,
And all the rooms were enormous. She said it gave her claus-
    trophobia
Living in small rooms. It would have. She was a fine, big
    woman,
With fine, big hates and her loves were the same size:
Even her husband, seemingly.
I should have thought him (except for this day)
A thin, forgettable man, the echo of manhood. Somehow
You never saw him really, even at table: he seemed
Like a thin spirit trapped once in a book's closing,
A rich and a fine book, beautifully bound—or else, perhaps,
Like a little spirit that got caught in a beautiful
Pot of Sèvres when somebody put the top on and replaced it
High on a shelf, and it was never opened,
It was so rare and choice: a collector's piece.
And I remember that Mrs. Fenimore fell from her horse in
    the field,
On this our first day's hunting, at a low wall, a low panel
(The sort of thing that does for the good riders now and
    then,
Because their horse swerved at so small a jump.)
And she might have righted herself except that the horse
    stumbled
And off she slid—I was near to her, seeing all this, and I
    held my breath,
For she headed straight for a rock, but her skirt caught
Just for a second on the high pommel and so
She landed thumpingly on the soft ground, and the horse
    stopped at once,
And fell to grazing.
She got up, smiling a wry smile, and she said, "Get on, get
    on,
It's nothing." She walked to the horse and took its bridle in
    her right hand.
"I've sprained my wrist, it's nothing. I'll pick up someone to
    drive me,
Over at Gibson's Farm, there, yonder. Get on, do!"
I wanted to stay there with her, but she wouldn't let me,
    saying,
"I will not spoil your first day in Virginia, no, it's nothing,
I'll go straight home. Tell Sam and Judith. My husband's
    home."

She smiled again, saying, "Theo is home, it's all right, he will
       look after me."
So I left her. When we got home we found her
Propped in her bed, with a broken wrist and a cracked collar-
       bone:
She had walked the two miles there, leading the horse, because
There was no one at Gibson's Farm.

And I remember this day because it ended a cycle—suddenly:
For Judith and I had grown out of our timing, being at odds,
But not from wanting or willing, but only
Because one tide does not always gee with another, and one is
       flooding
When the other ebbs; and my passion
Had run out when hers had returned, or the other way round;
And this had been so for two long months. I think we felt
Desperate about it, both of us, in silence, wondering, question-
       ing,
Saying: 'Is this the end? Is this what marriage does to you,
Finally? The ardours cool? The time for loving
Is all past and gone? You must content
Yourself with affection? Find passion elsewhere?'
But I was forever learning, in those days.

Sam and Judith and I had tea with Mrs. Fenimore. She lay
In a huge bed, big enough for eight people, comfortably,
Her arm and wrist in a cast and the cast in a sling, and her
       jacket
Bulging over the bandages and the straps
That held her collar bone. She looked gigantic,
With her black hair (never a spot of grey) piled up and up
In a mound of blackness on top of her fine head. We talked
Of this and that: she was fun, she made us laugh.
Sam said at length, "We must go, we must dress for dinner.
It's too bad about you. It is. We shall miss you. It's too bad,
And Harriet coming to dinner and there is Theo
All alone with Harriet, and you up here, alone, biting your
       nails,
And only one hand to work on. Poor, dear Mother!"
She said, "Ah, you remind me!
It's time to dress for dinner. Ring for the girl, then, Sam, do.
I've got to get dressed. I shall be slow about it."
He said to her, "Don't be silly. You stay right there."

She answered and said, "Do you think I want to miss it, the
      fun,
Do you think I'd leave you alone? I get up." He cried,
"You stay in bed or I'll call for Theo."
She looked at him and she said, "Oh, coward, Sam! Coward!"
He giggled and said to us, "See? I can do nothing, nothing.
She is my mother. She is a huge, great mountain of beauty,
But will she obey the mountain's son? Not her!
She only obeys the mouse." And he turned
Back to his mother and laughed and said, "And yes—
Perhaps dear Harriet is his piece of cheese?"
She said, "It has nothing to do with Harriet. No.
Judith, you know her, Harriet Sefton, pretty and forty—
If Theo wants to flirt with a pretty woman, well then,
Why not, in God's name? She is a pretty woman. What use
Is a wife with broken bones?" She said again,
"Either you ring the bell or I shall ring it.
Either the mountain or the son of the mountain.
And why don't you be like Tom and find you a valley,
To bear you some little hills? But ring the bell,
I'm going to get up."
Sam sighed and rose and he crossed the room and he rang the
      bell.
He said, "You could put the bell by your bed. Why don't you
      do it?"
She answered him, "I might ring the thing in my sleep. Or
      worse."
We laughed, and the door opened, but it was not the maid,
It was Theo Fenimore, sliding into the room. He closed
The door behind him, softly. He said, "I heard
The fire-alarm that you have for a bell go off, and I came,
For I don't trust you."
She said, "You are all agin me."
He smoothed his thinning hair with his hand and said,
"And what did you then propose?"
She said, "To get up. What use to stay in this bed? I've noth-
      ing
But a few cracked bones. They're strapped. What harm?" He
      said,
"No, Emmeline, I'm sorry. You stop in bed."
"I shall not do it!" He looked at her for a moment,
Smiling, vaguely, and said in his careful voice,
"Video meliora proboque, deteriora sequor. I follow

The wrong when I see and approve the right. Way back
In Ovid's day it was just the same. You stay
Just where you are."
She sighed and she said, "Oh, well." He answered, "Quite."
"And Harriet's coming to dinner." He said, "I know.
I shall get on faster without you." She laughed and said,
"It is the open season."
"Yes," he replied, "It is the open season. And Harriet,
She is a fine, broad-minded girl. And not too difficult.
And not too demanding. A man might flirt with her
For a short time, for a term. Perhaps I might describe her:
She is a girl—a woman—more wide than long."
He turned away and left us, so quickly, so gently,
That we hardly knew he was gone.
Mrs. Fenimore said again, "Oh well," and sighed and added,
"I'll stay right here then. Go along now and dress."
Sam said, "That's good. Can I get you anything, Mother,
Before I leave?" She answered, "Get you a wife." He said,
"Funny, I used to be after Tom to marry and he was against it.
And now he's married and I am not. But you never know
Your blessings, do you?" He laughed and left the room.
We said, "Good-night." She said, "Tell me, for how long now
Have you two children been married?"
Judith said, "Eight years now." "And he's been faithful?"
I said, "Oh yes, for I've never even been tempted."
"Pretty," said Mrs. Fenimore, "But so silly. And so untrue.
Of course you have. Have you lost your sight, your senses?
Don't be foolish. Of course you have been tempted, many
        times,
And the next time it happens—well, I don't know, perhaps
You must find your own way there. Go along now, you'll be
        late,
And dinner's at eight, and keep an eye on Harriet,
She's tempting, Tom. Good-night."

We went to our room but we hardly spoke at all. I think
We felt embarrassed. I wished
Judith would just say something. She didn't. She merely whis-
        tled:
Whistled while she undressed, and whistled while she was
        bathing,
And tried to whistle with cold cream on her face, but that
Made a silly noise of the whistling and she laughed then

And she said, "Ah there! And who gives you a thrill?"
I said, "Tit for tat. And you?" She was sitting then, facing
The mirror and doing her face. I loved to watch it. Her hands
Had a singular grace in motion. She said,
"Well, if you must know, many. And you, Tom, many?"
I said, "Is it wrong then, is it wrong? Of course—it's often.
You see them here and there, well, this one and that one,
Girls like Phyllis Gardiner, you can't help it.
But tell me, do you think it's wrong?" She said,
"Nothing is wrong, like that. How could we help it? I feel
Sometimes as though—well, dancing—or not that, only
Walking into a room, and seeing them—you hardly can bear
     it.
It isn't bad, it's just—it's overwhelming, a pleasure,
But why should you mind it? Are we dead or alive?
Are we so old, then?"
                    "No," I said, "we're not old, we're young,
We're in our prime, I reckon. Yes, sometimes dancing,
But it doesn't have to have anything done about it. But then,
It frightens me. I think: 'Have I fallen in love?' Do you
Think that too?"
                    She thought for a moment and she said, "No.
It's hiding it, trying to make believe that it didn't happen,
Trying to say it was untrue, couldn't be so, that's the thing
That harms us, isn't it? See, Tom. You give too much impor-
     tance
To a simple response. You say, 'If I feel like this, if I,
The good, pure husband, want to—well—go to bed
With this girl or with that, why, it must be love, it must'—
For how else can you ease your morality? Oh, I hate
That sort of morality! It's so thin and narrow, it binds
The body as well as the mind and when the bindings
Prove too weak and break, there's a fearful crash, because
You have gone to pieces over a little passion, a little
Natural attraction—because you gave it the big name, you
     gave it
The big word, Love, and didn't just say, 'Oh yes, here we are,
I'm attracted again, how nice, what fun, what pleasure!'"
She rose up then and she stretched her arms and the thin
Dressing gown of silk lay over her breasts and fell
In a straight line of long folds.
I said, "I see. Like Theo." She said, "Like Theo.
Or so I suppose. Like Tom; or even, like Judith."

I thought, Yes, it is so. I have known this for a long time,
But I didn't see it. And you: for a long time; but—
I always see you newly. And these others, the attractors,
It would be a long journey, and a new beginning, and much
    seeing,
And leading, where? To this? To the woman
I talk to, who talks to me, and our voices
Say what the words miss? And the wanting? Wanting?
But wanting is not to have, it is not to possess, to own,
It is not a door to open, but a long road to travel, slowly,
Toward a perfection, the perfecting of passion
Where love gives and is given, skilfully, equally, and time
Is clipped into the mould of two lovers, lying
In the conjunction of time and a conjoined passion;
And the wanting, only,
It is not to rise from possession with the need of it
Strong and clear, like a light in the darkness, the way-light,
The reef-light, the sound of bells in the fog, no!—oh, the
    wanting
Is but the beginning of this and the long knowing,
This grows over the years as a tree grows,
Slowly. And nothing matters, but you, you, Judith,
As long as the wanting is but wanting and you, Judith,
Are the satisfaction of want. I said,
"Come to me," and she came. And the light shone,
And the tides
Mounted together again.

2

And now we come to the time of Phyllis Gardiner:
Just three weeks then, no more, and it was over,
Leaving its hurt and its scar. We meet now, sometimes,
It's not unpleasant. She says, "Hello, Tom,
How are you?" and I answer, "Hello, Phyllis,
How are you doing?" And we smile—but hers
Is a quizzical smile: she looks at me, as though
Both smile and eyes said, 'You are an odd sort,
A faithful brute, still tagging to his wife.'
It speaks a little contempt.
               But it is over.
You see, we are near the end and the aim now.

378

All things tended to make love somewhat greater
Than its infractions. This was the single instance:
Stupidly entered, lightly, as though lightness
Itself made honesty. This began when Judith
Was bearing Beatrice.

                Judith, pregnant again,
Went up to Providence, to her mother's house:
Her father was not well. I did not go:
I was at work, and did not wish, just then,
The noise and vigour of that cheerful house
To interrupt me, nor to add temptation
Of Cottrellton, so near in the warm days
Of the May fishing. So she left me then,
Taking the boy to Providence with his nurse,
And I was home alone, with Agatha,
And on the whole content, although I missed her:
One cannot have a Judith and not miss her
When her step is not there, nor her sweet laugh,
Nor the response so ready and so full
For all demands upon it. But the house
Was now so quiet, and the work progressed
Miraculously well.

              And then one night,
I joined some friends for supper, and to my pleasure
Phyllis was there, and I sat next to her,
And we went out to dance, and we were paired,
Phyllis and I. She wore a soft, green dress,
With a bright diamond belt, a circular
Skirt that would swirl in motion. The green suited
Her light brown hair, her brownish-yellow eyes,
And her fair skin. She had a curious way
Of moving suddenly; it should have been so ugly,
But was not, for her youth and for her figure,
That made it graceful and intentional.
And all that evening (for we danced till late)
It was but pleasant, we were all old friends,
We drank a little, now and then, from flasks
That the men carried, but did not drink too much;
We joked and chattered: personalities,
The small and local topics—there was nothing
Out of the ordinary, except one remark
That Phyllis made to me. She said, "I think
That you have settled down. So very young!

Is Judith all your world?"
                              I said, "My world
Includes the devil if he'll dance like you
And look like you and wear your sort of dress
And make me laugh." She smiled at me and said,
"Are you ashamed to answer me?"
                                          "I have."
"No, not exactly. You avoided me.
And quite right, too. It's no concern of mine."
She turned the subject. We talked of other things
Till it was time to leave.
                              I took her home,
And said good-night outside the lighted door
Of her apartment house. She said, "Come up.
I'll give you one swift drink and you can go.
It's getting late."
                       "Perhaps it is too late?"
"No, not too late. Come on. We'll have one drink.
I'd like one and I hate to drink alone."
I said, "Good, that is fine. I want one too."
We went up to the pent-house on the roof;
She let us in the door. She said, "My people
Are all away. I might have had a party.
Perhaps I will. Or we might share a party—
How would that be?"
                        I said it would be fun,
And while we got the glasses and the ice
And found some whisky, we planned one for our friends,
Just a few people, dinner, perhaps dancing
To the victrola. While we drank, we talked.
It was so pleasant and so commonplace!
I thought, It's fun to be here, you are pretty,
And you're attractive, the evening was successful,
It's done me good. And then at last I rose.
"Thanks for the drink," I said. "We'll have the party,
I'll call my list up and do you call yours,
And we'll compare notes later."
                                    "Right," she said.
"Too bad that Judith's out of it." She held
The door wide open. I said good-night once more—
And then she looked at me. No more than that:
It was the same look she had given me then
When she had questioned me. Her full lips were open

In a half-smile, and her left hand was raised
And bent against her shoulder. And I dropped
My hat upon the floor and I reached out
And took her in my arms and then we kissed
In a whole passion.
                        So it all began;
So she became my mistress in this space
Of full three weeks, and in that feverish time
I only thought of pleasure and I stifled
The truths of conscience, and was satisfied
To drift uncharted ways.
                            She was not clever.
There was no brilliancy of mind, no common
Taste but our bodies—yet nothing to detract
That taste from satisfaction. She was pretty,
She was instructed in the arts of love,
Passionate but not wildly so; a cool
Head for the morrow, and never the least hint
That passion turned to the remorse of love.
What did we talk about? I don't remember:
Nothings and plans, and little, pointed words
Fitted to darkness and the naked bed,
And greetings and good-byes, perhaps, but these
Leave little image. We would meet for tea,
We'd walk in Central Park, or on the long
And dusty blackness of Exterior Street,
Seeing the Queensborough span dark-threaded beads
Of light across the water; or we'd dance,
Somewhere or anywhere, or we'd meet with friends
(Ignoring one another, for the time,
In simple wisdom) and I'd take her home,
Sedately, properly, and we'd mount the floors
In the prim presence of elevator-boys,
Up to her pent-house, and we'd say the words
That anyone could hear, till the door opened
And closed again on darkness and the spate
Of fresh and crude desire.
                            Time's meaningless:
I say three weeks—my diary tells me this—
My mind reports an age, an unclocked era,
Pressed into nothing, out of which there came
One little drop of pleasure, sweet, but never
Sweet to the taste now. Could I have been so wise

To see that all the flavour of the time
Lay in love's absence? I was not ready then
For wisdom's answer. And greed's satiety
We did not reach.
                    And then my Judith came
Home to her husband.
                        Noises in the front hall,
The sound of Judith's voice, of Agatha's.
And I ran down the stairs to give her welcome
Thinking, How odd a welcome! The whole hall
Was full of bags. I kissed her and the child,
Helped sort things out. I paid the taxi-driver:
It was a pleasant but robust confusion,
And took some time to settle.
                                Then we stood
At last alone in the soft springtime light
That filtered through the curtains of our room,
And she said, "Darling! I am home again,
Oh, good to have a home and have a Tom
That one comes back to!" She looked around the room,
Said, "I shall let dear Agatha unpack me,
I am so tired now." Then she sat down
In the deep chair and smiled at me. Her face
Was whiter than its usual. She said,
"I am exhausted by my happiness,
It's good exhaustion. Darling, I am home,
Isn't that wonderful?"
                        So the whole complexion
Changed on the instant: Judith in her home,
The smile and the known steps about the house,
The casual words, the little, common words
Made thought a torment.
                        There had been thoughtlessness
In all this interlude: now there was none.
Now it was all a lie: the little goings,
Not well accounted, the so small delays,
The afternoon that must be stretched and stretched
Out of its duties at this shop or that
Into the hours that could still include
Phyllis and me; the evenings that began
With men alone, but ended otherwise,
With her alone; and hurry, and go home,
And smooth the little lie, if it be needed,

Till it rolls easily upon the tongue,
And fear sharp angles of the truth. But fear
With Judith was impossible, it scored
Deeper than fear and turned to a distaste
With Tom for Tom, until he saw the truth,
And saw the past as tinctured as the present
With selfish greed.
                        And yet I put it off
With strange and tortuous arguments. I'd say,
'It is excess, of course. But some excess
Makes moderation tolerable to man.'
It didn't answer, and could not convince.
I saw, too clearly, all the difficult
And fearful months in which love grew so great
That it outgrew all difficulties, all fears,
And mounted into greatness, and had grown
Forever steadily to new heights. I saw
Judith too clearly, and I loved her more,
Great with her second child, beyond my passion,
Beyond the body, but dearer to the mind
In past desire and the future day
When this strong, willed, and merciless barrier
Should once more drop and open the long road
Of common happiness. Was she not my lover?
Could I debase love now into affection,
Or set a chaste companionship in place
Of full devotion? Or bear to wound a love
Whose vulnerable breast was but the flesh
That dropped its armour to receive me, hold me,
To nourish me, knowing no armour now
Could stop the arrow that spent love could speed?
And bear to wound, for what? Wound love for love?
But this was not love, this was a small passion,
A minor loving in a major key,
That touched the flesh, the senses, and the mind,
But could not touch the reaches of the heart
(That can alone transpose and make a song
Into a hymn of living) save with death,
And death's communicable.
                        So ended Phyllis:
The pretty girl, the girl of sudden motion,
The woman who had taken me, for a term,
Who gave her body, lightly and with grace,

Who did not give her heart nor ask for mine,
Who slept and woke forever to new day
As something new, but never as the effect
That yesterday had caused, that yesterdays
Could colour with their stain.

                                I like her, still.
We meet and speak, in spite of all the scorn
She voiced for me; in spite of the worse scorn
I poured upon myself that I had followed
Lightly a path made terrible by Clare,
A path made tortuous by Rosemary.

We met (as lovers) for the final time
Of a warm afternoon. She let me in,
Up at her pent-house. Then we sat outside
In wicker chairs on brown and sooty tiles
Of her high porch. I think she must have known
That I had come to end it, for she said,
"You have got something in your eye, a look
I do not like."

                        I said, "I've come to say
Thank you, dear Phyllis—thank you and good-bye."
"I thought as much," she answered. "I have seen
The whole thing coming. You are bored with me?"
I thought, How easy if I just said, 'Yes'
And let our tempers finish it. Instead,
I said, "I am a coward. Hit and run.
I shall just tell you—and then run away.
You will not understand. But yet I like you
Too much to lie to you."

                        "Oh. Serious words!
We have not yet been serious. It's a change.
What are you like, in this new mood?"

                                        I smiled,
And answered, "Very dull. You would not like it."
Then she rose up and came to me and sat
On the chair's edge and spoke: "Now listen, listen.
You're spoiling something that was grand and sweet.
I don't know why you want to, but you are.
I have not asked you, 'Do you love me, Tom?'
I have not tried to creep around your heart
Like the familiar tendril. We have had
Pleasure together at no cost to either,

And now you wish to spoil it, by thick words.
I know the words—fidelity, the home,
The right thing and the wrong, the decent thing,
All that—it's nonsense—and you know it is.
It is a pretty thing we have. Don't spoil it.
If you are bored or tired of me, or feel
Revulsion at me—say so. I could take
That sort of quitting, I could understand it.
I've felt that way, myself. But dearest Tom,
No homilies on duty and the state,
I beg you, beg you!"
                              I looked up at her.
She smiled as always, and her amber eyes
Were bright with her vivacity. I said,
"Well, that's all right. Suppose I leave it there,
Just leave and say 'so long' and sling my hook,
Will that be better? It is over, Phyllis.
I'm sorry, but it's so. Will it be better
Blankly, like that?"
                    "Oh, infinitely," she said,
"The sooner now, the better."
                              "Very well."
I rose up from the chair. She did not move,
But she was laughing. "Yes," I said, "I know.
We laugh and laugh. It is our generation.
We've lost our way and have not found another.
It has a funny sound, our way-lost laughter,
But how we need it!"
                    "Don't be serious.
Go home for that, you poet."
                              "Yes. I shall.
And we can meet?"
                    "Of course," she said, "of course!
Don't be so silly, so sentimental, Tom."
"Good-bye then, Phyllis." I held out my hand.
"Oh no," she said, "you kiss a girl good-bye
When she has been your mistress." I bent down
And kissed her, and she smiled and said, "So long.
Well, I'll be seeing you."
                              "Yes," I said, "So long."
I started back across the sunny porch
Toward the french doors that opened to the freedom
That I had mortgaged, but as I opened them

I heard her heels loud on the squares of tile
And she came up to me, a little breathless,
But smiling, and she said, "I'm but a woman,
And I must know."

      "Perhaps it's better not."
"I couldn't bear it."

      "You will have to now."
"Oh no," she said, "men are such silly fools,
I'd never know just to which grade of fool
I must assign you."

      "Any one will do."
"Not any one. Is it Duty and the Home,
The sterner calls of your New England Blood
That triumph o'er the Latin, o'er the land
They say is for the brave and free?"

        I laughed.
"No, not exactly. It is more than that."
She wrinkled up her brow. "I should have said
That you were not the dull, American fool
Who feels that virtue is its own reward
And anything outside the marriage circle
Is something fearfully regrettable—
And to be bragged about, like all good sins."
"No, not quite that, Phyllis."

      She stamped her foot.
"Tell me," she cried, "tell me! It isn't fair!
I've earned the answer, haven't I?"

       "You were paid
In just the coin that you could spend on me."
"Go on," she said, "I'm waiting for an answer,
A decent answer, please." I thought, Oh well!
Better to do it. There's no need to leave
A stupid grudge behind. "You won't believe me,
But here it is. I leave you because love
Is all too strong to be divided up
And parcelled categorically. I've found
No reason beyond this."

      "What do you mean?"
"I mean that I have but one love to give,
So large that it needs all component parts.
I may not chip a little off for you
Or anyone. The chips would fly and cut.
I may not cut—there's nothing to defend

Against such fragments and their edge is sharp.
Yes, sharper than I knew."
                              She cried, "Come down!
Come down to earth, and be specific, Tom.
You talk in circles."
                              "No," I said, "I won't.
I've told you. Puzzle it. When you fall in love,
Perhaps you'll understand."
                              She said, "Thank God
I didn't fall in love with you."
                              "Thank God!"
I echoed her. She looked at me, her face
Now for the first time had an angry look.
She said, "You say things I don't understand,
They're so high-flown and fancy, sound so pure.
You are a strange, abnormal sort of fool,
A lover tied to his wife's apron-strings."
I said, "They came untied. The wrong lies there,
While he's a lover."
                              But she laughed at me.
"While he's a lover! What sort of lover, you,
Who run the moment that her back is turned
To find a substitute?"
                              I bit my lip
To keep from cursing her. It was so true,
It hurt me, justly. "That is it," I said.
"You've said it. Yes. But what you have not said
Is that I see it clearly."
                              "And next time?
Another pretty face, another girl,
Another holiday from the apron-strings?"
I said, "I do not know. But time will tell.
I should be brash to say that all my life
I should not do stupidities."
                              "And I?
Am I stupidities?"
                              "For me, alone,
This was not clever. What you do, for you,
Is your own business."
                              "Yes," she cried, "it's mine.
I know my way, I see a certain truth,
I've seen all men alike, they differ only
In build, in colour. Why should I attach

387

Myself to one of you in what you call love,
When it must turn into the little pieces
You swear so grandly you will not detach?"
I answered slowly, "I have lost the right
To tell you of it, lost it by my fault.
But yet I know the truth and I shall follow
Only that truth hereafter."
                                        "Yes?" she said.
"And guaranties?"
                        "There are no guaranties.
Or only one. I'll tell you. You will laugh.
Laugh and be damned to you. There is but one love.
We are not others: we are what we are.
Don't quote the French at me, don't talk of Latins,
We run to our own rote—it's a hard rule.
But if we follow it, it pays a glory
That nothing else can match, and this I know,
And this I knew and I departed from it,
And I am but a fool, you're right. But see,
Folly is not destruction when it's seen
For what it is."
                    She said, "Now go away.
You have explained too well. Now go away.
I am not angry—really. Not too angry.
It will all fade away, as you will fade.
I'll back my system against yours. I hold
No grudge against you. But just go away,
And leave me to be free. You are the sort
That anchors people. I will not be anchored.
Good-bye."
                I said, "Good-bye," and left her then.

It is all gone now, it's a long way back.
It seemed so unimportant, till it built
Into a weight that weighed upon my mind
And choked my heart. So little and so large!
You dally—and in dalliance you pawn
Your love for little.
                        So I turned again,
Ashamed, to Judith. And the tides washed out
In time the marks of footsteps on the smooth
And treacherous sands. I did not walk those sands

Ever again. My feet knew happiness
On Judith's road, that we had paved with stones
Carved out of loving.

BLOWN FROM the dreary miles of endless ocean
Now is the air unruly from the south—
(Oh let my heart persist in its devotion!)
There is a winter-bitterness in my mouth.
My mind's unhappy in each falser notion,
Now is the struggle more than I can bear—
(Oh let my heart be true in its devotion!)
The very images corrupt the air.
Suspect and black arises each emotion,
Now is the meaning of all life obscure—
(Oh let my heart be single in devotion!)
What good is thought when all thought is impure?
Drink! There is strength and joy within this potion
If yet the heart be strong in its devotion.

THIS DAY began in one fashion and ended in another:
But the ending was the beginning of a long time of happi-
　　　ness,
And the beginning was the end of troubles that piled up,
　　　high, high
(Like the great cumulus clouds that foreshadow tempest
In the days of the first heat).
There was no warmth, now, only cold, the bitter, harsh
February air, no wind, but penetrating stillness.
Leaving the stable and coming home, I saw the covering snow
On the box hedge, and the soft yellow of the filtered day,
And I heard the washing, the repeated monotony, of the rest-
　　　less sea
That moved and moved from habit but no wind.
Now in the stable there could have been a certain peace, with
　　　John Ward,

And the familiar sounds of the stamping feet of the horses,
And the good smell of leather and the sharp smell, acrid,
Of the horses' bedding, and the dusty
Smell of the loft: but there was no peace, for our talk
Was of sale and disposal: and now, nearing the house,
These were put in the back of the mind, replaced
By what the house meant and what it contained and all
That life meant now and the long and troubled
Business of living.
And Cora would be there. Sitting. Eternally
Sitting, a beautiful woman, with a petulant face, sitting,
And talking of this and that, bitterly, in the disjointed
Phrases of her distaste. Up in my room would lie, silent,
The sheets of paper that had been covered with the thin
Issue of my mind, and beside them
The sheets of paper, blank, endless, sheet upon sheet,
That needed to be covered, but were not, that I could
    not cover
Now in the dead time, when the mind
Was empty, was but an eye to see the reach of winter, an ear
To hear only the dreary wash of the sea, a memory
To cover the city house with a fine glow of happiness, of right-
    ness,
Of desire, giving it all the attributes of comfort: the place
Where thoughts had once flowed freely down through the
    nervous fingers
To the blank pages that being covered
Were joy, and that being blank,
Were a torture. But that house,
It was gone now, sold, it was all past remedy. One had
This house only, for winter, and this for spring, for summer,
    and for all
The hastening months of the long years that lay
Blank like the pages.
But where was the money now to buy the quickening
Of the living streets, of the fantastic need that lifted
Shafts of shadow and light, of the quick tongues and the rich
    answers,
Of the mad tonic of the wintry air, the good sounds
Of the horns blowing, the rattle of hurry, the living
Breath that could breathe life into an empty page?
Now the pages were blank: but in their blankness,
There was no money to buy the life that once more

Could fill them. And Judith's father:
Dead now; and her mother poor, and Cora poor—
Cora who threw away her husband, a kind man, George Free-
     man, and only
Because she was bored, because she said he was small, small-
     town,
And never would rise above it. Never would rise
Above what level? Who sat there, bitterly,
Saying this and that to you, sneering, deriding—she
Who had not yet made life, to sneer at life?
But what could you do? Could you say, 'Get out, it makes
No difference if you hate it, get out, go live with your mother
In the city that you hated, George Freeman's city,
The small town: it will feed you, we will not feed you
For all you are a sister? Oh, not now, no,
Not on the very porch of her father's death, of the long
Tale of his failure, of the great sheets with figures,
The balance sheets that would not balance now, the sheets
That were better blank, like mine, not covered
With the little red figures written in the blood
That Isaac Carpenter could no longer spare. The sky
Showed a rift to the eastward, watery blue,
But there was no promise there, it was just a sign
Of what had been.
                    So I approached the house,
Wondering, worrying: and Judith would not be home
Till later in the day, and there was Cora, waiting—
Bored, but waiting. By God! it was not my fault
That she was bored! And I thought: If I get angry, if I let
The anger grow, will it help me, will I write then?
So I returned to the house.
                              I went to my room directly,
And I sat down at my desk, and stared
At the pages done and the pages to be done and I said:
Now I must work. Now! I must. But then,
The noise of the children came through the old house
In waves of sound, and I rose up, and my anger rose too,
And I went down the corridor to the nursery and I flung
The door wide open and I said to the nurse, harshly,
"Isn't it possible to have less noise here. This racket
Drives me crazy. How can I work here
With this sort of noise?"
And she looked at me and she said, "Yes, Mr. Cottrell.

It is so wet outside. They had to stop in. I'll try
To keep them quiet—they're having
A beautiful time."
And Henry called out, "Hi!" and his sister
Called out, "Hi! Hi!" and they rolled on the floor, laughing,
Wildly laughing and bumping into each other and calling
Hi! and Hi! and Hi! and their laughter
Was too much for me, and I said 'Hell!' under my breath,
And I left, thinking, I am defeated, it is no use,
Damn all children! And back in my room
I looked at the sheets of paper, and said, 'And this,
It's no use, now, it's dead. I'll go down to Cora.
Perhaps it is better to go and to get angry
Than to sit here doing nothing.' So I went down
But not in a Christian spirit, no, looking for trouble,
Looking for anything that would stir me, that would rouse
The power again and send
This doldrum of my gloom into the past before
Some wind, some wind, oh, any sort
Of a good blow! But I went slowly:
You want and you don't want; indecision settles
On the in-between moods.
                    On the way down
I passed the picture of Clare in the dark hall-way,
And I paused. I switched the light on and I looked at it,
For a long time. Then I turned off the light and I thought,
'You could stir me now,' and I thought,
'And Rosemary, what a pity! We never did. I wonder
What she was like in a bed. I'll always have to wonder.
God, what a fool I was!' And then I thought,
'If Phyllis were here,' but I shied off that, then, in my mind,
For it was not good to remember, even like this, being
A little thing and a light thing, a matter
Drifted into, politely, but not the stirring
Wind that had blown from these. But still I stood here,
Thinking, 'If only Cora weren't her sister! God,
I'll bet she'd change her tune in the dark night, with nothing
Between us but our skins.' And I thought, 'Oh no,
I don't want you, no, not your sort, not any sort except Judith.
I'd rather be boiled in oil than get myself tangled
Into a coil with you. But I'll go down now,
And perhaps you'll sneer at me, and if you do sneer,

I shall get angry, and you won't like it, you
Who have never seen me angry, and oh, I need
Something! And why the hell is Judith away,
When most I need her?' And this
Was the way things stood with me, at that day's beginning.

I entered the room, and there was Cora, reading—and in those
    days
She was a beautiful woman, and I remembered
How lovely she was when she was a very young woman, and
    I remembered
How she had liked me and made much of me, and how
All this was gone now, for some reason,
And that I minded it, having accepted it, having had it.
I thought: You dislike me, perhaps because I married
And you are not married but are divorced—as Joss is,
Who broke the only pattern, the first pattern, of his life, be-
    cause Molly
Seemed stupid and marriage only a trammel, and his daughter
Too young to care, now, and the future (when care might
    blossom into a sad flower)
A long way off. And like Joss, you, Cora,
You could not stick it: but I am married, yes,
I am still married, and your sister
She is my wife and that, perhaps, is bitter to you, who threw
A man away because he was born in the wrong city.
She lowered her book as I came in and she said, at once,
"Tom, I've been thinking. I'm going to leave, soon. This
Is getting me nowhere. I've sponged on you too long."
I thought, You never can tell, now can you? But just then
I said nothing. She went on:
"I like you, Tom, and I love my sister Judith—once
I used to admire you. But this house, this house!
It's stultifying!" I thought, Aha! that's better,
Now you are warming up, my girl. But I said nothing;
I sat in a chair and faced her, and I looked at her,
Thinking, You are a beautiful woman, even
With petulance on your face. You look like Judith,
But she has grace and you have none. Go on. I want
To hear you. Yes. Funny—I want to hear you:
I am sick of my own thoughts.
She said, "The trouble with you is—shall I tell you

393

The trouble with you?" I said, "Yes, do. It's nice
To hear what's the trouble. You see, I have no troubles, so
    this
Will give me the thing I lack."
She said, "No troubles? don't fool yourself. Your trouble
Is a great big one. I have studied you. Yes, Tom. You need
To be shaken roughly." I said, "Go on and shake me."
She said, "Do you want to hear?" I said, "I'll hear it
Whether I want or not." She puckered her brow. She tapped
With her fingers on the book that she held. She opened
Her mouth to speak, and closed it. I said "Go on."
"All right, I will. You have a lot of talent. And what
Do you do with it? You write about Cottrellton. You write
About riding, you do poems on fishing, or nature, or the silly
People about New York, the so-called
Upper Classes. Bah! They make me sick! They—
Oh, what are they? The poems are thin, the stories,
They are so futile. The world has moved on past you, past
    you:
Can't you see it? You are still living, writing
In the nineteenth century." She stopped. I thought,
What shall I say now, that will most provoke her?
I said, "I am trying to cultivate miniature-writing:
It's awfully important." She cried, "Good God!
You can't be serious?" "Oh yes, dead serious. And style,
And euphony, and clarity, all in miniature, so that in time
I can make small things great."
                                    "Make small things great!"
She echoed my words. She said, "Now listen to me.
You take a brace or you will be done for, Tom.
You leave the small things, leave them all, all, all!
Oh, can't you see the world's changed? Miniatures, hell!
Write with some sort of guts, write of the big matters, the
    terrible
Things that happen, write of the small people
Whose lives are the great lives now. Get drunk and write!
Write of passion and love, and not of the pretty, little, stupid
World you inhabit where people say 'How are you?'
And bow and hide their thoughts. Get out and learn.
Forget the birds and flowers, forget the sea-scapes,
Forget the sunsets over the pretty rocks, the charming
Songs of thrushes, or robins, or any damn bird
You happen to think of. Machines—have you heard of them?

They have changed our lives, they are big and oh, exciting,
    new, wonderful!
The world is rising, the people all are rising—
Can't you hear them? Must you go on thinking in little,
In terms of the individual when the masses cry
Freedom in a great voice? Ah, what you need
Is to leave my sister—yes, even leave my sister, the perfect
Wife of your bosom, the woman, the companion, the comfort.
The pillow for your head, the shock-absorber—
Get out and suffer! Love! For God's sake, love!
Have an affair, live with another woman, anyone, anyone,
Suffer a little, God! you are so small.
It would even do you good if you fell in love
With another man, I'd rather you were a fairy
Than what you are. You're small, and you grow complacent,
You'll be a little, third-rate, small-time poet,
Unless you get out and live."
                              "Hooray!" I said.
She looked at me then, sharply. She said, in a quiet voice,
"Oh no, it's useless. You have set, set already,
So young to set, too. A young man, down in a deep rut.
A young man, married, to one of his own class,
A faithful husband, a darling, sweet little father,
Fond of his horses, kind, so kind to his servants,
Sweet to his sister-in-law, houses her, feeds her, looks
With real compassion at her because she had—
The guts to divorce a jelly-fish. You belong
In Providence where I came from, small-town Providence,
That I've escaped from. You will grow old so soon.
And someday you will see it happen, yes, you, you'll see it—
Revolution and change, and you'll sigh and say:
'Ah for the good old days!' and you'll walk with a fine
Aristocratic smile to the scaffold, but only
The smile will be remembered—and all the talents,
They will be buried with you—you—who know now
Nothing of life, nothing of tragedy,
Nothing of love except conventional marriage,
Nothing of poetry newer than poems by Swinburne,
Nothing of writing beyond dear Walter Pater,
Nothing of this great world, beyond Rhode Island
And perhaps New York to the east of Central Park,
Nothing of pain, nor sorrow, nothing of greed,
Nothing of poverty nor the slums, and nothing

395

Of the great masses toiling and making steel
For the days to come. Oh nothing! Poor little Tom,
I pity you, for I fear you are too small
To fit to the big place."
                            I said, "Are you finished, now?"
She said, "Not me—you are."
                                "Is the lecture finished?"
"The lecture never began," she said. "No lecture
Is given to deaf ears. If I could reach you
By making signs with my thumbs, I'd try."
                                            I thought,
The only sign you could make to me, my girl,
Would be with your pretty legs, and I don't want that.
So I rose and said "Well, thanks. I'm sorry you're going.
There won't be any reason to peek from the rut
After my Cora's left."
                        She cried, "There won't!
If only Judith would curse at you!" I said,
"Judith is too polite. She never would curse. You see,
It's all good manners, dear." And I left her then,
And climbed to my own room, and the writing table
Still was covered with things done and things
Still to be done. And I looked at them, and I thought,
I didn't get angry. Why?
                            And I thought then
Of the things she'd said: suppose she were right, at that?
You go on thinking
In terms of the individual when the masses cry
Freedom . . . I didn't know the masses. Who were they?
Not the individuals I had known, here and there, they were
    not the masses?
How could I write of the things I did not know?
Get out and learn . . Go where then, and learn what?
Live where and work at what? Use what for money?
Go be a bum and learn of bums? I thought,
If prosperity hangs too long around its corner,
We'll all be bums, yes, willy-nilly.
You'll be a little, third-rate, small-time poet
Unless you get out and learn . . . *get out and suffer,*
Love! For God's sake, love . . . But love, to Cora,
What did that mean? And what did she mean by suffer?
There had been Father and Martin, there'd been Clare—
There'd been Tom in his pretty attempt at loving

Phyllis Gardiner, was that love? *Anyone, anyone!*
Well, she was anyone. Did it make you suffer
Less because Martin's father was prosperous, owning
His great, rich farm? Would you have felt it more
If he'd died as he dug a ditch for a sewer line
Or fallen into a smelter? Or felt it more
If Jake had murdered your father as they two worked
In a factory or a mill? Ah, hell! I thought,
What does she mean, and how does she see the light
Who couldn't make life go for herself, who turned away
From what individual to what masses now?
You couldn't be sure with Cora,
She might go live in a slum.
Well, let her live there,
What did it matter? And write, write, as you saw it,
You couldn't be someone else, or you'd be a failure,
Trying to change.
Or be a failure trying
To be yourself?
I looked at the blank pages,
And I thought, it is time to work, not time to listen to bitter
Thoughts of the might-be, prophecies of disaster
From sister Cassandra. But as I took
The pencil up in my hand to write, I felt
The blood run up to my head, and a fine anger
Blazed inside me, and rose up higher and higher, and I flung
The pencil on the table and I got up then, saying,
'I'll go below and give you a bit of my mind, you little,
Pretty young fool, with your women and your fairies,
And your gibes at Judith and me.' And I went to the door
To fling it open. It opened. There stood Judith,
Cheeks flushed, smiling, dressed in a black sweater,
A grey tweed skirt, her hair so dark and the eyes grey
And wide with pleasure. "Oh Tom," she said. "how good
To be home again! How silly to feel this way
After four hours of divorce. How silly!
But oh, how nice!"
          I said, "You were just in time."
"In time for what?"
          "To save your sister's life."
"Has Cora been after you?"
          "Yes," I said, "with a hatchet,
But I was going down with an axe, to hew her

397

Limb from pretty limb."
                    "They're pretty," said Judith. "Leave them.
I bet I know what she said. She has been after me
For a long time now. She thinks that we are too happy."
"Listen to me," I said, and I told her then, and the words
Spouted out of me, angrily, and I told
All she had said and what I'd said and something
Of things I did not say. I felt the anger
Ebbing a little, now. And Judith sat there, her eyes
Grew dark and darker, and her face flushed
And when I was done, she cried, "She'll go tomorrow
And I shall bless her going."
                    I said, "You're angry?"
She said, "I am angry that she has made you angry,
And angrier at her folly, her stupid folly—why,
You know she's a fool, she's just the silliest part
Of our generation. Don't you see that? don't you?
They hate ideals and they hate manners and fashions,
They laugh at decency and they laugh at love,
They think it is shameful and small to be married, happily,
For a man to love one woman with all his heart,
For a woman to hang to one man—yes, as shameful—
The fools, the fools! They think a woman
Stultifies herself if she gives her life
To the job of marriage, the husband and the children.
'What is the matter with her?' they say. 'She's crazy,
Why doesn't she work in a shop, work in a office, work
In a dance hall, in a brothel, go into politics, anything—
But for God's sake why does she waste her time on this
Pettiness of her home—her home!' They say,
'You are just mediaeval, you're back in the Dark Ages, you let
Your husband run you.' I like it. I like my husband—
I love my husband. I'm proud to have his children.
Damn them, they forget that! They say, 'It's only
A small matter, loving, unless it's done
In an unblessed bed and then it is fine and animal,
And the animals are fine.' But they forget
That animals never work in an office, or go
Into politics. And look you, Thomas,
They tell me, 'You have married an artist.' But an artist
Who writes with craftmanship, caring about it,
Who writes but what he knows of, who writes for clarity,
Who's lucid, simple, dealing with simple, eternal

398

Matters like love and death and marriage and all the poor
Small moments of the heart rising, they think him
But a political slacker, he isn't worth
The powder to blow him to hell. Think of it, think of it!
He doesn't write propaganda! My God! How awful!
He's a pimp to capital, bourgeois, stupid, he's small, he's mean—
Oh, what do we care what they say, you and I,
What do we care?"
                                    She leaped at me and she seized me
Hard by the coat and she said, "Come on, let's go,
Let's go downstairs and sneer. I'm tired of kindness,
I'm sick of listening to this, I'm sick
Of being put in the negative, I want
To be positive for a change. Come on, come on,
Let's sneer at my sister Cora."
I said, "That's fine."
She grabbed my arm and together we ran downstairs
And into the living room, where Cora was sitting,
And we danced around her and we sang
(For the words and the tune came to us as we danced):
"For we are still married today, today,
For we are still married today!"
Then we stood still and I said, "We're happily married."
And Judith said, "We're happily married, and we thank God!"
And I said, "Yes, and you, you are the failure, who broke
The circle of marriage because you hadn't the simple wisdom
To see it was the one circle you might complete, for now
Your heart is divided, and your life
Will always divide, and your son will tell you
All these things some day."
And Judith cried, "Yes, Cora, it is the truth, and what's more,
What do you know, or what will you know that we
Cannot know? There is more to be learned in marriage
Than years to learn it, and there is more to be done
Than years to do it, and the emotion
Is great and deep and incessant, and all this
You didn't know, and you won't know—you'll fritter
Your life away, by yourself, but we
Will spend it here, together, enriching, always
Enriching each other. Oh yes,
You are the failure, and we
Are married, married, married, happily married!"
And we danced and sang again, and we made faces at Cora,

But she just sat there, smiling a wry sort of a smile,
Saying nothing, and shaking her head, slowly, and we left her,
Singing, singing, up the stairs and into our own bedroom,
And we closed the door of it, and I said,
Breathlessly, "Come here, Judith,
I want to kiss you," and she said,
"Come here yourself, for I want
Much of the same."

After a while, after the blood had ceased
To drum in our ears, I said,
"We have been mean, and unkind."
She said, "I don't care, we follow
Our own way and she can follow
Her way, any way. And what
Does she know of us, or of our love?
And why were we mean?"
                                        I said,
"We were three against one."
She questioned me with her eyes. I answered them:
"There is you and there is me, and always now
There is Us."
She nodded, saying, "Yes, there is us, now,
It's a strange thing and a strong thing. And you,
Are you happy now?" And I said
"I am happy now, but I am not always happy, no,
There is so much to do, and so much
That is not done, and so much
To grow that has not yet grown."
"Would you be happy, then, if it were all grown?"
I shook my head.
She said, "You have been full of trouble, and we,
We have been full of trouble, and now,
Is it so bad now?"
"Not so bad now. It will never be bad
With us to face it. It is not big trouble,
It is a lot of little, mean, petty troubles
That gathered into a heap. They blocked
My view of you."
                        "They blocked
Not me but the star we follow. Tell me,
Is it an odd star that we follow?
Tell me, are there so many

400

People following our star?"
I thought, if they had you, Judith,
They could follow our star. I said,
"It is the star the whole world tries to follow, the star
Of the unity of love—or of life—but when they fail,
From disappointment they turn to bitterness
And they curse the star then: but some
Follow it on. There was your father.
There was Grandfather and his star, Francesca,
That was a big star. He followed it,
Always, sure of it, being unsure
Of life or death, or memory,
Or life everlasting, or his art, and only
Sure of this one star, and at the last, crying
Thanksgiving to it. And this
Has remained with me, and his wife, Francesca,
And his love for her, these remain, and so
We may remain, or a pattern we make, or life—
This many continue in our children, or for them, and their
        pattern
Will be of us, and of him and of Francesca, and of a love
That they saw, and one that they did not see, as I
Saw only the pattern of his love left, and it made
A warmth for me. Oh yes, his star
Is a big star and we follow it, and can point
The star to the children, saying, 'It is there, see it,
It is to follow.' "
She said, "Yes. And now,
The temper is over, and we must go down, Tom,
And we must say, Sorry, to Cora."
I laughed at her and I said, "Cora will say
That is just useless manners."
"Yes," she said, "it is true, she will say this,
But then—it doesn't matter,
We are in love, and our love
Needs no hurt to Cora."
"All right, then, let us go down. Let us
Go down together, you and I
And us—to Cora."
                    She sighed and smiled and said,
"You and I and us. It is like
Our Mr. People, who once sat between us.
He is a fine man."

401

I said, "You have remembered Mr. People?"
She answered, "I have forgotten nothing, I have remembered
Joys and pains and quarrels and love and kisses,
And the moon in the window and the dark Medici shadows,
And Madrid in spring and the smell
Of the acacias, and Carmino Cella,
And the sound of the black duck, rushing
Over the dusk, and Jake,
And Mrs. Mallory and the sound of the bells coming
Across the grass green in December,
And the agony of birth, and the soft
Lips of Henry, and Beatrice at my breast, and the long, long
Accountancy of the days as the pain of birth
Faded and one lay
In the bed that marriage had made and birth had made.
Oh, I have remembered
The small things and the big things and all these,
They are for you, Tom, for you and for me,
And for us together."
She sighed and I repeated, "For us together,
And beyond question."
"Ah, beyond question, no, Tom. Always question,
Question all things, but lean on my love now and let
Me lean on your love, for in the leaning
We are so strong, we three, our love, and you
And I together. Forever. I hope and pray
It will be forever."
"Yes," I said, "forever, now. How long
It took to learn!" She said, "It will be longer
Before we may forget."
I thought, Before we forget: but that's death:
In death we may forget? or perhaps remember?
But this is life now, and death may mean an ending,
Or else a meeting, I do not know: but only
That love may last forever, if forever
Be in the pulse of life, and time
Lie in the clock of the heart, and love
Grows to the word slowly, earning
Forever slowly, slowly, nearing
The full stature of its remembrance, the long, slow
Progress to that one, fearful word, slowly—
But with me,

It is a long bliss and now
It is mine, I have known this,
I have known its shadow: its light:
I remember and, for the uncharted span of memory,
It is forever.

THESE ARE the tethers never are forgot,
These are the plants on which a future's fed,
These are the fruits that love and fear begot
Lying with passion on a marriage bed.
This is the field we sowed to pasture hope,
These are the walls we built to bar distress,
These borders dug that sun might warm their slope—
So do our four hands harvest happiness.
There is no magic here, for on this soil,
The nights and days, the seasons in their kind,
Rain and the sun, and long, incessant toil
Must pass, and passing, leave a love behind.
Are you impatient, sweet, that it is slow?
The roots of happiness are deep to grow.

THIS IS FOR Beatrice, and for Henry—see,
    It is her birthday and the August sun
        Shines prettily,
Casting long shadows on the grass to mark
    Her two years over and her third begun.
Look over yonder, where the girl with dark
    Italian eyes is standing, melancholy,
        Because her bubble burst,
            Her bright balloon:
That is the child of Joss, the child of Molly,
    The last one and the first.
And there, behind the tree, emerging soon,
    That boy is Cora's boy:

His name is Freeman. Though his mother wears
Another now, his father is—his father?
In his prayers
He mentions two where once was only one.
But there are other children here. Their joy.
Is loud in cries:
Potato races frantically run,
And eggs that spill from spoons that shook too much,
And donkeys' tails that fastened to their eyes,
Of such
They shall be happy while they still are young
And on their tongue
No name more glamourous, none of more surprise
Than this (at which a dozen fists will clutch):
Jack Horner Pies.
And here the elders sit, who must be able
To run and help, to tie into a sack
The bouncing candidates of this coming race.
Here is my mother, she is dressed in black,
And Cora's here, a smile upon her face,
And nurses busy with the supper table.
And Beatrice, on that August afternoon
Fell on her egg and bent the kitchen spoon,
And Henry, in his eagerness
Helping himself to more of apple jelly,
Put most of it upon her party dress,
And in his race, fell down
Flat on his belly:
He would have yelled if he had had the wind—
He got false credit for his manliness,
And not a frown;
And Beatrice strews the lawn with bits of paper,
Unwrapped from gifts,
As with a most unbalanced heave she lifts
The burden to herself and tries to caper.
Here is my Judith and here too am I
To watch, to help, to guide, to be umpire,
To keep an anxious and parental eye,
To be a host to elders and a liar
About the charms of someone else's child.

The sun is low now, and the air is mild,
The nurses roam,

Gathering in the young, to take them home.
The air at once is full of shrill good-byes,
We stand and say Good-bye and Come again
To children hid below balloons of blue,
To children clutching an important prize
(Found at the counters of the five-and-ten).
And Mother sadly leaves,
And Cora follows with her handsome son,
And all are gone but just one child, who heaves
A sigh and says, "It was such lovely fun—
If I could only always stay with you."
It is my niece who goes
Back to her father? But he is away;
Back to her mother? to a wind that blows
Two ways to loving—there's an echo there?
Forget it now, the day
Is full of its enchantment and the air
Is soft with musk,
The children must go in, in disarray,
To let excitement fade, to sleep by dusk,
And dream of more.
Judith and I, aweary, may undress,
And happily at the shore
Shatter the opal mirror of the bay
In dives to sea-weed's browner wilderness.
And dress and dine,
And see the lighthouse that begins to blink,
(Ours, that at first was mine)
Sitting in revery on the porch to think
Of unimportant things;
And going in, she holds the coloured thread
With which I tie a fly's bright-feathered wings—
Oh, on such little matters love is fed
And we,
Judith and I together, may survey
The lengthening hours
In which love built a refuge, lengthily,
A fortress with strong towers,
Where we might keep a watch upon the deep
Seas of our living, till its night of sleep.

PART EIGHT

*N*OW THE immaculate bed of your delight
Must bear an impress deeper than a stain,
And its four marches, boundaried by night,
Are the four edges of your spirit's pain.
Now is the hollow empty that was full,
Now on the pillow is an image-head,
Now is a cold beyond the warmth of wool,
Now have the last sweet whispers all been said.
Here is a pause that is not of today,
Nor yesterday, nor will be of tomorrow,
Here is the timeless moment when the clay
Assumes the shape of unbelieving sorrow.
Now is the silence heavier than stones
Where moveless sheets lie over moveless bones.

WE ARE NEAR the end, then?

Yes, we are near the end, we have done
The journey, now: the journey
Together.

*Is there not more to say, may you
Not linger a little, telling
The years between?*

No. See: they are like Deer River, that feeds and renews
On a hundred small trickles, numberless springs,
Little brooks and drains, and the soft
Rain of spring and the heavy, spent
Rain of summer, and the long
Drench of the fall skies, and the white
Snow and the grey ice of the hard
Months of winter—all these
Feed the river, it flows greatly,

But of a thousand
Smaller sources, blent, mixed
Into a great flow. We have followed
The major springs to their source.

We are near the end, then.

Yes, it is close—but still, linger a little
On this day and the day before, for here
Is matter for the heart: November
Colours among the leaves, and the pink
Grasses and the green leaves
Of the catbriar, and the purple
Leaf on the fierce spine of the blackberry and the haze
Of autumn under Virginia sun.
Linger a little, there are still a few
Voices, voices speaking, lips
That move and speak, laughing.

And we were shooting, Sam and Judith and I, idly,
For it was hot, and there were not many quail,
On that November afternoon, and the dog
Panted and worked slowly.
And toward evening
It grew cooler, and the shadows lay like a tangible
Blue veil over the hollows, where creeks
Lay in still small pools, lay in the dry
Beds of their gravel, and the air
Was full of the dusty smell of the dry
Leaves we stirred, and the sound
Of the rustling grasses and the stillness
In no sound of the bird-voices.
And Sam said, "You didn't have a party—
Even for fifteen years, no party?"
Judith answered him, "It was in October,
Everyone leaves then. They run away
At the fine time of the year. We'll have one
Later, perhaps New York. A big one.
Will you come, Sam?"
He said, "I couldn't miss it, Judith, I'll come
With a crystal heart for you,
And a large crystal
Loving-cup for Tom."

"Oh, good!" she said. And then,
"Why are you not married?"
He said, "I should be, should be."
I asked him, on that evening, because the light
Was soft now, and the air still, and the fields
Were shadowed and peace
Lay like a sweet air over the land enclosing
All three of us then, saying,
"Are you averse from marriage?"
"No," he said, "not I—why should I be?
There was my father and mother, and now
There is Theo and my mother, and always
It has been happy for them and that
Was happy for me. And there is always you two—
Yes, you the doubter,
You and your dark Judith, always
To lead on a chap." And we asked him
(Because the evening bade us to ask him, because
There was stillness around us that lifted
The heart up, gently)
"Why, then?"
And he said, with a smile, "Because—
She would not have me. And since then—
Oh, long ago—I have waited—
For her, or another, but neither
Comes my road." And Judith said,
"Oh, we are sorry," and I said,
"Yes, we are sorry," and Sam replied,
"It is the breaks, that's all. It matters
Only at the odd moments. I'll bring you
Crystal for your next party and I shall bring
Fifteen kisses for Judith and fifteen
Kicks in the pants for Tom." And he said,
"Let's start home," and we nodded and he took
Judith's arm and they walked ahead and I followed,
Looking at them, and hearing
Their laughter, and hearing
The rustle our feet made in the dry broom-sedge, and seeing
The last light on a tree's top across the creek, on the hill,
And smelling the dust, and I felt
Sad and content, and happy, and loving,
And all these together: as a man feels
When the years, accumulating,

Have added to peace in the long evening
Of a November day and love
Walks with a quick rustling noise before him,
Through the grasses.

And now? What now?

We linger a moment more. There was the moment
Outside the door to Mrs. Fenimore's room. She stood
Straight-backed and ample there and she said,
"We shall be off early. I've ordered
Breakfast and such like. You haven't
Forgotten your boots, like last time?"
And Judith laughed. She said, "No,
I actually have them, right here,
Right in my room. And Tom
Has his breeches, too." And we three
Laughed again, and we said, "Good-night."
But Mrs. Fenimore looked at us, a rather
Piercing sort of a look, and she said,
"You are a couple. I tell you—
There are not many couples. The world
Is full of people like cooks and butlers: always
The man is wonderful, the woman's a slut, a termagant;
Or the woman's the best cook in ten counties
And the man drinks, or walks off
With bits of silver, or beats
The best cook in ten counties. Truly
It is not often that people make a couple,
And you—yes, you two,
You are a couple. There should be
Another word to describe it."
The thin voice
Of Theo Fenimore came through his closed door,
Saying, "The half is more than the whole: it comes
From Hesiod, Works and Days."
She cried out, "Shush!
You are a lap behind." He said,
"No, I am a lap ahead of you, Emmeline."
She said again, "You shush!" and to us, "I bid you
A fond good-night—couple." She smiled. And we
Smiled too, leaving her, and going
To the room that housed us, the room

That contained us each, but what each
Contained was the half of a whole and it lay
Always warm in our hearts then, in those days,
And warm on that day. And this
I have remembered.

And now?

It is the end now, but of this
I cannot tell you, I cannot, the end
Has merged into blankness, now.
I have told
Many things, we have travelled
A long way together, but this—
It is gone, it has fused, running together. It is become
Nothing but the bare, bare ribs
Of its being.
I can tell you that we rose up,
Yes, in the first light of day,
That we dressed, that we ate together,
And the day
Was a fine day, and the sun rose,
And Mrs. Fenimore and Sam and I and Judith
Drove to the meet and the grooms
Stood there, holding the horses and we mounted,
And there were many people, on foot, mounting,
Men and women and fine
Horses and that the dew
Lay heavily on the fields. And the hounds drew
Coverts and found, and they ran well;
And that I followed
Close to the Master, and that I thought
Nothing of Judith, being
Immersed in the speed of the day. And I tell you
That time passed like wind on the face, rushing, blowing:
That time fled to the sound of the drum of the feet of the
        horses:
That time flew like the sun over the high heaven: and then,
I tell you I jumped into a road, and a man—
With a car, some sort of a car—yelled at me,
And I pulled up and he said,
"Get off, I'll take it, the animal—
Take my car and drive to the Witter Cross Roads,

413

Your wife's had a fall."
I tell you I did this: as he said: driving
Fast on the yellow dirt road, and the dust
Blew over me in a cloud as I stopped
At the Cross Roads and there
Were several people, I think, and they were bending
Over a woman on the ground and the woman
Was Judith, and I ran to her, and
Kneeling beside her, I called her
And there was no answer, and I felt
For her pulse and her heart
And there was
No pulse but only
Stillness, and the voices of people, I think of people.
And I can tell you
Nothing of what the day was, nor its colour,
Nor what the earth smelt of, nor what
Sounds there were, but only
Of the silence, the silence,
Of a heart's silence: and now
This is what I have told and this
Is all, it is all, now, and there are only
The bones of grief.

And then, Tom?

Judith all over the house: a terrible music:
Tempting the heart to move; fingers at the black tie,
The hair to brush again. Brush for Judith.
Cover the look in your face, cover it—you must,
Soon They'll be looking.
The air is Judith, breathe the good air:
The air is your heart, the sound of the sea is your flesh,
The waves are your pulse. It is all distant.
So. Go down the stairs—they are used to it:
There have been mourning feet upon these stairs
Over and over again. The walls say so. The dark doors
Rich with time say, Live and die and remember,
And love and remember, always
Remember Grandfather and remember Judith.
This floor was for them to tread, for them to walk on,
The flowers are new flowers, caught in the halls,
In the air of the old flowers gathered and gathered and gone.
The day's November and death is in November,

414

But say, instead, in a steady sort of a voice,
Welcome Sam, and welcome, Arthur and Edward,
And welcome, Mrs. Carpenter,
But don't say: Judith. And don't cry out November,
But shut your lips on the minutes that spell the hours
And the hours that spell the age since November crumbled
Into an empty space without a meaning,
Without a lover.
Mother is dressed in black, and Joss in black,
And Sam and I, we've got on black ties, yes,
And black is the seal of sorrow, the sign of mourning,
And Mother in black of a sorrow beyond all reason—
Oh—Judith all over the house like a fine scent
Sprayed in November crystals of scented air.

Now we go into the room: into the old room, this
Is papered with love and the echo of old love.
The room is different? Faces, the solemn faces,
Only a well-bred rustle—you must not think this. Look!
The room is empty of people, the world is empty,
Only a white-clad image, advancing, advancing,
Toward your Judith—cry Stop! and run:
But you just stand still,
The legs and the feet stand still and the heart stands still,
And a great fear runs all through, and the sweat comes,
And the knees are shaking. The image in white?
The people's faces are white, the globes of faces
Dim in the room of people—the image in white:
This is the minister, only the Reverend Munson,
And your hands flutter the pages and pass the pages,
And past the Morning Service and Evening Service,
And past the Litany and the Marriage Service,
And past the words there, shining, Each to the Other,
And on to the big words and the fine words, on, on—and
      here—
I am the Resurrection and the Life. And the voice
Stuttering slightly, only the Reverend Munson,
And Judith is not beside you, no, and this,
This was everything good in the whole wide world—
And suddenly over the beat of the words you hear
Life Everlasting as though it bore a sense
Beyond the words as a horn plays over the gale
Of the short and the long taut strings.

415

The globes of faces are weeping, but some are smiling
Over their tears. You smile at Mrs. Carpenter,
You smile at Arthur and Edward, you smile at Mother,
But without looking at her, only the corner
Of the eye perceives.

And thank you, Sam, and thank you, Arthur and Edward,
And thanks then, Joss, and Cora: thanks for the roses,
And thank you, Mrs. Standeven, yes, Aunt Rachel,
I'm sorry, I shouldn't forget—
Oh thank you, Mother dear, and cheer up, Mother,
And Joss will take you on in the car with him,
And hello there, Miss Darnley, thanks for the flowers,
Thanks for the lilies, Mr. Waterman, yes,
This was Grandfather's room, that is his window,
Howd'ye do, Mrs. Hallowell, Howd'ye do
Caroline and Maude—but you've changed your dresses,
For Maude's in grey and Caroline's wearing black,
And thanks for coming, Miss Brown, the room looks pretty,
        yes,
And oh, Mr. Babcock,
Howd'ye do, I hope the music's sticking
Well on the doors for in the music there
Judith and I and love are embedded forever—
She was a Carpenter, now she is a Cottrell
Leaving the Cottrell's house.

And a great voice calls in my mind, it calls out loudly:
'Love is a bliss and a pain, love's end is sorrow,
What does it matter? Love is the one preserver.'

Put them right in the car, Sam, in that car,
Both of them there, and Joss, look after Mother,
And the car starts off from the sea of the globes of faces,
From the soft women's voices, the low men's voices,
The wet sad face of Mother who has no voice,
And then—
It is the sound of Dr. Munson's voice,
It is ashes to ashes, it is the rattle,
Rattle as earth falls down in the deep pit, down
To lips not speaking, lips no longer whispering,
Lips enjoining terror, entreating love.

And then,
It is all over, now, it is all over,
And you are alone—
Memories over this house, memories upstairs
Tempting the eyes to cry and the lips to quiver,
Giving the word 'alone' a fearful meaning.
And life's before you,
But all alone? But now
Here the one lamp is out, and the room is dark,
And the stairs are dark, and this is Grandfather's room:
Always the same now, here is the same paper
Clothing the walls, the walls that could absorb us,
Retain our image. The cupboard is full now,
It is full of dresses.
The bureau is covered now, with its little bottles,
There are pictures here, here on the mantel,
These are photographs, and these are jars and vases,
These are the same now, and the flowers they hold—
These are our flowers, for us?
These are flowers—
These are different flowers, white and white,
And only,
Only the bed remains, yes, only
The bed remains.

Only the dark now, only the dark,
Only the one poor spirit striving, only
The two poor hands, clasped, each to the other;
Only the dark now, and the small words,
And the lips that speak, and
The terrible acquiescence.
What is the dark now in so fierce a light?
Where is love now in the dark lightning,
The noiseless thunder of blood
In the long veins,
The searching,
The pain and the passion, the whole, lonely passion,
The love that rears
Love in its search to find
All pain, all love—
Swift to your love, it grows
Fast to your heart, the pain

417

Is the knife of the mind in the heart,
Is the fire of death
That scorches and sears and burns
The dross of your mind,
But the mystery of your love
Is your own possessing, possessing,
Your own . . .
                    And now . . .
Only the dark now, only the dark
And the beat of the heart,
And the taste of tears,
And the crowding thoughts and the keen
Impulse to everlasting
Love and remembrance, and the hurt
Of the pain of the knife in the heart,
Of the mind's knife,
Cutting the old away, for a new day—
In the dark now, in the dark—
There is a long time yet
Till the light grows,
When love will be seen, for now
There is the last trial of love, there is the pain
All in the darkness.

EPILOGUE

SO TO THE END. It's been of me and mine,
These words piled up and gathered to a heap
Under your eyes. And yet, I shall confess
There's not an ending, for I am alive,
Moving and living, feeling, tasting, seeing,
Hearing the sounds yet that must more betoken
The living tissue. And not yet tragedy.
What! death a tragedy? No, it is sorrow,
It is a pain so deep that it delays
Always the breath a little. But not tragic.
No, there'd be tragedy in the small, the false
Hatreds and jealousies, in the petty spites,
The mean dilemmas of divided love,
Passions turned outward till the seams were rotted
In such exposure to the almighty sun
That rises and that shines, yes, and that burns
All such inversions. There'd be tragedy
In the poor, lonely path that was not hedged
With the rich planting of another's love,
The starved and dessicated life that fed
Only on its own juice, forever sucking
Vainly the arid air of the wide and desert
And solitary ways. But tragedy
Where once a love consumed and burnt and fed
On the whole article? At such flames as these
We warm forever, till our molecules
Are past all warming and grow chill and soon
Seek death that is implicit in all life,
Death that is yours before you pull the air
In one sharp cry of birth, death that is wound
Into the coil of you. May you insulate
The wires of death, will not their current run
A while, a while, and will not the long load
At length make fusible your coil in death's
Transcendent heat?
Because my dear love

(The living, moving essence that I knew)
Is but the dust now, shall I then despair,
Till mood and movement are at last as one
And all the junctures of my living bones
Speak tragedy? How small, how weak a love
That could not lift the burden of its grief
Into a further living, could not hold
Erect, but stooped to a bent, mournful pose
In weak, unpassioned grief.
                              No, it was mine!
I had it, I, the grandson and the son,
The boy, the lover and the husband, I,
The father and the man, the eager fool,
The fool whose wisdom came to salvage life
From fretful, piecemeal folly—it was mine:
Love, love, and love—oh that by writing this
One word ten thousand times, I might somehow
Capture its essence, that is caught in me
Past death, past sorrow, past the changing days,
And by a last strange alchemy transform
The letters into: Judith.
                              Tragedy?
No, I have loved and married and been loved,
And these are mine forever, past all death,
Past theft—perhaps, perhaps they will be mine
Down reaches of the undeciphered days
When I too am a part of earth again
And join my lover. But it does not matter,
For I am thus immortal that my love
For being given was returned to me
Forever greater, and forever mine.

THE END